THE
CATALOGUE
OF BRITISH & FOREIGN

CIGARETTE CARDS
1888 - 1986

Published by
The London Cigarette Card Company Ltd.

1986 edition

I.S.B.N.   0 903790 44 0

HOW TO USE THE CATALOGUE

This catalogue is published in two sections. Section 1 covers the cigarette card issues of British tobacco manufacturers for the home market together with certain export series (indicated by 'export' in brackets). Section 2 deals with cards issued outside the United Kingdom.

In each section manufacturers are featured in alphabetical order, and the issues of each firm are catalogued alphabetically within suitable sub-divisions, such as, in Section 1, 'Pre-1919 Issues', 'Post-1920 Issues', 'Silks', 'Miscellaneous' and, in Section 2, 'With Brand Name', 'Without Brand Name', 'Silks', etc. Where a brand name, but no maker's name, is shown on the card, reference should be made to the appropriate Index of Brands. Anonymous series, that is those with printed backs but no brand or maker's name, are listed under the firms to which the issue has been attributed. Anonymous British issues are also listed at the end of Section 1.

Information is given in the columns from left to right as follows:

Size
(a) British issues: the code letter refers to the size of the card as indicated in the chart on page 4. A number 1 or 2 after the letter means that the card is slightly larger or smaller than shown.
(b) Foreign issues: the absence of a code letter indicates that the series is of standard size. A code letter 'L' defines the card as being large (about 80×62 mm). Other codes are 'K' = smaller than standard, 'M' between standard and large, and 'EL' = larger than large.

Printing
(a) British issues: the code indicates the printing on the front of the card. BW = black-and-white; C = coloured; CP = colour photograph; P = photograph; U = uni-coloured (monochrome).
(b) Foreign issues: the letter 'P' is used to show that a series consists of photographs.

Number in Set
This figure gives the number of cards in the series. A question mark alongside shows the exact number is unknown.

Title and Date
Where a series title is printed on the cards, this is used in the catalogue. For cards which do not exhibit a series title, an 'adopted' title is shown (indicated by an asterisk in the British section). Where a firm issued more than one series with the same title, these are distinguished by the addition of 'Set 1', 'Set 2', etc. or a code letter. The date of issue, where known, is shown in brackets.

Reference Code
(a) British issues: un-numbered series, series issued by more than one manufacturer, and different series of the same title issued by a single firm, have been given an 'H' or 'Ha' number cross-referencing to Handbooks Parts I and II respectively. 'RB' after the series title refers to the reference book covering a particular manufacturer, and 'W' after the title refers to the Wills Reference Book (details of these publications will be found on page 5).
(b) Foreign issues: 'RB18' followed by a number refers to the B.A.T. and Tobacco War reference book. 'WI' and WII' refer to World Tobacco Index Part I and Part II respectively. A reference number following a Wills' series relates to the Wills' Reference Book (details of these publications will be found on page 5).

Prices
The last two columns show the London Cigarette Card Company's selling prices for odd cards and complete sets in very good condition. Where no price is shown, this does not necessarily mean that the Company are permanently unable to supply, and if you require items in this category, please request a quotation enclosing a self-addressed envelope either with an International Reply Coupon or ready-stamped for posting in Britain.

HOW TO ORDER CARDS

Availability

We have the world's largest stocks of cigarette cards and the chances are that we will be able to supply your requirements for most series at the prices shown in the catalogue. However, certain odd cards, particularly from rarer series, may not be available in top condition and in such cases it is helpful if you indicate whether cards of a lower standard are acceptable at reduced prices. If a complete set is not in stock, we may be able to offer a part set, with one or two cards missing, at the appropriate fraction of full catalogue price. In some instances we can supply sets on request in fair to good condition at half catalogue price. If in doubt, please write for a quotation, enclosing a stamped, self-addressed envelope.

End Numbers

When ordering odd cards, please allow treble price for end numbers, for example, numbers 1 and 50 of a set of fifty, because these are the cards most frequently damaged in collections and consequently are more difficult to obtain in top condition.

Postage

Inland second class post is included in all prices quoted. Overseas postage is charged at cost.

Overseas payments in currencies other than sterling are acceptable, but allow £1 for bank conversion charges.

Value Added Tax where applicable is included in all prices shown.

Ordering

Please ensure that your name and full address are clearly shown. State the maker's name and the set title required (with 'first series', 'second series', date of issue, etc. as appropriate). For odds, please list each individual number wanted. Make your crossed cheque or postal order payable to The London Cigarette Card Company Limited and enclose with order. Notes and coins should be registered. Foreign remittances will be credited after conversion and deduction of bank charges. Please allow 14 days for delivery. Send your order to:

> The London Cigarette Card Co. Ltd.
> Sutton Road
> Somerton
> Somerset TA11 6QP
> England
> Telephone No. Somerton (0458) 73452

Remember that your cards will look their best when displayed in one of our albums, for which please see back cover.

Guarantee

In the unlikely event that you, the collector, are not satisfied with the cards supplied, we guarantee to replace them or refund your money, provided the goods are returned within 14 days of receipt. This guarantee does not affect your statutory rights.

Personal Callers

Personal callers are welcome at our Somerton offices on Mondays to Fridays from 9.30 a.m. to 1.00 p.m. and from 2.30 p.m. to 4.30 p.m., so if you are in the area, please call in and our staff will be able to assist you. However, being largely a mail order business, we do not have displays.

CARD SIZES (Applies to British issues only)

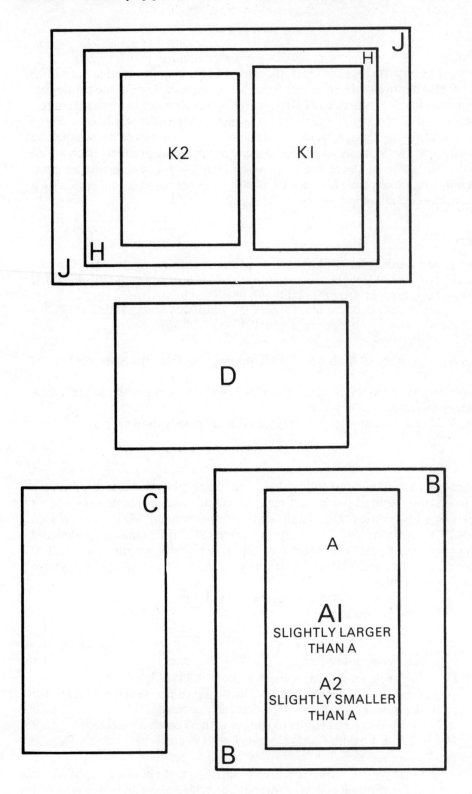

J

H

K2

K1

H

J

D

C

B

A

AI
SLIGHTLY LARGER
THAN A

A2
SLIGHTLY SMALLER
THAN A

B

BOOKS FOR THE COLLECTOR

The Catalogue of Trade Card Issues, 1986 Edition (Illustrated). This catalogue details a magnificent selection of different series issued by non-tobacco companies including Barrett and Brooke Bond from the 19th century to the present day. Contains hundreds of mint condition sets priced at only 75p each plus 16 pages of illustrations £3.50

Cigarette Cards & Novelties by Frank Doggett. 96 very large pages with more than 1,200 cards illustrated in full colour. Deals with the history and development of cigarette cards, popular themes, rarities and collecting hints £5.00

Collecting Cigarette Cards and Other Trade Issues by Dorothy Bagnall. An interesting paperback dealing with cigarette and trade cards from their origin through to the post-war period. 112 pages with 126 cards illustrated   £3.95

Reference Books

Handbook Part I (1888 to 1919) 172-page reference book (no prices) listing subjects of unnumbered series, etc. Illustrated, hardback. Covers British Cigarette Cards issued between 1888 and 1919, cross-referenced to the catalogue (964 cards illustrated) £5.00

Handbook Part II (1920 to 1940) 164-page reference book (no prices) listing subjects of unnumbered series, etc. Illustrated, hardback. Covers British Cigarette Cards issued between 1920 and 1940, and all silk issues, cross-referenced to the catalogue (906 cards illustrated) £5.00

World Tobacco Card Index & Handbook Part I (701 pages and nearly 2,000 cards illustrated) £10.00

World Tobacco Card Index Part II (supplement to Index I, 452 pages with approximately 3,600 cards illustrated) £10.00

World Tobacco Card Index Part III (supplement to Index I and II, 504 pages with more than 650 cards illustrated) £10.00

The Card Issues of Abdulla/Adkin/Anstie (20 pages) £1.95
The Card Issues of Ardath Tobacco (28 pages) £1.95

Australian and New Zealand Card Issues (over 300 pages with 600 cards illustrated) £10.50

The Card Issues of B.A.T. & Tobacco War (336 pages with nearly 3,000 cards illustrated) £10.00

The Card Issues of Churchman (36 pages with 29 cards illustrated) £1.95
The Card Issues of Faulkner (12 pages) £1.95
The Card Issues of Gallaher (40 pages) £1.95
The Card Issues of Hill (28 pages) £1.95
The Card Issues of Lambert & Butler (32 pages with 25 cards illustrated) .   £1.95

The Card Issues of Ogdens including Guinea Gold (244 pages with 356 cards illustrated) £10.00

The Card Issues of Godfrey Phillips (40 pages with 225 cards illustrated) .   £1.95
The Card Issues of John Player (44 pages with 26 cards illustrated) £1.95
The Card Issues of Taddy (32 pages with 30 cards illustrated) £1.95
The Card Issues of Wills (200 pages with 559 cards illustrated) £5.00
Guide Book No. 1 Ty-Phoo Tea Cards (36 pages with 68 cards illustrated)   £1.95
Guide Book No. 2 F & J Smith Cards (36 pages with 79 cards illustrated)   £2.00

Guide Book No. 3 A. & B. C. Gum Cards (44 pages with 29 cards illustrated) £2.75

British Trade Card Index Part I (pre-1945 issues, 216 pages with 423 cards illustrated) £7.00

British Trade Card Index Part II (1945-1969 issues, 232 pages with 274 cards illustrated) £7.00

Directory of British Tobacco Issuers (36 pages with 16 cards illustrated) . .   £1.95
Glossary of Cartophilic Terms (40 pages with 27 cards illustrated) £1.95

All the above books are available from
THE LONDON CIGARETTE CARD COMPANY LTD.
SUTTON ROAD, SOMERTON, SOMERSET, ENGLAND. TA11 6QP.
Tel: Somerton (0458) 73452

AUCTIONS
Please see back page for details.

SECTION I
BRITISH CIGARETTE CARDS

INDEX OF BRANDS

The following is a list of the cases so far known where cards appear without the name of issuer, but inscribed with a Brand Name or other indication which is the collector's only clue to the identity of issuer.

A. INDEX OF BRANDS and initials found on British issues of cards or silks.

All Arms Cigarettes—see Carreras

B.D.V. Cigarettes—see Godfrey Phillips
Bandmaster Cigarettes—see Cohen Weenen and Drapkin
Big Gun Cigarettes—see Sandorides
Black Cat Cigarettes—see Carreras
Blush of Day Cigarettes—see Robinson & Barnsdale
Broadway Novelties—see Teofani
The Buffs—see Drapkin

Cake Walk Cigarettes—see Pezaro
Casket and Critic Cigarettes—see Pattreiouex
The Challenge Flat Brilliantes—see Gloag
Citamora Cigarettes—see Gloag
Club Member Cigarettes—see Pattreiouex
Club Mixture Tobaccos—see Continental Cigarette Factory
Colin Campbell Cigars—see Robinson & Barnsdale
Crowfoot Cigarettes—see Hill
Cymax Cigarettes—see Coudens

Eldona Cigars—see Drapkin & Millhoff
Erinmore Cigarettes—see Murray
Explorer Cigars—see Drapkin & Millhoff

The Favourite Magnums Cigarettes—see Teofani
The Flor de Dindigul Cigar—see Bewlay
Forecasta—see B. Morris
Fresher Cigarettes—see Challis

G.P.—see Godfrey Phillips
Gainsborough Cigarettes—see Cohen Weenen
Gala Cigarettes—issuers unknown, see under Miscellaneous
General Favourite Onyx—issuers unknown, see under Anonymous
Gibson Girl Virginia, Madrali Turkish and Hungarian—see Hill
Gold Flake Cigarettes—see Hill

Gold Flake, Honeydew and Navy Cut Medium Cigarettes—see Hill
The Greys Cigarettes—see United Kingdom Tobacco Co.

Hawser, Epaulet and Honey Flake Cigarettes—see Wholesale Tobacco Supply Syndicate
Heart's Delight Cigarettes—see Pritchard & Burton

Jersey Lily Cigarettes—see Wm. Bradford
Cigarette Job—see Societe Job
Junior Member Cigarettes—see Pattreiouex

Kensitas Cigarettes—see J. Wix

Leon de Cuba Cigars—see Eldons
Levant Favourites—see B. Morris
Life Ray Cigarettes—see Carreras
Lucana Cigarettes—see Sandorides

Matossian's Cigarettes—see Henly & Watkins
Max Cigarettes—see A. & M. Wix
Mayblossom Cigarettes—see Lambert & Butler
Mills—see Amalgamated

New Orleans Tobacco—see J. & T. Hodge

Oracle Cigarettes—see Tetley

Pibroch Virginia—see Fryer
Pick-Me-Up Cigarettes—see Drapkin & Millhoff
Pinnace—see Godfrey Phillips
Pioneer Cigarettes—see Richmond Cavendish
Polo Mild Cigarettes—see Murray
Private Seal Tobacco—see Godfrey Phillips

Q.V. Cigars—see Webster

R.S.—see Robert Sinclair

Reina Regenta Cigars—see B. Morris
De Reszke Cigarettes—see Millhoff and
  Godfrey Phillips
Ringers Cigarettes—see Edwards,
  Ringer & Bigg
Roseland Cigarettes—see Glass

Senior Service Cigarettes—see
  Pattreiouex
Spinet Cigarettes or The Spinet House—
  see Hill
The Spotlight Tobaccos—see Hill
Star of the World Cigarettes—see J.L.S.
State Express Cigarettes—see Ardath

Summit—see International Tobacco Co.
Sunripe Cigarettes—see Hill
Sweet Alva Cigarettes—see Drapkin

T.S.S.—see Tobacco Supply Syndicate
Tatley's Cigarettes—see Walker's
  Tobacco Co.
Three Bells Cigarettes—see J. & F. Bell
Tipsy Loo Cigarettes—see H. C. Lloyd
Topsy Cigarettes—see Richards & Ward
Trawler, Critic and King Lud
  Cigarettes—see Pattreiouex

W.T.C.—see Walker's Tobacco Co.

B. INDEX OF INSCRIPTIONS found on British issues of cards

'The Cigarettes with which these Picture Cards are issued are manufactured in England
  and are Guaranteed Pure'—see Hill.
'England expects that Every Man will do his duty—By Purchasing these Cigarettes you
  are supporting British labour'—issuers unknown, see Anonymous
'Issued with these Famous Cigarettes'—see Teofani
'Issued with these Fine Cigarettes'—see Teofani
'Issued with these High Grade Cigarettes'—see Teofani
'Issued with these Well-known Cigarettes'—see Teofani
'Issued with these World Famous Cigarettes'—see Teofani
'Presented with these well-known choice cigarettes'—see Teofani
'Smoke these cigarettes always'—see Teofani
'These Cigarettes are Guaranteed Best British Manufacture'—see Hill.

C. INDEX OF OTHER INDICATIONS found on British Tobacco Issues

THE B.I. Co.—see Burstein Isaacs
Chantler & Co., Bury—see Lea
'Eagle, Cork'—see Lambkin
Agnes D. Eld, Dudley—see Lea
L. & Y. Tobacco Co.—see Lancs. and Yorks. Tobacco Manufacturing Co.
Orient Line Steamships—see Singleton & Cole
P. O. Box 5764, Johannesburg—see A. & M. Wix
S. C. Peacock Sales Co.—see Lea

ABDULLA & CO. LTD., London

Illus. No.	Size	Printing	Number in set		Handbook ref.	Price per card	Complete set
A. Export Issues Post-1920							
	A	BW	50	Beauties of To-Day (1938)	Ha.514	£1.70	—
	A	C	25	British Butterflies (1935)	Ha.517–1	36p	£9.00
	A	P	52	Cinema Stars—Set 1	Ha.515–1B	£2.50	—
	A2	U	30	Cinema Stars—Set 2	Ha.515–2	£2.50	—
	A2	U	30	Cinema Stars—Set 3	Ha.515–3	£2.50	—
	A2	U	32	Cinema Stars—Set 4	Ha.515–4	80p	£25.00
	A2	C	32	Cinema Stars—Set 5	Ha.515–5	80p	£25.00
	A2	C	30	Cinema Stars—Set 6	Ha.515–6	£2.50	—
161	D	C	25	Feathered Friends (1935)	Ha.516	44p	£11.00
	A2	C	50	Film Favourites (1934)	Ha.517–2	£1.70	—
	A	C	50	Film Stars (1934)		£7.00	—
	—	C	24	*Film Stars (128 × 89 mm.)	Ha.517–3	—	—
	A	C	25	Old Favourites (1936) (Flowers)	Ha.517–4	16p	£4.00
	A	C	40	Screen Stars (1939):—			
				A. Normal Abdulla back		30p	£12.00
				B. "Issued by the Successors to …" back		70p	£28.00
	A2	C	50	Stage and Cinema Beauties (1935)	Ha.517–5	£2.50	—
	A	U	30	Stars of the Stage and Screen		£3.00	—
B. Miscellaneous							
		?	4	Bridge Rule Cards (various sizes)		£11.00	—
				Great War Gift Packings Cards		£27.00	—
				Message Cards (letters of the alphabet)		£4.00	—

ADCOCK & SON, Norwich

Illus. No.	Size	Printing	Number in set		Handbook ref.	Price per card	Complete set
Post-1920 Issue							
	A1	U	12	Ancient Norwich (1928–29)		—	£40.00
			11/12	Ancient Norwich (No. 6 missing)		70p	£8.00

ADKIN & SONS, London

Illus. No.	Size	Printing	Number in set		Handbook ref.	Price per card	Complete set
A. Pre-1919 Issues							
	D	BW	25	*Actresses—French, Nd. 126–150	H.1/Ha.1	£35.00	—
	A	C	15	*Beauties—"PAC"	H.2/Ha.2	£35.00	—
	A2	C	12	Character Sketches:—	H.3/Ha.3		
				A. Black printing on back (1901)		£4.00	£50.00
				B. Green printing on back (1902–3)		£4.00	£50.00
	A2	C	12	A Living Picture:—	H.5/Ha.5		
				A. "Adkin & Sons" at top back			
				(i) crimson		£4.00	£50.00
				(ii) scarlet		£4.00	£50.00
				B. "These cards are …" at top back		£4.00	£50.00
	A	BW	25	Notabilities (1915)	H.6	£2.40	£60.00
	A1	C	12	Pretty Girl Series (Actresses)	H.7/Ha.7	£22.00	—
	A2	C	12	*Pretty Girl Series—"RASH" (1897):—	H.8/Ha.8		
				I. 1–6 Head and shoulders:			
				A. Calendar back		£22.00	—
				B. Advertisements back		£10.00	£60.00
				C. Figure and verse back		£10.00	£60.00
				II. 7–12 Full length:			
				A. Calendar back		£22.00	—
				B. Advertisements back		£10.00	£60.00
				C. Figure and verse back		£10.00	£60.00
	D	C	12	A Royal Favourite	H.9/Ha.9	£8.00	£100.00
	A	BW		Soldiers of the Queen (1899–1900)—	H.10		
			50	A. Series of 50:—			
				(a) Nos. 1–25 "… and exclusively with"		£16.00	—
				(b) Nos. 1–50 and variety "… and issued with …"		£3.00	£150.00
			61	B. Series of 60, 59 numbers and varieties		£2.40	—
	A	BW	31	*Soldiers of the Queen and Portraits (1901)	H.11/Ha.11	£3.50	£110.00
	A	C	30	Sporting Cups & Trophies (1914)		£9.00	—
	A	BW	25	War Trophies (1917)		£3.20	£80.00
B. Post-1920 Issues							
	A	C	50	Butterflies and Moths (1924)	H.80	80p	£40.00
228	A	C	50	Wild Animals of the World (1922–23)	H.77	80p	£40.00
C. Miscellaneous							
			12	Character Sketches (premium issue)		—	—
		C	? 4	*Games—by Tom Browne, postcard back (135 × 85 mm.)	H.4/Ha.4	—	—
			12	A Living Picture (premium issue)		—	—

H. J. AINSWORTH, Harrogate

Illus. No.	Size	Printing	Number in set		Handbook ref.	Price per card	Complete set
Pre-1919 Issue							
	D	C	30	*Army Pictures, Cartoons, Etc.	H.12	£50.00	—

ALBERGE & BROMET, London

Illus. No.	Size	Printing	Number in set		Handbook ref.	Price per card	Complete set
Pre-1919 Issues							
	A	C	? 25	*Boer War and General Interest:—	H.13/Ha.13		

Illus. No.	Size	Print-ing	Number in set		Handbook ref.	Price per card	Complete set
				A. "Bridal Bouquet" and "El Benecio" wording on green leaf design back......		£40.00	—
				B. "La Optima" and "Federation" wording on green leaf design back..........		£40.00	—
				C. "Bridal Bouquet" and "El Benecio" wording on brown leaf design back.....		£40.00	—
	D1	C	40	*Naval and Military Phrases:—	H.14		
				A. "Bridal Bouquet" and "El Benecio"....		£45.00	—
				B. "La Optima" and "Federation"........		£45.00	—
	D1	C	30	*Proverbs................................	H.15	£40.00	—

PHILLIP ALLMAN & CO. LTD., London _____

Post-1940 Issues							
359	A	C	50	Coronation Series (1953)..................		30p	£15.00
	A1	C		Pin-up Girls (1953):— A. First 12 subjects:—			
			12	Ai unnumbered "For men only".........		40p	£5.00
			12	Aii numbered "Ask for Allman always"..		40p	£5.00
			12	Aiii unnumbered "Ask for Allman always"		85p	£10.00
	A1	C	12	B. Second 12 subjects.....................		£1.25	—
	A1	C	24	C. Inscribed "1st series of 24"............		—	—
	—	C	24	D. Large size (75 × 68 mm.)..............		£1.25	£30.00

AMALGAMATED TOBACCO CORPORATION LTD. ("Mills" Cigarettes) _____

A. Post-1940 Issues							
	—	C	25	Famous British Ships "Series No. 1" (75 × 48 mm.) (1952)...................		10p	£0.75
	—	C	25	Famous British Ships "Series No. 2" (75 × 48 mm.) (1952)...................		10p	£0.75
	—	C	50	History of Aviation (75 × 48 mm.) (1952)			
				A. Nos. 1 to 16, 18 to 25 and 27		£1.00	—
				B. Nos. 17, 26 and 28 to 50		10p	£2.00
	A	C	25	Kings of England (1954).................		80p	£20.00
	A	C	25	Propelled Weapons (1953).................		10p	£0.75
B. Export Issues							
	A	C	25	Aircraft of the World (1958)		10p	£0.75
	A	C	25	Animals of the Countryside (1957).........		10p	£1.00
	A	C	25	Aquarium Fish (1961)....................		10p	£1.00
356	A	C	25	Army Badges—Past & Present (1961)		10p	£2.00
	A	C	25	British Coins & Costumes (1958)...........		10p	£1.00
	A	C	25	British Locomotives (1961)		10p	£2.50
	A	C	25	British Uniforms of the 19th Century (1957).		16p	£4.00
	A	C	25	Butterflies & Moths (1957)...............		10p	£0.75
	A	C	25	Cacti (1961)............................		10p	£0.75
	A	C	25	Castles of Britain (1961)		24p	£6.00
248	A	C	25	Coins of the World (1961)		10p	£1.00
	A	C	25	Communications (1961)...................		36p	£9.00
	A	C	25	Dogs (1958)............................		10p	£1.50
	A	C	25	Evolution of the Royal Navy (1957)........		10p	£2.00
	A	C	25	Football Clubs and Badges (1961)..........		60p	£15.00
	A	C	25	Freshwater Fish (1958)...................		10p	£0.75
	A	C	25	Geurriers A Travers Les Ages (French text) (1961)................................		50p	£12.50
	A	C	25	Historical Buildings (1959)		20p	£5.00
	A	C	25	Histoire de L'Aviation, 1st series (French text) (1961)...........................		10p	£0.90
	A	C	25	Histoire de L'Aviation, 2nd Series (French text) (1962)...........................		10p	£0.75
	A	C	25	Holiday Resorts (1957)....................		10p	£0.75
148	A	C	25	Interesting Hobbies (1959).................		10p	£2.50
	A	C	25	Into Space (1958)		10p	£1.00
	A	C	25	Les Autos Moderns (French text) (1961)		16p	£4.00
300	A	C	25	Medals of the World (1959)................		10p	£1.75
	A	C	25	Merchant Ships of the World (1961)........		10p	£1.25
	A	C	25	Merveillers Modernes (French text) (1961) ..		30p	£7.50
	A	C	25	Miniature Cars and Scooters (1959)........		50p	£12.50
	A	C	25	Nature (1958)..........................		10p	£0.75
65	A	C	25	Naval Battles (1959).....................		10p	£1.00
	A	C	25	Ports of the World (1957).................		10p	£0.75
	A	C	25	Ships of the Royal Navy (1961)		20p	£5.00
	A	C	25	Sports and Games (1958)		30p	£7.50
	A	C	25	Tropical Birds (1959)....................		60p	£15.00
	A	C	25	Weapons of Defence (1961)................		10p	£2.50
	A	C	25	Wild Animals (1958)		10p	£0.75
	A	C	25	The Wild West (1960)		16p	£4.00
	A	C	25	World Locomotives (1959)		16p	£4.00

THE ANGLO-AMERICAN CIGARETTE MAKING CO., LTD., London _____

Pre-1919 Issue							
	A	C	20	Russo-Japanese War Series (1906)	Ha.100	—	—

THE ANGLO CIGARETTE MANUFACTURING CO., London

Illus. No.	Size	Printing	Number in set		Handbook ref.	Price per card	Complete set
A. Pre-1919 Issue							
	A	C	36	Tariff Reform Series (1909)	H.16	£14.00	—

E. & W. ANSTIE, Devizes

Illus. No.	Size	Printing	Number in set		Handbook ref.	Price per card	Complete set
Pre-1919 Issues							
	A	C	16	*British Empire Series (1904)	H.17/Ha.17	£10.00	£160.00
		C	8	Puzzles (1902) (26 × 70mm.)	H.18/Ha.18	£50.00	—
		C	5	Royal Mail (1899) (70 × 50mm.)	H.19/Ha.19	£90.00	—
B. Post-1920 Issues							
119	A2	C	25	Aesop's Fables (1934)	Ha.518	60p	£15.00
	A	U	50	People of Africa (1926)		£1.80	£90.00
	A	U	50	People of Asia (1926)		£1.80	£90.00
	A	U	50	People of Europe (1925)		£1.80	£90.00
	A2	BW	40	Places of Interest (1939):—			
				A. Varnished front		15p	£6.00
				B. Unvarnished front		60p	£24.00
223	A	C	50	*Racing Series (1922):—			
				1–25—Racing Colours		£1.20	£30.00
				26–50—Horses, Jockeys, Race-courses, etc.		£1.20	£30.00
207	A	C	50	Scout Series (1923)		£1.60	£80.00
	A2	C		Sectional Series:—	Ha.519		
			10	Clifton Suspension Bridge (1938)		30p	£3.00
			10	Stonehenge (1936)		30p	£3.00
			10	The Victory (1936)		60p	£6.00
			20	Wells Cathedral (1935)		40p	£8.00
			20	Wiltshire Downs (1935)		50p	£10.00
			10	Windsor Castle (1937)		30p	£3.00
322	A2	BW	40	Wessex (1938).		50p	£20.00
221	A	U	50	The World's Wonders (1924)		£1.20	£60.00

C. Silks. Anonymous unbacked woven silks. Width sizes only are quoted as the silks were prepared in ribbon form and length sizes are thus arbitrary.

Illus. No.	Size	Printing	Number in set		Handbook ref.	Price per card	Complete set
—		C	? 9	*Flags, large (width 95 mm.).	Ha.495-1	£2.50	—
—		C	? 31	*Flags, small (width 42 mm.)	Ha.495-1	70p	—
—		C	? 80	*Regimental Badges (width 32 mm.).	Ha.495-3	From 70p	—
—		C		*Royal Standard and Portraits:—	Ha.495-2		
			1	Royal Standard (width 61 mm.).		—	£2.00
			1	King George V:—			
				(a) Large (width 71 mm.), black frame		—	£45.00
				(b) Large (width 71 mm.), gold frame		—	£35.00
				(c) Small (width 35 mm.)		—	£45.00
			1	Queen Mary:—			
				(a) Large (width 71 mm.)		—	£25.00
				(b) Small (width 35 mm.)		—	£45.00
			1	Lord French (width 71 mm.)		—	£55.00
			1	Lord Kitchener (width 71 mm.)		—	£10.00

H. ARCHER & CO., London

Illus. No.	Size	Printing	Number in set		Handbook ref.	Price per card	Complete set
Pre-1919 Issues							
	C	C	? 30	*Actresses—Selection from "FROGA A and B".	H.20/Ha.20		
				A. "Golden Returns" back		£30.00	—
				B. "M.F.H." back		£35.00	—
	C		50	*Beauties—"CHOAB":—	H.21/Ha.21		
		U		A. "Bound to Win" front		£11.00	—
		C		B. "Golden Returns" back		£30.00	—
		C		C. "M.F.H." back		£30.00	—
	C	C	20	*Prince of Wales Series	H.22	£15.00	—

ARDATH TOBACCO CO. LTD., London

Illus. No.	Size	Printing	Number in set		Handbook ref.	Price per card	Complete set
A. Pre-1919 Issues. All export.							
	—	U	30	Boucher Series (77 × 62 mm.)		£1.50	—
	—	U	30	Gainsborough Series (77 × 62 mm.)		£1.50	—
	A1	U	50	Great War Series.		£4.00	—
	A1	U	50	Great War Series "B"		£4.00	—
	A1	U	50	Great War Series "C"		£4.00	—
	A1	U	40	Franz Hals Series, Dutch back		—	—
				Hollandsche Oude Meesters, Dutch back (70 × 60 mm.):—			
	—	U	25	A. First 25 subjects		£6.00	—
	—	U	25	B. Second 25 subjects		£6.00	—
	—	U	30	Raphael Series (77 × 62 mm.)		£1.50	—
	—	U		Rembrandt Series:—			
			30	A. Large size (77 × 62 mm.), English back .		£2.00	—
			40	B. Large size (77 × 62 mm.), Dutch back. . .		£2.50	—
			30	C. Extra-large size (101 × 62 mm.).		£2.75	—
	—	U	30	Rubens Series (77 × 61 mm.):—			•
				A. English "State Express" back		£1.50	—
				B. English "Winfred" back		—	—
				C. Dutch back		—	—
				D. New Zealand "State Express" back		—	—

Illus. No.	Size	Print-ing	Number in set		Handbook ref.	Price per card	Complete set
	—	U	30	Velasquez Series:—			
				A. Large size (77 × 62 mm.)		£1.75	—
				B. Extra-large size (101 × 62 mm.)		£2.50	—

B. Post-1920 Non-photographic Issues

Illus. No.	Size	Print-ing	Number in set		Handbook ref.	Price per card	Complete set
	A1	C	50	*Animals at the Zoo (export):—	Ha.520		
				A. Back with descriptive text		80p	£40.00
				B. Back without description, "Double Ace" issue		£4.00	—
	A	C	96	Ardath Modern School Atlas (export)		£1.00	—
	A	C	25	Big Game Hunting (export):—			
				A. Back in blue		£1.60	£40.00
				B. Back in black		£4.00	—
	A	U	50	Britain's Defenders (Dec. 1936) (see RB21/463B)		25p	£12.50
		U	50	British Born Film Stars (export):—			
	A2			A. Small size, back white semi-glossy		70p	—
	A2			B. Small size, back cream matt		70p	—
	—			C. Medium size (67 × 53 mm.)		70p	—
		U		Camera Studies (see RB21/268–2B):—			
	—		36	A. Small size (70 × 44 mm.)		50p	£18.00
	—		45	B. Large size (79 × 57 mm.)		50p	£22.00
	—	C	25	Champion Dogs (95 × 67 mm.) (Nov. 1934) (see RB21/370B)		32p	£8.00
	A	C	50	Cricket, Tennis and Golf Celebrities (Jul. 1935):—			
				A. Home issue, grey back		25p	£12.50
				B. Export issue, brownish-grey back, text revised		80p	£40.00
	—	U	25	Dog Studies (95 × 68 mm.) (Sep. 1938)		50p	£12.50
	A	C	25	Eastern Proverbs (export)	Ha.521	80p	£20.00
	A	C	48	Empire Flying-Boat (sectional) (Jan. 1938) . .		36p	£18.00
	A	C	50	Empire Personalities (Apr. 1937)		40p	£20.00
122	A	C	50	Famous Film Stars (Aug. 1934)		32p	£16.00
	A	C	50	Famous Footballers (Oct. 1934)		25p	£12.50
	A	C	25	Famous Scots (Jun. 1935)		32p	£8.00
	—	C	25	Fighting and Civil Aircraft (96 × 68 mm.) (Apr. 1936)		£1.00	£25.00
	A	C	50	Figures of Speech (Feb. 1936)		20p	£10.00
	A	C	50	Film, Stage and Radio Stars (Sep. 1935)		40p	£20.00
	—	C	25	Film, Stage and Radio Stars (96 × 68 mm.) (Jun. 1935)		20p	£5.00
	—	C	50	From Screen and Stage (96 × 68 mm.) (Dec. 1936)		40p	£20.00
	A	U	50	Life in the Services:—			
				A. Home issue (May 1938), adhesive		20p	£10.00
				B. Export issue, non-adhesive		70p	£35.00
135	A	C	50	National Fitness:—			
				A. Home issue (Sep. 1938), adhesive		18p	£9.00
				B. Export issue, non-adhesive		70p	£35.00
	A	U	50	Our Empire (export)	Ha.522	80p	£40.00
302	A	C		Proverbs:—			
			25	A. Home issue (Sep. 1936) Nos 1–25		16p	£4.00
			25	B. Export issue Nos 26–50		80p	£20.00
		U	100	Scenes from Big Films (export):—			
	A			A. Small Size White Back		70p	—
	A			B. Small Size Cream Back		70p	—
				C. Medium Size (67 × 52 mm.)		70p	—
	A	C	50	Silver Jubilee (Mar. 1935)		25p	£12.50
	A	C	50	Speed—Land Sea and Air:—			
				A. Home issue (Jul. 1935), "Issued with State Express"		40p	£20.00
				B. Export issue, Ardath name at base		80p	—
	—	C	25	Speed—Land, Sea and Air (95 × 68 mm.) (Apr. 1938)		40p	£10.00
	A	C	50	Sports Champions (1935):—			
				A. Home issue, with album offer, "State Express" at base		22p	£11.00
				B. Export issue, without album offer, "Ardath" at base		80p	£40.00
224	A	C	50	Stamps—Rare and Interesting (Jan. 1939) . . .		70p	£35.00
	A	C	50	Swimming, Diving and Life-Saving (Mar. 1937) (export)	Ha.523	80p	—
	A	C	50	Tennis (Sep. 1937) (export)	Ha.524	80p	—
	A	C	48	Trooping the Colour (sectional) (May 1939) .		70p	£35.00
98	A	C	50	Who is This? (May 1936) (Film Stars)		18p	£9.00
	—	BW	24	World Views (No. 13 not issued) (95 × 68 mm.) (Oct. 1937)		13p	£3.00
297	A	C	50	Your Birthday Tells Your Fortune (Jul. 1937)		16p	£8.00

C. Post-1920 Photographic Issues

Illus. No.	Size	Print-ing	Number in set		Handbook ref.	Price per card	Complete set
	A2	P	54	Beautiful English Women (1928) (export) . . .		£1.50	—
	A2	P	35	Hand Shadows (export)		—	—
	A2	CP	50	New Zealand Views (1928) (export)		£1.80	—
	H	P		Photocards—Numbered Series (Aug. 1936–Jan. 1937)*—			
			110	"A"—Football Clubs of Lancashire		32p	£35.00
			110	"B"—Football Clubs of North East Counties		45p	£50.00
			110	"C"—Football Clubs of Yorkshire		45p	£50.00
			165	"D"—Football Clubs of Scotland		30p	£50.00
			110	"E"—Football Clubs of Midlands		40p	£45.00

ARDATH TOBACCO CO. LTD. *(continued)*

Illus. No.	Size	Print-ing	Number in set		Handbook ref.	Price per card	Complete set
			110	"F"—Football Clubs of London and Southern Counties..................		23p	£25.00
			99	"Z"—General Interest:—			
				Nos. 111–165		13p	£2.50
				Nos. 166–209 (Cricket etc.)		13p	£3.00
			11	"A.s." (1), "C.s." (2–3), "E.s." (4–10), "F.s." (11)—Football Clubs (supplementary)................................		80p	£9.00
	H	P		Photocards—"A Continuous Series of Topical Interest" (Jul. 1937–May 1938):—	Ha.525		
			22	Group A—Racehorses and Sports		14p	£3.00
			22	Group B—Coronation and Sports		—	£14.00
			21	Different (minus Walter Neusel)		20p	£4.00
			22	Group C—Lancashire Personalities........		—	£20.00
			21	Different (minus Gracie Fields)		50p	£10.00
			22	Group D—Irish Personalities, etc.		40p	£9.00
			22	Group E—Film Stars and Sports		25p	£5.50
			22	Group F—Film Stars and Sportsmen		70p	£15.00
			66	"G.S."—Miscellaneous subjects (export)		75p	£50.00
	H	P		Photocards—"A Continuous Series of General interest", with Album Offer (May–Nov. 1938):—	Ha.526		
			11	Group G—Australian Cricketers		£12.00	—
			22	Group H—Film, Radio and Sporting Stars..		50p	£11.00
			22	Group I—Film Stars and Miscellaneous.....		80p	£17.50
		P		Photocards—"A Continuous Series of General Interest", without Album Offer—Uncoloured (Dec. 1938–Oct. 1939):—	Ha.527		
	H		22	Group J—Film Stars and General Interest...		18p	£4.00
	H		22	Group K—Film, Radio and Sporting Stars:—			
				1. With "Kings" Clause..................		50p	£11.00
				2. Without "Kings" Clause (export)		70p	£15.00
	H		44	Group L—Film Stars and Miscellaneous....		23p	£10.00
368	C		45	Group M—Film Stars and Miscellaneous:—			
				1. Small size........................		40p	£18.00
	—			2. Large size (80 × 69 mm.), with "Kings" Clause		45p	£20.00
	—			3. Large size (80 × 69 mm.), without "Kings" Clause		45p	£20.00
		P	45	Group N—Film, Stage and Radio Stars:—			
	C			1. Small size........................		45p	£20.00
	—			2. Large size (80 × 69 mm.)		45p	£20.00
	H	CP		Photocards—"A Continuous Series of General Interest", without Album Offer—Hand Coloured (export) (Dec. 1938):—	Ha.528		
			22	Group 1—Views of the World		36p	£8.00
			22	Group 2—Views of the World		36p	£8.00
			22	Group 3—Views of the World		23p	£5.00
				Real Photographs:—			
	—	P	45	Group O—"A Continuous Series of General Interest"—Films, Stage and Radio Stars (Oct. 1939).....................	Ha.529	40p	£18.00
	C	P	45	"1st Series of 45"—Film and Stage Stars (Jun. 1939).........................		55p	£25.00
	C	P	54	"2nd Series of 54"—Film and Stage Stars (Aug. 1939).........................		55p	£30.00
	J2	P	18	"First Series"—Views (Jun. 1937)..........		£1.10	£20.00
	J2	P	18	"Second Series"—Film and Stage Stars (Jun. 1937)...............................		£1.10	£20.00
	J2	P	18	"Third Series"—Views (Nov. 1937)		£1.10	£20.00
	J2	P	18	"Fourth Series"—Film and Stage Stars (Nov. 1937)...............................		£1.10	£20.00
	J2	P	18	"Fifth Series"—Views (Feb. 1938)		£1.10	£20.00
	J2	P	18	"Sixth Series"—Film and Stage Stars (Jan. 1938)................................		£1.10	£20.00
	H	P	44	"Series One" "G.P.1"—Film Stars (export) (Aug. 1939).........................		34p	£15.00
	H	P	44	"Series Two" "G.P.2"—Film Stars (export) (Nov. 1939).........................		13p	£3.50
	H	P	44	"Series Three" "G.P.3"—Film Stars (export) (Nov. 1939).........................		£1.50	—
	H	CP	44	"Series Three" "C.V.3"—Views (export) (Aug. 1939).........................		34p	£15.00
	H	CP	44	"Series Four" "C.V.4"—Views (export) (Nov. 1939).............................		13p	£4.00
	J2	P	36	"Series Seven"—Film and Stage Stars (Mar. 1938)................................		70p	—
	J2	P	54	"Series Eight"—Film and Stage Stars (Jul. 1938)................................		37p	£20.00
		P	54	"Series Nine"—Film and Stage Stars (Oct. 1938):—			
	H			A. Medium size		33p	£18.00
	J2			B. Extra-large size....................		33p	£18.00
		P	54	"Series Ten"—Film and Stage Stars:—			
	—			A. Large size (80 × 69 mm.) (Feb. 1939)....		33p	£18.00
	J2			B. Extra-large size (Jun. 1939)		40p	£22.00
	—	P	54	"Series Eleven"—Film and Stage Stars 1939.			
	—			A. Large size (80 × 69 mm.)		30p	£16.00

ARDATH TOBACCO CO. LTD. *(continued)*

Illus. No.	Size	Print-ing	Number in set		Handbook ref.	Price per card	Complete set
J2				B. Extra-large size		70p	—
—		P	54	"Series Twelve"—Film and Stage Stars (80 × 69 mm.) (Sep. 1939)................		28p	£15.00
—		P	54	"Series Thirteen"—Film and Stage Stars (80 × 69 mm.) (Dec. 1939)................		28p	£15.00
		P	36	"of Famous Landmarks" (Aug. 1939):—			
—				A. Large size (80 × 69 mm.), titled "Real Photographs"......................		£1.50	—
J2				B. Extra-large size, titled "Real Photographs of Famous Landmarks".......		80p	£30.00
		P	36	"of Modern Aircraft":—			
—				A. Large size (80 × 69 mm.) (Jun. 1939)....		£1.25	£45.00
J2				B. Extra-large size (Mar. 1939)...........		£1.00	£36.00

D. Miscellaneous

Illus. No.	Size	Print-ing	Number in set		Handbook ref.	Price per card	Complete set
—		C	30	Girls of All Nations (78 × 66 mm.)		£6.00	—
			25	Historic Grand Slams (folders) (101 × 70 mm.).....................................		•	—
			48	How to Recognise the Service Ranks (holed for binding)		£1.50	—
			150	Information Slips (holed for binding)		£1.20	—
				Ministry of Information Cards (1941–3):—			
			? 5	A. Calendar—"It all depends on me"		50p	£2.50
				B. Greeting Card—"It all depends on me"		—	—
			24	C. "It all depends on me" (80 × 63 mm.)		32p	£8.00
				D. Union Jack Folder		—	—
			? 4	Wonderful Handicraft......................		£7.00	—

THE ASSOCIATED TOBACCO MANUFACTURERS, LTD. ———

Post-1920 Issues

Illus. No.	Size	Print-ing	Number in set		Handbook ref.	Price per card	Complete set
C2		C	25	Cinema Stars (export):—	Ha.530		
				A. "Issued with Bond Street Turkish Cigarettes"		—	—
				B. "Issued with John Bull Virginia Cigarettes"		—	—
				C. "Issued with Club Virginia Cigarettes" .		—	—
				D. "Issued with Heliopolis Turkish Cigarettes"		—	—
				E. "Issued with Sports Turkish Cigarettes"		—	—

A. ATKINSON, London ———

Pre-1919 Issue

Illus. No.	Size	Print-ing	Number in set		Handbook ref.	Price per card	Complete set
D		C	30	*Army Pictures, Cartoons, etc...............	H.12	—	—

AVISS BROTHERS LTD., London ———

Pre-1919 Issue

Illus. No.	Size	Print-ing	Number in set		Handbook ref.	Price per card	Complete set
D1		C	40	*Naval and Military Phrases.................	H.14	£45.00	—

J. A. BAILEY, Swansea ———

Pre-1919 Issue

Illus. No.	Size	Print-ing	Number in set		Handbook ref.	Price per card	Complete set
D1		C	40	*Naval and Military Phrases.................	H.14	—	—

A. BAKER & CO. LTD., London ———

Pre-1919 Issues

Illus. No.	Size	Print-ing	Number in set		Handbook ref.	Price per card	Complete set
A		BW	20	*Actresses—"BLARM," "A. Baker & Co. Ltd." at foot:—	H.23		
				A. Long design back		£14.00	—
				B. Design altered and shortened		£14.00	—
A		BW	10	*Actresses—"HAGG A"...................	H.24	£12.00	£120.00
		BW		*Actresses "Baker's 3-sizes":—	H.25/Ha.25		
A			25	Small cards.............................		£9.00	£225.00
			25	Medium cards (56 × 75 mm.)		£20.00	—
			? 5	Extra Large Cards (67 × 127 mm.)		£60.00	—
C		BW	? 41	*Baker's Tobacconists' Shops:—	H.26/Ha.26		
				A. "Try our 3½d Tobaccos" back.........		£45.00	—
				B. "Cigar, Cigarette, etc. Manufacturers" back..................................		£45.00	—
C		C	25	Beauties of All Nations:—	H.27		
				A. "Albert Baker & Co. (1898)..." back ..		£9.00	£225.00
				B. "A. Baker & Co. ...." back............		£7.00	£175.00
C		BW	16	*British Royal Family.....................	H.28	£22.00	—
A1		BW	20	Cricketers Series	H.29	£55.00	—
A1		C	25	*Star Girls...............................	H.30	£65.00	—

BAYLEY & HOLDSWORTH ———

Pre-1919 Issue

Illus. No.	Size	Print-ing	Number in set		Handbook ref.	Price per card	Complete set
?		C	26	*International signalling Code		£65.00	—

BELFAST SHIPS STORES CO. LTD., Belfast

Illus. No.	Size	Print- ing	Number in set		Handbook ref.	Price per card	Complete set

Pre-1919 Issue

		C	? 1	*Dickens' Characters (79 × 40 mm.)	H.31	—	—

J. & F. BELL LTD., Glasgow

Pre-1919 Issues

	A	BW	10	*Actresses—"HAGG A" ("Three Bells Cigarettes")	H.24	£25.00	—
	C	C	25	*Beauties—Tobacco Leaf Back:—	H.32/Ha.32		
				A. "Bell's Scotia Cigarettes" back.........		£45.00	—
				B. "Three Bells Cigarettes" back..........		£45.00	—
	A	C	25	Colonial Series............................		£20.00	—
	A	BW	30	*Footballers		£10.00	£300.00
	A	C	25	Scottish Clan Series No. 1	H.33	£7.00	£175.00

B. BELLWOOD, BRADFORD

Pre-1919 Issue

	C	C	18	Motor Cycle Series........................	Ha.469	£50.00	—

RICHARD BENSON, LTD., Bristol

231		U	24	Old Bristol Series:—			
—				A. 80 × 70 mm. pre-1940.................		£1.50	£36.00
—				B. Reprint (88 × 78–83 mm.) (1946)		90p	£22.00

BENSON & HEDGES, London

Post-1940 Issue

A2		C	1	Advertisement Card The Original Shop (1973).................................		—	£1.00

FELIX BERLYN, Manchester

Pre-1919 Issue

		C	25	Golfing Series (Humorous):—			
	A1			A. Small size...........................		£60.00	—
	—			B. Post Card size (139 × 87 mm.).........		—	—

BERRY, London

Pre-1919 Issue

	D	U	? 1	London Views	H.34	—	—

BEWLAY & CO. LTD., London

Pre-1919 Issues

	D1	U	12	Bewlay's War Series (Generals, etc.):—	Ha.477	—	£100.00
				A. "Caps the Lot" Smoking Mixture......		£8.00	£100.00
				B. Try Bewlay's "Caps the Lot" Mixture..		£8.00	£100.00
				C. Try Bewlay's "Modern Man" Mixture .		£8.00	£100.00
	D1	U	25	Bewlay's War Series (Photogravure War Pictures)................................	H.35	—	£125.00
				A. "Modern Man" Mixtures etc..........		£5.00	—
				B. "Modern Man" Cigarettes.............		£5.00	—
				C. "Two Great Favourites"		£5.00	—
	A	C	? 5	*Comic Advertisement Cards (1909)	H.36	£100.00	—

W. O. BIGG & CO., Bristol

Pre-1919 Issues

	A	C	37	*Flags of All Nations:—	H.37		
				A. "Statue of Liberty" back, 4d oz.........		£4.50	—
				B. As A:—(a) altered to 4½d by hand		£4.50	—
				(b) 4½d red seal over 4d		£5.00	—
				C. Panel design "New York" Mixture.....		£5.00	—
	A	C	50	Life on Board a Man of War...............	H.38	£7.00	£350.00

JAS. BIGGS & SONS, London

Pre-1919 Issues

	C	C	26	*Actresses—"FROGA A"..................	H.20	£16.00	—
	C	C	26	*Actresses—"FROGA B"..................	H.20/Ha.20	£25.00	—
	A	C	25	*Beauties, with frameline—"CHOAB":—	H.21/Ha.21		
				A. Blue type-set back		£30.00	—
				B. Overprinted in black on Bradford cards		£35.00	—
	C	C		*Beauties, no framelines—selection "BOCCA":—	H.39		

JAS. BIGGS & SONS *(continued)*

Illus. No.	Size	Print-ing	Number in set		Handbook ref.	Price per card	Complete set
			? 4	A. Blue back		£40.00	—
			? 3	B. Black back		£40.00	—
	C	C	30	*Colonial Troops	H.40	£16.00	—
	C	C	30	*Flags and Flags with Soldiers	H.41	£15.00	—
	A1	C	25	*Star Girls	H.30	£85.00	—

R. BINNS, Halifax

Post-1920 Issue

	A	U	? 2	*Halifax Footballers	Ha.531	—	—

THE BOCNAL TOBACCO CO., London

Post-1920 Issues

56	A2	U	25	Luminous Silhouettes of Beauty and Charm (1938)		60p	£15.00
308	A2	C	25	Proverbs Up-to-Date (1938)		50p	£12.50

ALEXANDER BOGUSLAVASKY, LTD., London

Post-1920 Issues

	—	C	12	Big Events on the Turf (133 × 70 mm.)		£3.50	—
194	A2	C	25	Conan Doyle Characters (1923):—			
				A. Back in black, white board		£1.40	£35.00
				B. Back in grey, cream board		£1.40	£35.00
				C. Back in green		£1.40	£35.00
	A2	C	25	Mythological Gods and Goddesses (1924)		44p	£11.00
107	A	C	25	*Sports Records, Nd. 1–25 (1925)		60p	£15.00
	A	C	25	Sports Records, Nd. 26–50 (1925)		26p	£6.50
		C	25	Winners on the Turf (1925):—			
	A			A. Small size, captions "sans serif"		70p	£17.50
	A			B. Small size, captions with "serif"		£1.50	—
	B			C. Large size		80p	£20.00

R. & E. BOYD, LTD., London

Post-1920 Issues

	—	U	25	Places of Interest (72 × 55 mm.)		£32.00	—
	—	U	25	Wild Birds at Home (75 × 57 mm.)	Ha.626	£32.00	—

WM. BRADFORD, Liverpool

Pre-1919 Issues

	C	C	50	*Beauties—"CHOAB"	H.21	£16.00	—
	D	U	? 5	Beauties—"Jersey Lily Cigarettes"	Ha.488	£150.00	—
	D2	BW	20	Boer War Cartoons	H.42	£50.00	—

T. BRANKSTON & CO., London

Pre-1919 Issues

	C	C	30	*Colonial Troops:—	H.40		
				A. Golf Club Mixture		£16.00	—
				B. Red Virginia		£16.00	—
				C. Sweet as the Rose		£16.00	—

BRIGHAM & CO., Reading

Pre-1919 Issues

	B	U	16	Down the Thames from Henley to Windsor		—	—
	A	U	16	Reading Football Players		£60.00	—
	—	BW	3	Tobacco Growing in Hampshire (89 × 79 mm.) (1915)		£10.00	£30.00

BRITANNIA ANONYMOUS SOCIETY

Pre-1919 Issue

	—	C	? 10	*Beauties (60 × 40 mm.)	Ha.532	£75.00	—

BRITISH & COLONIAL TOBACCO CO., London

Pre-1919 Issue

	A1	C	25	*Armies of the World	H.43	£65.00	—

J. M. BROWN, Derby

Pre-1919 Issue

	D	C	30	*Army Pictures, Cartoons, Etc.	H.12	£25.00	—

JOHN BRUMFIT, London

Illus. No.	Size	Print-ing	Number in set		Handbook ref.	Price per card	Complete set
Post-1920 Issue							
360	A	C	50	The Public Schools' Ties Series (Old Boys) (1925)		£1.40	£70.00

G. A. BULLOUGH, Castleford

Pre-1919 Issue							
	D	C	30	*Army Pictures, Cartoons, Etc.	H.12	—	—

BURSTEIN, ISAACS & CO., London
(The BI-CO Company, B. I. & Co., Ltd.)

Post-1920 Issues							
354	D	BW	25	Famous Prize-Fighters, Nd. 1–25 (1923).....		£1.40	£35.00
	D	BW	25	Famous Prize-Fighters, Nd. 26–50 (1924) ...		£1.40	£35.00
	D	P	28	London View Series (1922)		£1.60	—

BYRT WOOD & CO., Bristol

Pre-1919 Issue							
	A2	U	? 47	*Pretty Girl Series—"BAGG"	H.45/Ha.45	£50.00	—

PERCY E. CADLE & CO. LTD., Cardiff

Pre-1919 Issues							
	A1	BW	20	*Actresses—"BLARM"....................	H.23	£13.00	—
	C	U	26	*Actresses—"FROGA A"..................	H.20	£20.00	—
	C	C	26	*Actresses—"FROGA B"..................	H.20	£22.00	—
	C	BW	12	*Boer War and Boxer Rebellion Sketches.....	H.46	£27.00	—
	C	BW	? 12	*Boer War Generals—"FLAC".............	H.47/Ha.47	£32.00	—
	A	BW	20	*Footballers	H.48	£10.00	—

CARRERAS LTD., London

A. Pre-1919 Issues							
—		C	6	*Flags of the Allies (shaped):—	H.49/Ha.49		
				1. Grouped Flags:—			
				A. "All Arms" Cigarettes.............		£16.00	—
				B. "Black Cat" Cigarettes............		£16.00	—
				2. Allies Flags (5):—			
				A. "Black Cat" Cigarettes............		£16.00	—
				B. "Life Ray" Cigarettes		£32.00	—
353	A	C	140	Raemaeker's War Cartoons (1916):—			
				A. "Black Cat" Cigarettes		80p	£110.00
				B. Carreras Cigarettes....................		£1.70	—
183	A	C	50	The Science of Boxing (1920):—			
				A. "Black Cat" back		£1.00	£50.00
				B. Carreras Ltd. back		£1.70	—
	A	C	80	Types of London (1919)		90p	£70.00
	A	C	50	Women on War Work......................		£4.50	£225.00
B. Post-1920 Issues. Mostly home issues, export only issues indicated.							
	A	CP	24	Actresses and Their Pets (Oct. 1926) (export)		£2.20	£55.00
254		C	48	Alice in Wonderland (Jun. 1930):—			
	A			A. Small size, rounded corners		16p	£8.00
	A			B. Small size, square corners.............		70p	£35.00
	B2			C. Large size.........................		20p	£10.00
			1	Instruction Booklet		—	£8.00
130	A	C	50	Amusing Tricks and How to Do Them (Jan. 1937)..		25p	£12.50
		C		Battle of Waterloo (Jul. 1934):—	Ha.533		
			1	1. Paper insert, with instructions.........		—	£4.00
			15	*2. Soldiers and Guns, large size (67 × 70 mm.)		£2.00	—
	A			*3. Soldiers and Guns, small size:—			
			10	Soldiers—Officers' Uniforms		£1.00	£10.00
			12	Soldiers and Guns.................		£1.00	£12.00
319	C1	C	50	Believe it or Not (Oct. 1934)		15p	£7.50
	A	C	50	Birds of the Countryside (Mar. 1939)........		16p	£8.00
284	A	C	50	Britain's Defences (Sep. 1938)		18p	£9.00
175		C	25	British Costumes (Jul. 1927):—			
	C2			A. Small size...........................		60p	£15.00
	B2			B. Large size..........................		70p	£17.50
	A	P	27	British Prime Ministers (Oct. 1928) (export) .		90p	£25.00
	A	C	50	Celebrities of British History (Sep. 1935):—			

Illus. No.	Size	Print- ing	Number in set		Handbook ref.	Price per card	Complete set
				A. Brown on cream back (two shades of ink).............................		13p	£4.00
				B. Pale brown on bluish black		13p	£4.00
	A	C	25	Christie Comedy Girls (June 1928) (export)..		£1.20	£30.00
	A	U		Cricketers (May 1934):—			
			30	A. "A Series of Cricketers"		£1.00	£30.00
			50	B. "A Series of 50 Cricketers":—			
				1. Front in brown and white		£1.00	£50.00
				2. Front in black and white		£10.00	—
329	A	BW	50	Dogs and Friend (Sep. 1936)................		13p	£5.50
	A	C	50	Do You Know? (Sep. 1939).................		13p	£3.50
	A	C	50	Famous Airmen and Airwomen (Jan. 1936) .		60p	£30.00
		C		Famous Escapes (Feb. 1926):—			
	A		25	A. Small size.............................		50p	£12.50
	B2		25	B. Large size............................		40p	£10.00
	—		10	C. Extra-large size (133×70 mm.).........		70p	£7.00
	A2	C	96	Famous Film Stars (Apr. 1935):—			
				A. Set of 96		37p	£37.00
				B. Alternative pictures for six numbers	Ha.534	£3.00	£18.00
327	A	C		Famous Footballers (Sep. 1935):—			
			48	A. Set of 48		16p	£8.00
			24	B. Nos. 25–48 redrawn		70p	£17.50
	A	C	25	Famous Men (Dec. 1927) (export)		90p	£22.50
	B2	P	24	Famous Naval Men (May 1929) (export)....		60p	£15.00
	B2	P	12	Famous Soldiers (Mar. 1928) (export)......		£2.50	—
	A	P	27	Famous Women (Apr. 1929) (export)		£1.00	£27.00
	A	C	25	Figures of Fiction (Apr. 1924)		80p	£20.00
38		P	54	Film and Stage Beauties:—			
	A2			A. Small size, titled "Film and Stage Beauties" (Jan. 1939)...................		13p	£4.50
	—			B. Medium size (70×60 mm.) titled "Film and Stage Beauties" (Mar. 1939):—			
				(a) Without full point after "Carreras Ltd"		14p	£7.00
				(b) With full point after "Carreras Ltd."		18p	£9.00
		P	36	Film and Stage Beauties			
	B1			A. Large size (Feb. 1939)		22p	£8.00
	J2			B. Extra-large size (Nov. 1938)............		28p	£10.00
	A	C	50	Film Favourites (Apr. 1938)		32p	£16.00
306	A	P	54	Film Stars—"A Series of 54" (Oct. 1937)		18p	£9.00
252		P	54	Film Stars:—			
	A			A. Small size, "Second Series of 54" (Jul. 1938)		13p	£5.50
	—			B. Medium size (68×60 mm.) "A Series of 54" (Aug. 1938).....................		28p	£15.00
	J2	P		Film Stars (export):—			
			36	"A Series of 36"..........................		£1.00	—
			36	"Second Series of 36"		£1.00	—
			36	"Third Series of 36"......................		£1.00	—
			36	"Fourth Series of 36"		£1.00	—
	A2	C	50	Film Stars, by Florence Desmond (Jan. 1936)		15p	£7.50
318	—		72	Film Stars, oval (70×30 mm.) (Jun. 1934):—			
		P		A. Glossy brown photoprints		50p	£36.00
		U		B. Semi-glossy brown half-tones		40p	£30.00
29	A	C	50	Flowers (May 1936)......................		13p	£5.00
	A2	C	75	*Footballers (Aug. 1934):—			
				A. "Carreras Cigarettes" on front 27 mm. long		17p	£13.00
				B. "Carreras Cigarettes" on front 26 mm. long		17p	£13.00
20		C	36	"Fortune Telling" (Jul. 1926):—			
	A			A. Small size—			
				1. Card inset.........................		42p	£15.00
				2a. Head inset, black framelines		24p	£8.50
				2b. Head inset, brown framelines		42p	£15.00
	B2			B. Large size—			
				1. Card inset		24p	£8.50
				2. Head inset.......................		42p	£15.00
			1	Instruction Booklet		—	£3.00
		P		Glamour Girls of Stage and Films (Aug. 1939):—			
	A2		54	A. Small size............................		13p	£4.00
	—		54	B. Medium size (70×60 mm.)		13p	£4.50
	—		36	C. Large size (76×70 mm.)		13p	£4.50
	J2		36	D. Extra-large size		15p	£5.50
		C	50	"Gran-Pop" by Lawson Wood (Dec. 1934):—			
	C1			A. Small size...........................		13p	£5.50
	B			B. Large size..........................		13p	£3.00
		C	52	Greyhound Racing Game (May 1926):—			
	A			A. Small size...........................		13p	£4.00
	B2			B. Large size..........................		13p	£3.00
			1	Instruction Booklet		—	£2.50
		C	48	Happy Family (Jun. 1925):—			
	A1			A. Small size...........................		30p	£15.00
	B2			B. Large size..........................		13p	£6.00
	A	C	25	Highwaymen (Jul. 1924)....................		£1.20	£30.00
149	A	C	50	History of Army Uniforms (Jun. 1937)......		70p	£35.00
	A	C	50	History of Naval Uniforms (Sep. 1937)......		25p	£12.50

Illus. No.	Size	Print- ing	Number in set		Handbook ref.	Price per card	Complete set
		C		Horses and Hounds (July 1926):—			
	A		25	A. Small size		70p	£17.50
	B2		20	B. Large size		40p	£8.00
	—		10	C. Extra-large size (133 × 70 mm.)		70p	£7.00
357		C	50	Kings and Queens of England (1935):—			
	A			A. Small size		50p	£25.00
	B2			B. Large size		80p	£40.00
358	A	U		A "Kodak" at the Zoo:—			
			50	"Series of Fifty" (Sep. 1924)		25p	£12.50
			50	"2nd Series of Fifty" (Jan. 1925)		25p	£12.50
	A	P	27	Malayan Industries (Oct. 1929) (export)		13p	£2.75
		P	24	Malayan Scenes:—			
	A			A. Small size (Oct. 1928)		80p	£20.00
	—			B. Medium size (70 × 60 mm.) (Nov. 1928)		13p	£3.00
	—	C	53	*Miniature Playing Cards (44 × 32 mm.)		13p	£3.75
156		C	50	The "Nose" Game (Jul. 1927):—			
	A			A. Small size		20p	£10.00
	B2			B. Large size		16p	£8.00
			1	Instruction Booklet		—	£2.50
		C	50	Notable M.P.s (May 1929):—			
	A			A. Small size		18p	£9.00
	—			B. Medium size (69 × 60 mm.)		13p	£4.00
	A	P	25	Notable Ships—Past and Present (Mar. 1929) (export)		70p	£17.50
159		C		Old Staffordshire Figures (Sep. 1926):—			
	A		24	A. Small size		36p	£9.00
	—		12	B. Extra-large size (134 × 71 mm.)		£1.50	£18.00
	B	C	24	Old Staffordshire Figures (different subjects) (Sep. 1926)		80p	£20.00
		C	24	Orchids (Oct. 1925):—			
	A			A. Small size		13p	£3.50
	B			B. Large size		13p	£3.50
	—			C. Extra-large size (133 × 70 mm.)		£1.50	£36.00
60	A	C		Our Navy (Mar. 1937):—	Ha.536		
			20	A. Thick card, selected numbers		32p	£6.50
			50	B. Thin card		40p	£20.00
243	C1	C	50	Palmistry (Dec. 1933)		13p	£5.00
	A	P	27	Paramount Stars (June 1929) (export)		24p	£6.50
	A	C	25	Picture Puzzle Series (Apr. 1923)		70p	£17.50
	—	C	53	Playing Cards (68 × 42 mm.)	Ha.535–1A	90p	—
		C		*Playing Cards and Dominoes (May 1929):—	Ha.535–1B		
	C		52	A. Small size—(a) Numbered		25p	£12.50
				(b) Unnumbered		25p	£12.50
	—		26	B. Large size (77 × 69 mm.)			
				(a) Numbered		18p	£4.50
				(b) Unnumbered		26p	£6.50
44	A	C	48	Popular Footballers (Jan. 1936):—			
				A. White back		13p	£5.00
				B. Cream back		13p	£5.50
112	—	C		Popular Personalities, oval (70 × 30 mm.) (Feb. 1935):—	Ha.629		
			72	1. Normal issue		22p	£16.00
			10	2. Replaced subjects (Nos. 1–10) for issue in Eire		—	—
		C		Races—Historic and Modern (Mar. 1927):—			
	A	C	25	A. Small size		56p	£14.00
	B		25	B. Large size		56p	£14.00
	—		12	C. Extra-large size (133 × 69 mm.)		£1.50	£18.00
		C		Regalia Series (July 1925):—			
	A		25	A. Small size		16p	£4.00
	B		20	B. Large size		30p	£6.00
	—		10	C. Extra-large size (135 × 71 mm.)		60p	£6.00
	—	C	50	"Round the World" Scenic Models (folders) (83 × 73 mm.)		20p	£10.00
		C		School Emblems (Oct. 1929):—			
	A		50	A. Small size		30p	£15.00
	B		40	B. Large size		25p	£10.00
	—		20	C. Extra-large size (134 × 70 mm.)		50p	£10.00
	C1	C	48	Tapestry Reproductions of Famous Paintings (sectional) (June 1938)		35p	£17.50
	A	C	50	Tools—And How to Use Them (Mar. 1935)		35p	£17.50
	A	P	27	Views of London (export)		13p	£2.75
	A	P	27	Views of the World (export)		40p	£11.00
	A	C	25	Wild Flower Art Series (Aug. 1923)		40p	£10.00
C. Post-1940 Turf Slide Issues							
	A	U	50	British Aircraft (1953)		30p	£15.00
	A	U	50	British Fish (1954)		18p	£9.00
	A	U	50	British Railway Locomotives (1952)		25p	£12.50
	A	U	50	Celebrities of British History (1951)		35p	£17.50
	A	U	50	Famous British Fliers (1956)		40p	£20.00
	A	U	50	Famous Cricketers (1950)		£1.20	—
	A	U	50	Famous Dog Breeds (1952)		20p	£10.00
	A	U	50	Famous Film Stars (1949)		25p	£12.50
	A	U	50	Famous Footballers (1951)		40p	—
	A	U	50	Film Favourites (1948)		40p	—
	A	U	50	Film Stars (1947)		35p	£17.50
	A	U	50	Footballers (1948)		40p	—
	A	U	50	Olympics (1948)		50p	£25.00
	A	U	50	Radio Celebrities (1950)		25p	£12.50

CARRERAS LTD. *(continued)*

Illus. No.	Size	Printing	Number in set		Handbook ref.	Price per card	Complete set
	A	U	50	Sports Series (1949)		25p	£12.50
	A	U	50	Zoo Animals (1955)		25p	£12.50

(N.B. These prices are for the full slides. If only the cut slides are required these will be half Catalogue price.)

D. Post-1940 Issues

Illus. No.	Size	Printing	Number in set		Handbook ref.	Price per card	Complete set
	A	C	50	British Birds (1976)		10p	£1.50
				Album £1.00			
355	A	C	50	Flowers all the Year Round (1977)		18p	£9.00
				Album £1.00			
	A	C	50	Kings & Queens of England (1977)		17p	£8.50
				Album £1.00			
	A	C	50	Military Uniforms (1976)		10p	£1.50
				Album £1.00			
361	A	C	50	Palmistry (1980)		50p	—
				Album—			
	A	C	50	Sport Fish (1978)		10p	£1.50
				Album £1.00			
	A	C	50	Vintage Cars (1976):—			
				A. With word "Filter" in white oval:—			
				i Thin card, bright red oblong at top ..		15p	£7.50
				ii Thick card, bright red oblong at top .		12p	£6.00
				iii Thin card, dull red oblong at top		20p	£10.00
				B. Without word "Filter" in white oval....		10p	£1.50
				Album £1.00			

E. Miscellaneous Pre-1919 Issues

Illus. No.	Size	Printing	Number in set		Handbook ref.	Price per card	Complete set
			5	The Black Cat Handy French-English Dictionary (Booklets)		£8.00	—
			180	The Black Cat Library (Booklets)		£7.00	—
			?	*Lace Motifs*		£6.00	—

F. Miscellaneous Post-1940 Issues

Illus. No.	Size	Printing	Number in set		Handbook ref.	Price per card	Complete set
	A	C	60	Flags of All Nations (Prepared but not issued)		13p	£7.50
	—	C		Guards Series (68 × 50 mm.):—			
			4	A. Military Mug Series (1971).............		60p	£2.50
			8	B. Order Up the Guards (1970)		60p	—
			16	C. Send for the Guards (1969)		60p	—
	—	C	7	Millionaire Competition Folders (68 × 30 mm.)..................................		60p	£4.25

CARRICK & CO., Hull

Pre-1919 Issue

Illus. No.	Size	Printing	Number in set		Handbook ref.	Price per card	Complete set
	D	C	12	*Military Terms (1901)	H.50	£30.00	—

P. J. CARROLL & CO. LTD., Dundalk, Glasgow and Liverpool

A. Pre-1919 Issues

Illus. No.	Size	Printing	Number in set		Handbook ref.	Price per card	Complete set
	D	C	25	British Naval Series	H.51	£14.00	—
	A	P	20	County Louth G.R.A. Team and Officials (1913)............................		£7.00	—
	D	BW	25	*Derby Winners (1914–15):—	H.52		
				A. Back in Black		£40.00	—
				B. Back in Green........................		£40.00	—

B. Post-1920 Issues

Illus. No.	Size	Printing	Number in set		Handbook ref.	Price per card	Complete set
	D	C	25	Ship Series (1937)		£3.20	£80.00
	D	U		Sweet Afton Jig-Saw Puzzles (1935):—			
			8	1. Inscribed "1" in centre of back.........		£7.00	—
			8	2. Inscribed "2" in centre of back.........		£7.00	—
			8	3. Inscribed "3" in centre of back.........		£7.00	—

C. Miscellaneous

Illus. No.	Size	Printing	Number in set		Handbook ref.	Price per card	Complete set
	D	C	25	Birds (prepared but not issued)	Ha.537	13p	£3.50

THE CASKET TOBACCO & CIGARETTE CO. LTD., Manchester

Pre-1919 Issues

Illus. No.	Size	Printing	Number in set		Handbook ref.	Price per card	Complete set
	A2	U	? 2	Cricket Fixture Cards, Coupon Back (1905–06)................................		—	—
	A2	U	? 2	*Football Fixture Cards, Coupon Back (1905–11)................................	H.53	£80.00	—
	A2	BW	? 2	Road Maps...............................	H.54/Ha.54	—	—

S. CAVANDER & CO., London & Portsea

Pre-1919 Issue

Illus. No.	Size	Printing	Number in set		Handbook ref.	Price per card	Complete set
	D	BW	? 1	*Beauties—selection from "Plums"	H.186/Ha.186	—	—

CAVANDERS LTD., London and Glasgow

Post-1920 Issues

Illus. No.	Size	Printing	Number in set		Handbook ref.	Price per card	Complete set
	A	C	25	Ancient Chinese (1926).....................		40p	£10.00
	A	C	25	Ancient Egypt (Jul. 1928)...................		50p	£12.50
	B	C	25	Ancient Egypt (different subjects)		20p	£5.00
63	A	P	36	Animal Studies		13p	£3.25
		CP	50	Beauty Spots of Great Britain (1927):—			
	A			A. Small size		20p	£10.00
	—			B. Medium size (76 × 52 mm.)		50p	£12.50

CAVANDERS LTD. *(continued)*

Illus. No.	Size	Print- ing	Number in set		Handbook ref.	Price per card	Complete set
		CP		Camera Studies (1926):—			
	A		54	A. Small size............................		16p	£8.00
	—		56	B. Medium size (77 × 51 mm.)		16p	£8.00
	A	C	30	Cinema Stars—Set 6 (1934).................	Ha.515–6	27p	£8.00
	—	CP	30	The Colonial Series (77 × 51 mm.) (1925):—			
				A. Small caption, under 1mm. high.......		30p	£9.00
				B. Larger caption, over 1 mm. high		40p	£12.00
	—	C	25†	Coloured Stereoscopic (1931).............		22p	£11.00
	D	C	25	Feathered Friends or Foreign Birds (1926):—	Ha.516		
				A. Titled "Feathered Friends"		£1.00	£25.00
				B. Titled "Foreign Birds"		60p	£15.00
	—	C	25†	Glorious Britain (76 × 51 mm.) (1930).......		24p	£12.00
				The Homeland Series (1924–26):—	Ha.539		
	A			Small size—			
		CP	50	A. Back in blue.........................		40p	£20.00
		CP	50	B. Back in black, glossy front		35p	£17.50
		CP	54	C. Back in black, matt front		25p	£12.50
	—			Medium size (77 × 51 mm.):—			
		CP	50	D. Back inscribed "Hand Coloured Real Photos"		15p	£7.50
		CP	56	E. As D, with "Reprinted..." at base.....		20p	£10.00
		CP	56	F. As D, but words "Hand Coloured" dropped		25p	£12.50
		P	56	G. As D, but words "Hand Coloured" dropped		25p	£12.50
	A	C	25	Little Friends (1924)......................	Ha.540	40p	£10.00
		C	25	The Nation's Treasures (77 × 51 mm.) (1925)		24p	£6.00
		P		Peeps into Many Lands—"A Series of ..." (1927):—			
	D		36†	A. Small size.....................		13p	£9.00
	—		36†	B. Medium size (75 × 50 mm.)		15p	£11.00
	—		36	C. Extra-large size (113 × 68 mm.).......		£1.40	—
		P	36†	Peeps into Many Lands—"Second Series..." (1928):—			
	D			A. Small size.....................		13p	£9.00
	—			B. Medium size (75 × 50 mm.)		15p	£11.00
		P	24†	Peeps into Many Lands—"Third Series ..." (1929):—			
	D			A. Small size.....................		14p	£7.00
	—			B. Medium size (75 × 50 mm.)		14p	£7.00
	—			C. As B, but inscribed "Reprinted by Special Request"......................		25p	£12.50
		P	24†	Peeps into Prehistoric Times—"Fourth Series..." (1930):—			
	D			A. Small size....................		22p	£11.00
	—			B. Medium size (75 × 50 mm.)		25p	£12.50
	—	P		*Photographs (54 × 38 mm.) (1924):—	Ha.541		
			30	1. Animal Studies......................		90p	£27.00
			3	2. Royal Family		£2.50	—
	—	C	48	Regimental Standards (76 × 70 mm.)	Ha.502–7	—	—
	C	C	25	Reproductions of Celebrated Oil Paintings (1925)................................	Ha.542	70p	£17.50
		CP	108	River Valleys (1926):—			
	A			A. Small size......................		25p	£27.00
	—			B. Medium size (75 × 50 mm.)		29p	£30.00
288	A	C	25	School Badges:—	Ha.543		
				A. Back in dark blue		16p	£4.00
				B. Back in light blue....................		20p	£5.00
	—	CP	30	Wordsworth's Country (76 × 51 mm.) (1926)		34p	£10.00

†Stereoscopic series, consisting of a Right and a Left card for each number, a complete series is thus **double** the number shown.

R. S. CHALLIS & CO. LTD., London

Post-1920 Issues

364	D1	C	50	Comic Animals (1936)......................		16p	£8.00
	A	BW	44	Flicketts (Greyhound Racing Flickers)......	Ha.589–1	—	—
370	D1	U	36	Wild Birds at Home (1935):—	Ha.626		
				A. Inscribed "Issued with Baldric Cigarettes"		13p	£4.00
				B. Above wording blocked out in black ...		60p	£22.00

H. CHAPMAN & CO.

Pre-1919 Issues

	D	C	30	*Army Pictures, Cartoons, etc................	H.12	—	—

CHARLESWORTH, & AUSTIN LTD., London

Pre-1919 Issues

	C	U	50	*Beauties—"BOCCA"	H.39	£11.00	—
	C	BW	16	*British Royal Family......................	H.28	£20.00	—
	C	C	30	Colonial Troops:—	H.40		
				A. Black back...........................		£17.00	—
				B. Brown back...........................		£17.00	—
	A1	BW	20	Cricketers Series	H.29	£55.00	—

CHARLESWORTH, & AUSTIN LTD. *(continued)*

Illus. No.	Size	Printing	Number in set		Handbook ref.	Price per card	Complete set
	C	C	30	*Flags and Flags with Soldiers	H.41	£16.00	—

CHESTERFIELD CIGARETTES

Post-1940 Issue

		C	6	Cocktails 1980 (76 × 45 mm.)		17p	£1.00

A. CHEW & CO., Bradford

Pre-1919 Issue

	D	C	30	*Army, Pictures, Cartoons, etc.	Ha.12	—	—

W. A. & A. C. CHURCHMAN, Ipswich

A. Pre-1919 Issues

Illus. No.	Size	Printing	Number in set		Handbook ref.	Price per card	Complete set
	C	C	26	*Actresses—"FROGA A"	H.20	£20.00	—
	C	C	26	*Actresses—"FROGA B"	H.20	£25.00	—
	C	U	? 23	*Actresses, "For the Pipe" back	H.55/Ha.55	£30.00	—
	A	C	25	Army Badges of Rank (Mar. 1916)	H.56	£4.00	£100.00
	A	C	12	*Beauties—"CERF" (Oct. 1904)	H.57	£26.00	—
	C	U	25	*Beauties—"FECKSA"	H.58	£75.00	—
				*Beauties—"CHOAB":—	H.21/Ha.21		
	—	C	25	I. Circular cards, 55 mm. diameter		£325.00	—
	C	C	25	II. Five different backs		£110.00	—
	C	C	25	*Beauties—"GRACC"	H.59	£32.00	—
	A	C	50	Birds & Eggs (May 1906)	H.60	£4.00	£200.00
	D	BW	20	*Boer War Cartoons	H.42	—	—
			20	*Boer War Generals—"CLAM":—	H.61		
	A2	BW		A. Black front		£17.00	—
	A	U		B. Brown front		£17.00	—
	A	C	50	Boy Scouts (Jan. 1916)	H.62	£2.60	£130.00
	A	C	50	Boy Scouts, 2nd Series (Aug. 1916)	H.62	£2.60	£130.00
	A	C	50	Boy Scouts, 3rd Series (Oct. 1916):—	H.62		
				A. Brown back		£2.60	£130.00
				B. Blue back		£5.00	—
	D	P	41	*Celebrities—Boer War Period	H.63		
				26 Generals, etc.		£10.00	—
				15 Actresses		£10.00	—
53	A	C	38	Dogs and Fowls (Apl. 1908)	H.64	£4.50	£170.00
	A		50	East Suffolk Churches:—			
		BW		A. Black front, cream back (1912)		£1.30	£65.00
		BW		B. Black front, white back (1912)		£1.50	£75.00
		U		C. Sepia front (1917, re-issued 1923)		£1.30	£65.00
	A	C	50	Fish & Bait (May 1914)	H.65	£3.00	£150.00
	A	C	50	Fishes of the World (Sep. 1911):—	H.66	—	£185.00
				30 cards as re-issued 1924		£1.50	£45.00
				20 cards not re-issued		£7.00	—
	A	C	50	Flags & Funnels of Leading Steamship Lines (Feb. 1912)	H.67	£4.00	—
	A	C	50	Football Club Colours (Jan. 1909)	H.68	£4.50	£225.00
	A	U	50	*Footballers—Photogravure Portraits		£10.00	—
	A	C	50	Footballers—Action Pictures & Inset (Nov. 1914)		£4.00	£200.00
	C	C	40	*Home and Colonial Regiments:—	H.69		
				20 Caption in Blue		£20.00	—
				20 Caption in Brown		£20.00	—
	A	C	50	Interesting Buildings (Jul. 1905)	H.70	£3.50	£175.00
	A	C	50	*Medals (Jan. 1910)	H.71	£3.60	£180.00
	A	C	50	*Phil May Sketches (Feb. 1912):—	H.72		
				A. "Churchman's Gold Flake Cigarettes"		£3.00	£150.00
				B. "Churchman's Cigarettes"		£5.00	—
	A	C	50	*Regimental Colours and Cap Badges (Aug. 1912)	H.73	£3.00	£150.00
	A	C	50	Sectional Cycling Map (Aug. 1913)	H.74	£3.00	£150.00
	A	C	50	Silhouettes of Warships (Feb. 1916)		£4.00	£200.00
	A	C	50	A Tour Round the World (Jan. 1911)	H.75	£4.00	£200.00
	A1	C	25	*Types of British and Colonial Troops	H.76	£40.00	—
	A	C	50	Wild Animals of the World (Jun. 1907)	H.77	£3.60	£180.00

B. Post-1920 Issues

Illus. No.	Size	Printing	Number in set		Handbook ref.	Price per card	Complete set
	—	C	48	Air-Raid Precautions (68 × 53 mm.) (Aug. 1938)	Ha.544	14p	£7.00
	A	U	50	Association Footballers (Sep. 1938)		13p	£4.50
10	A	U	50	Association Footballers, 2nd Series (Sep. 1939)		16p	£8.00
	A	C	25	Boxing (Dec. 1922)	H.311	£1.60	—
	A	U	50	Boxing Personalities (Dec. 1938)		20p	£10.00
	A	U	25	British Film Stars (Feb. 1934)		70p	£17.50
	A	C	55	Can You Beat Bogey at St. Andrews? (Mar. 1933):—			
				A. Set of 55, and three alternatives for No. 55		65p	£35.00
				B. Overprinted in red "Exchangeable..."		65p	£35.00
		U		Cathedrals & Churches (Nov. 1924):—	Ha.545		
	A		25	A. Small size		£1.20	£30.00
	J		12	B. Extra large size		£4.00	—
	A	C	50	Celebrated Gateways (Apr. 1925)		£1.20	£60.00

Illus. No.	Size	Print-ing	Number in set		Handbook ref.	Price per card	Complete set
	A	C	25	Civic Insignia and Plate (May 1926).........		90p	£22.50
	A	C	50	Contract Bridge (June 1935)................		13p	£6.50
	A	C	50	Cricketers (June 1936).....................		90p	£45.00
		C		Curious Dwellings:—			
	A		25	A. Small size (Jan. 1926).................		£1.00	£25.00
	B		12	B. Large size (Nov. 1925)...............		£1.70	£20.00
	A	C	25	Curious Signs (Sep. 1925)..................		£1.00	£25.00
		C		Eastern Proverbs:—	Ha.521		
				A. Small size—			
235	A		25	1. "A Series of 25" (Aug. 1931)		14p	£3.50
	A		25	2. "2nd Series of 25" (Aug. 1932)......		30p	£7.50
				B. Large size—			
	B		12	1. "A Series of 12" (Jan. 1931)		£1.70	£20.00
	B		12	2. "2nd Series of 12" (1933)...........		60p	£7.50
	B		12	3. "3rd Series of 12" (1933)...........		30p	£3.50
	B		12	4. "4th Series of 12" (1934)		25p	£3.00
	A	C	50	Empire Railways (Oct. 1931)		£1.10	£55.00
	A	C	25	Famous Cricket Colours (May 1928)........		£1.40	£35.00
		U		Famous Golfers:—			
	A		50	A. Small size (Oct. 1927).................		£1.00	£50.00
				B. Large size—			
	B		12	1. "A Series of 12" (Oct. 1927)		£2.50	£30.00
	B		12	2. "2nd Series of 12" (Mar. 1928)		£2.50	£30.00
		C		Famous Railway Trains (see RB21/ 210/54):—			
	A		25	A. Small size (Oct. 1929).................		£1.40	£35.00
				B. Large size—			
	B		12	1. "Series of 12" (Nov. 1928)..........		£2.00	£24.00
	B		12	2. "2nd Series of 12" (Jul. 1929).......		£2.00	£24.00
301	A	C	52	"Frisky" (May 1925).......................		32p	£16.00
	A	C	50	History and Development of the British Empire (Apr. 1934)		60p	£30.00
	—	U	48	Holidays in Britain (Views and Maps) (68 × 53 mm.) (May 1937):—			
				A. White card.........................		14p	£7.00
				B. Cream card		14p	£7.00
	—	C	48	Holidays in Britain (Views only) (68 × 53 mm.) (June 1938)		18p	£9.00
173	A	C	25	The Houses of Parliament and Their Story (Dec. 1931)..............................		70p	£17.50
		C		Howlers:—			
	A		40	A. Small size (July 1937).................		13p	£4.50
	B		16	B. Large size (Oct. 1936).................		19p	£3.00
	A	C	25	The Inns of Court (Feb. 1922)		80p	£20.00
	A	C	25	Interesting Door-Knockers (Mar. 1928).....		£1.20	£30.00
	A	C	25	Interesting Experiments (Nov. 1929) (see RB21/210/79)		50p	£12.50
	A	C	50	"In Town To-night" (May 1938)............		13p	£4.50
	B	C	12	Italian Art Exhibition, 1930 (Jan. 1931)		90p	£11.00
	B	C	12	Italian Art Exhibition, 1930—"2nd Series" (Aug. 1931)		90p	£11.00
		C		The King's Coronation:—			
	A		50	A. Small size (Jan. 1937).................		13p	£4.50
	B		15	B. Large size (May 1937)		33p	£5.00
	A	U	50	Kings of Speed (May 1939)		13p	£5.00
		C		Landmarks in Railway Progress:—			
	A		50	A. Small size (Jan. 1931).................		£1.20	£60.00
				B. Large size—			
	B		12	1. "1st Series of 12" (Jan. 1932)		£1.25	£15.00
	B		12	2. "2nd Series of 12" (Mar. 1932)		£1.25	£15.00
		U		Lawn Tennis:—	Ha.546		
	A		50	A. Small size (Sep. 1928).....		40p	£20.00
	B		12	B. Large size (Jul. 1928)		£1.50	£18.00
317		C		Legends of Britain (Aug. 1936):—			
	A		50	A. Small size...........................		36p	£18.00
	B		12	B. Large size.........................		75p	£9.00
		C		Life in a Liner:—			
	A		25	A. Small size (Feb. 1930)		28p	£7.00
	B		12	B. Large size (Apr. 1930)		£1.25	£15.00
202		C		Men of the Moment in Sport:—			
	A		50	A. Small size (Dec. 1928)		£1.00	£50.00
				B. Large size—			
	B		12	1. "1st Series of 12" (Mar. 1929)		£1.75	£21.00
	B		12	2. "2nd Series of 12" (May 1929)......		£1.75	£21.00
	—	C	48	Modern Wonders (68 × 53 mm.) (Feb. 1938).		18p	£9.00
	A	C	25	Musical Instruments (Jul. 1924).............	Ha.547	£1.40	£35.00
		C		Nature's Architects:—			
	A		25	A. Small size (Oct. 1930).................		30p	£7.50
	B		12	B. Large size (May 1930)		£1.25	£15.00
	—	U	48	The Navy at Work (68 × 53 mm.) (Oct. 1937)		13p	£5.00
	A	C	25	Pipes of the World (Jan. 1927)		£1.60	£40.00
		C		Prominent Golfers:—			
	A		50	A. Small size (May 1931)		£1.00	£50.00
	B		12	B. Large size (Aug. 1931)................		£2.25	£27.00
81		C		The "Queen Mary":—			
	A		50	A. Small size (Apr. 1936)		50p	£25.00
	B		16	B. Large size (June 1936)'................		60p	£10.00
	A	C	50	Racing Greyhounds (Aug. 1934)............		60p	£30.00

Illus. No.	Size	Print-ing	Number in set		Handbook ref.	Price per card	Complete set
—		C	48	The R.A.F. at Work (68 × 53 mm.) (Dec. 1938)..........		22p	£11.00
		C		Railway Working:—	Ha.548		
				A. Small size—			
75	A		25	1. "Series of 25" (Oct. 1926)		£1.40	£35.00
	A		25	2. "2nd Series of 25" (July 1927)		90p	£22.50
				B. Large size—			
	B		12	1. "Series of 12" (Sep. 1926)		£3.00	—
	B		13	2. "2nd Series, 13" (Oct. 1927)		£3.00	—
	B		12	3. "3rd Series, 12" (1927)		£3.00	—
	A	BW	50	Rivers and Broads (1922):—			
				A. Titled "Rivers & Broads"............		£3.00	—
				B. Titled "Rivers & Broads of Norfolk & Suffolk"		£3.00	—
12	A	C	50	Rugby Internationals (Sep. 1935)		32p	£16.00
201	A	C	50	Sporting Celebrities (Dec. 1931)		70p	£35.00
200		C		Sporting Trophies:—			
	A		25	A. Small size (Apr. 1927)		65p	£16.00
	B		12	B. Large size (May 1927)		£2.00	£24.00
54	A	C	25	Sports & Games in Many Lands (Aug. 1929) (see RB21/210/133)		44p	£11.00
		C		The Story of London (May 1934):—			
	A		50	A. Small size.......................		50p	£25.00
	B		12	B. Large size.......................		£1.00	£12.00
		C		The Story of Navigation:—			
	A		50	A. Small size (July 1937).............		13p	£4.50
33	B		12	B. Large size (1935)		50p	£6.00
	A	C		3 Jovial Golfers in search of the perfect course (May 1934):—			
			36	A. Home issue		55p	£20.00
			72	B. Irish issue, with green over-printing		£1.50	—
		C		Treasure Trove:—			
	A		50	A. Small size (Aug. 1937)		13p	£5.50
	B		12	B. Large size (1935)		33p	£4.00
		C		Warriors of All Nations (see RB21/210/144):—			
	A		25	A. Small size (Dec. 1929)		90p	£22.50
				B. Large Size—			
	B		12	1. "A Series of 12" (Nov. 1929)		£1.00	£12.00
263	B		12	2. "2nd Series of 12" (May 1931)......		£1.50	£18.00
		C		Well-known Ties (1934):—			
	A		50	A. Small size........................		35p	£17.50
				B. Large size—			
	B		12	1. "A Series of 12"		60p	£7.50
	B		12	2. "2nd Series of 12"		50p	£6.00
	A	C	50	Well-known Ties, "2nd Series" (1935).......		13p	£6.00
	A	U	25	Wembley Exhibition (1924).................		£1.20	£30.00
	A	U	50	West Suffolk Churches (July 1919)		£1.40	£70.00
	—	C	48	Wings Over the Empire (68 × 53 mm.) (July 1939).........................		13p	£3.25
		C		Wonderful Railway Travel (Apr. 1937):—			
	A		50	A. Small size........................		20p	£10.00
	B		12	B. Large size........................		50p	£6.00

C. Miscellaneous

—			1	Australian Cricket Fixture Booklet (1899)...		—	—
—			1	Christmas Greetings Card (1938)		—	80p
—			1	Mystery Wording Revolving Card (1907)....		—	—
—		U	55	Olympic Winners Through The Years (Package Designs, 30 small, 25 large)......		—	—
—		C	48	Pioneers (68 × 53 mm) (Prepared but not issued)		—	—
—		U	40	The World of Sport (Package Designs, 30 small, 10 large)		—	—
	A	C	50	World Wonders Old and New (prepared but not issued)............................		20p	£10.00

WM. CLARKE & SON, Dublin

Pre-1919 issues

	Size	Print-ing	Number in set		Handbook ref.	Price per card	Complete set
	A	C	25	Army Life (1915)......................	H.78	£5.00	£125.00
	A1	BW	? 16	*Boer War Celebrities—"CAG"	H.79	£14.00	—
	A	C	50	Butterflies & Moths (1912)................	H.80	£4.00	£200.00
	A	BW	30	Cricketer Series (1901)...................		£55.00	—
	A1	BW	66	Football Series (1902)	H.81	£5.00	—
	A	C	25	Marine Series (1907)		£6.00	£150.00
	A	C	50	Royal Mail (1914)......................	H.82	£4.00	£200.00
		C	50	Sporting Terms (38 × 58 mm.):—	H.83/Ha.83		
				14 Cricket Terms......................		£14.00	—
				12 Cycling Terms		£14.00	—
				12 Football Terms		£14.00	—
				12 Golf Terms		£14.00	—
—		C	? 19	*Tobacco Leaf Girls (shaped)...............	H.84	£300.00	—
—		C	25	Well-known Sayings (71 × 32 mm.).........	H.85	£9.00	£225.00

J. H. CLURE, Keighley

Pre-1919 issues

	Size	Print-ing	Number in set		Handbook ref.	Price per card	Complete set
	D	C	30	*Army Pictures, Cartoons, etc..............	H.12	£45.00	—
	A	U	50	War Portraits	H.86	—	—

J. LOMAX COCKAYNE, Sheffield

Illus. No.	Size	Print-ing	Number in set		Handbook ref.	Price per card	Complete set
Pre-1919 Issue							
	A	U	50	War Portraits.............................	H.86	£40.00	—

COHEN WEENEN & CO. LTD., London

A. Pre-1919 Issues

Illus. No.	Size	Print-ing	Number in set		Handbook ref.	Price per card	Complete set
	—	P	? 35	*Actresses, Footballers and Jockeys (26 × 61 mm.)..................."FROGA A"....	H.87	£14.00	—
	A1	U	26	*Actresses—"FROGA A".	H.20	£25.00	—
	A	C	? 21	*Beauties—selection from "BOCCA"........	H.39/Ha.39	£32.00	—
	A1	C	25	*Beauties—"GRACC".	H.59	£35.00	—
	D2	BW	25	*Boxers:—			
				A. Black back..............................		£7.00	£175.00
				B. Green back..............................		£6.00	£150.00
				C. Without Maker's Name................		£7.00	—
	A	BW		*Celebrities—Black and white:—	H.88		
			65	A. "Sweet Crop, over 250 ..." back.......		£2.50	£165.00
			?19	B. "Sweet Crop, over 500 ..." back.......		£5.00	—
4	A	C		*Celebrities—Coloured:—	H.89		
			45	I. 1–45 Boer War Generals etc. "Sweet Crop, over 100 ..." back:—		—	£115.00
				A. Toned back.........................		£2.50	—
				B. White back.........................		£2.50	—
				C. Plain Back.........................		—	—
			121	II. 1–121 Including Royalty, etc. "Sweet Crop, over 250 ..." back:			
				1–45 as in I...........................		£2.50	—
				46–121 additional subjects.............		£2.50	£190.00
	—	C		*Celebrities—"GAINSBOROUGH I":—	H.90/Ha.90		
			? 2	A. In metal frames (46 × 67 mm.)..........		£85.00	—
	D2		39	B. "Sweet Crop, over 250 ..." back.......		£25.00	—
	D		30	C. "Sweet Crop, over 400 ..." back.......		£8.00	—
			39	D. 1902 Calendar Back gilt border to front .		£85.00	—
			39	E. Plain Back.........................		£9.00	£360.00
	—	P	?157	*Celebrities—"GAINSBOROUGH II":— In metal frames (46 × 67 mm.)	H.91/Ha.91	£11.00	—
				A. Without frames showing Frame Marks ..		£4.00	—
				B. Without Frames no Frame Marks (as issued)...............................		£8.00	—
	A2	C	20	*Cricketers, Footballers, Jockeys:— "Sweet Crop, over 250 ..." back:—	H.92		
				A. Caption in brown.....................		£13.00	£260.00
				B. Caption in grey-black.................		£13.00	£260.00
	D	C	40	Fiscal Phrases, "Sweet Crop, over 500" back:—	H.93		
				A. "Copyright Regd." on front...........		£8.00	£320.00
				B. Without "Copyright Regd."		£8.00	£320.00
	A2	C	60	Football Captains, 1907–8—Series No. 5....	H.94	£4.00	£240.00
	A2	BW	? 65	*Heroes of Sport.........................	H.95/Ha.95	£26.00	—
	A	C	40	*Home and Colonial Regiments.............	H.69		
				A. "Sweet Crop, over 100 ..." back:—			
				20 Caption in blue.....................		£7.00	£140.00
				20 Caption in brown....................		£7.00	£140.00
				B. "Sweet Crop, over 250 ..." back:—			
				20 Caption in blue.....................		£9.00	—
				20 Caption in brown....................		£9.00	—
	A2	C	20	*Interesting Buildings and Views.............	H.96/Ha.96	£7.00	£140.00
	K2	C	52	*Miniature Playing Cards — Bandmaster" Cigarettes...........................		£2.50	—
	D2	C	20	*Nations:—	H.97/Ha.97		
				A. Blue back...........................		£8.00	£160.00
				B. Plain back—gilt border...............		—	—
				C. 1902 Calender back.................		—	—
	D	C	40	Naval and Military Phrases:—	H.14		
				A. Red back, "Series No. 1"..............		£10.00	£400.00
				B. "Sweet Crop, over 250 ..." back.......		£16.00	—
	D2	C	50	Owners, Jockeys, Footballers, Cricketers—Series No. 2...........................	H.98	£3.20	£160.00
	D2	C	20	Owners, Jockeys, Footballers, Cricketers—Series No. 3...........................	H.99	£5.00	£100.00
	D	C	30	*Proverbs, "Sweet Crop, over 400 ..." back ..	H.15	£11.00	—
	A	C	20	Russo-Japanese War Series.................	H.100	£12.00	—
	A	BW	25	*Silhouettes of Celebrities.................	H.101	£7.00	£175.00
	D1	C	50	Star Artistes—Series No. 4:—	H.102/Ha.102		
				20 With stage background.................		£7.00	£140.00
				30 No stage, plain background.............		£5.00	£150.00
	D	C	50	V.C. Heroes (of World War I), Nd. 51–100:—			
				51–75—dull greyish card.................		£5.00	£125.00
				Without Maker's Name on back........		£6.00	—
				76–100—glossy white card...............		£5.00	£125.00
	D	U	50	*War Series (World War I):— 1–25 Admirals and Warships:—	H.103		
				A. Thick card..........................		£5.00	£125.00
				B. Thin card...........................		£5.00	£125.00

COHEN WEENEN & CO. LTD. *(continued)*

Illus. No.	Size	Print-ing	Number in set		Handbook ref.	Price per card	Complete set
				26–50 Leaders of the War:—			
				A. Maker's Name on back...............		£5.00	£125.00
				B. *Without Maker's Name on back. See*			
				Anonymous		£7.00	—
	D1	C	30	Wonders of the World—"Series No. 6"	H.104	£4.00	£120.00
B. Post-1920 Issues							
	D2	U	25	*Cricketers (1926)...........................		£3.20	£80.00
205	D2	C	20	Nations (1923)...........................	H97	£1.50	£30.00
	D1	C	30	Wonders of the World (1923)	H.14	£1.00	£30.00
C. Silks							
	—	C	? 16	*Victoria Cross Heroes II (72 × 70 mm.)			
				(paper-backed)	Ha.504–2	£16.00	—

T. H. COLLINS, Mansfield

Illus. No.	Size	Print-ing	Number in set		Handbook ref.	Price per card	Complete set
Post-1920 Issues							
	A1	U	25	Homes of England (1924)...................		£2.20	£55.00
	A	C	25	Sports & Pastimes—Series I	H.225	£2.20	£55.00

F. COLTON Jun., Retford

Illus. No.	Size	Print-ing	Number in set		Handbook ref.	Price per card	Complete set
Pre-1919 Issues							
	D	C	30	*Army Pictures, Cartoons, etc...............	H.12	£30.00	—
	A	U	50	War Portraits.............................	H.86	£30.00	—

THE CONTINENTAL CIGARETTE FACTORY, London

Illus. No.	Size	Print-ing	Number in set		Handbook ref.	Price per card	Complete set
Post-1920 Issues							
	A	C	25	Charming Portraits:—	Ha.549		
				A. Back in blue, with firm's name		£2.60	—
				B. Back in blue, inscribed "Club Mixture			
				Tobacco"............................		£2.60	—
				C. Back in brown, inscribed "Club Mixture			
				Tobacco"............................		£2.60	—
				*D. Plain back		£2.60	—

COOPER & CO's STORES LTD., London

Illus. No.	Size	Print-ing	Number in set		Handbook ref.	Price per card	Complete set
Pre-1919 Issues							
	A	BW	25	*Boer War Celebrities—"STEW":—	H.105		
				A. "Alpha Mixture" back		£80.00	—
				B. "Gladys Cigars" back		£80.00	—

CO-OPERATIVE WHOLESALE SOCIETY LTD., Manchester

Illus. No.	Size	Print-ing	Number in set		Handbook ref.	Price per card	Complete set
A. Pre-1919 Issues							
	A2	C	? 4	*Advertisement Cards......................	H.106/Ha.106	£250.00	—
	A	C	25	Boy Scout Series		£8.00	—
	A	C	50	British Sport Series†	H.112	£14.00	—
	A	C	28	*Co-operative buildings and Works	H.107	£9.00	£250.00
	A	C	25	Parrot Series.............................		£15.00	—
	A	C	18	War Series...............................		£10.00	—

†Note: Cards advertise non-tobacco products, but are believed to have been packed with cigarettes and/or tobacco.

Illus. No.	Size	Print-ing	Number in set		Handbook ref.	Price per card	Complete set
B. Post-1920 Issues							
	A	C	24	African Types (1936)		13p	£3.00
	—	U	50	Beauty Spots of Britain (76 × 51 mm.)		13p	£4.50
	A2	C	50	Boy Scout Badges (1939)		30p	£15.00
259	A	C	48	British and Foreign Birds (1938)		15p	£7.50
	D	C	25	*Cooking Recipes (1923)		£1.40	£35.00
	A	C	24	English Roses (1924)		£2.00	£50.00
	A	C	50	Famous Bridges (48 + 2 added) (1937).......		32p	£16.00
110	A	C	48	Famous Buildings (1935)		15p	£7.50
	A2	C	25	How to Do It (1924)......................	Ha.550	£1.00	£25.00
	A	C	48	Musical Instruments (1934).................		£1.20	£60.00
	A	C	48	Poultry (1927)		£1.30	£65.00
	A	C	48	Railway Engines (1936)		£1.70	£85.00
	A	C	24	Sailing Craft (1935)		70p	£17.50
	A2	C	48	Wayside Flowers, brown back (1923)........		£1.10	£55.00
	A2	C	48	Wayside Flowers, grey back (1928).........		13p	£6.50
	A2	C	48	Wayside Woodland Trees (1924)...........		£1.20	£60.00
C. Post-1940 Issue							
	A	C	24	Western Stars (1957)		08p	£0.75

COPE BROS. & CO. LTD., Liverpool

Illus. No.	Size	Print-ing	Number in set		Handbook ref.	Price per card	Complete set
A. Pre-1919 Issues							
		BW	20	*Actresses—"BLARM":—	H.23		
	A1			A. Plain backs, Name panel $\frac{1}{4}$" from border		£15.00	—
	A1			B. Black design back, Name $\frac{1}{4}$" from			
				border................................		£15.00	—
	D			C. Black design back, Name panel $\frac{1}{16}$" from			
				border................................		£17.00	—

Illus. No.	Size	Print-ing	Number in set		Handbook ref.	Price per card	Complete set
	A	U	? 6	*Actresses—"COPEIS"	H.108	£65.00	—
	A	U	26	*Actresses—"FROGA A"	H.20	£45.00	—
	D1	P	50	*Actresses and Beauties	H.109	£7.00	—
	K1	P	? 17	*Beauties, Actors and Actresses	H.110	£14.00	—
	A	C	52	*Beauties—P.C. inset	H.111	£25.00	—
	A	C	15	*Beauties—"PAC"	H.2	£35.00	—
	A1	C	50	Boats of the World		£4.00	£200.00
	D2	BW	126	Boxers:—			
				1–25 Boxers		£2.20	£55.00
				26–50 Boxers		£3.00	£75.00
				51–75 Boxers		£3.00	£75.00
				76–100 Boxers		£8.00	£200.00
				101–125 Army Boxers		£3.20	£80.00
				126 "New World Champion"		—	£10.00
199	A1	C	35	*Boy Scouts and Girl Guides	H.132	£4.50	£160.00
	D	BW	25	British Admirals	H.103	£9.00	£225.00
	A2	C	50	British Warriors:—			
				A. Black on white backs		£4.00	£200.00
				B. Grey on toned backs		£4.50	£225.00
	A	C	50	Characters from Scott:—			
				A. Wide card		£3.50	£175.00
				B. Narrow card—officially cut		£3.50	—
		U	115	Chinese Series:—	H.113		
	A1			Nos. 1–20		£7.00	—
	A1			21–40		£7.00	—
				41–65:—			
	D			A. Thick brown card		£7.00	—
	A1			B. Re-drawn, smaller format		£10.00	—
	A2			66–115		£7.00	—
	A	C	50	Cope's Golfers:—			
				A. Wide card		£12.00	—
				B. Narrow card—officially cut		£12.00	—
	A	C	50	Dickens' Gallery		£3.50	£175.00
	A	C	50	Dogs of the World		£3.00	£150.00
	A	C	25	Eminent British Regiments— Officers' Uniforms:—		—	£200.00
				A. Yellow-brown back		£8.00	—
				B. Claret back		£8.00	—
	A2	C	30	*Flags of Nations:—	H.114		
				A. "Bond of Union" back		£8.00	£240.00
				B. Plain back		£7.00	—
	D	C	24	*Flags, Arms and Types of Nations:—	H.115		
				A. Numbered		£6.00	£150.00
				B. Unnumbered		—	—
		U	20	*Kenilworth Phrases (80 × 70 mm.)	H.116	—	—
	A2	C	50	Music Hall Artistes:—			
				A. Inscribed "Series of 50"		£12.00	—
				B. Without the above		£3.60	£180.00
	A	U	472	Noted Footballers—"Clips Cigarettes":—	Ha.474		
				1. Unnumbered—Wee Jock Simpson		—	£14.00
				120. Series of 120:—			
				A. Greenish-blue frame		£2.50	—
				B. Bright blue frame		£2.50	—
				162. Series of 282:—			
				A. Greenish-blue frame		£2.50	—
				B. Bright blue frame		£2.50	—
				189. Series of 500. Bright blue frame		£2.50	—
	D	P	195	Noted Footballers—"Solace Cigarettes":—		£3.00	—
	A	C	24	*Occupations for Women	H.117	£90.00	—
	A	C	52	*Playing Cards "Rulers" as Court Cards:— Blue backs:—	H.118		
				A. Rounded Corners, Court cards		£16.00	—
				Other than Court cards		£16.00	—
				B. Square Corners, Court cards		£11.00	—
				Other than Court cards		£11.00	—
	—	C	24	Photo Albums for the Million:—	H.119		
				12 Buff cover (25 × 39 mm.)		£14.00	—
				12 Green cover (25 × 39 mm.)		£14.00	—
	A	C	50	Shakespeare Gallery:—			
				A. Wide card		£3.50	£175.00
				B. Narrow card—officially cut		£3.50	—
	A1	C	25	*Uniforms of Soldiers and Sailors:—	H.120		
				A. Circular Medallion back, wide card		£17.00	—
				B. Circular Medallion back, narrow card, officially cut		—	—
				C. Square Medallion back, wide card		—	—
				D. Square Medallion back, narrow card, officially cut		£16.00	—
	D	BW		V.C. & D.S.O. Naval & Flying Heroes:—			
			50	Unnumbered (1916)	H.121	£3.40	£170.00
			25	Numbered 51–75 (1917)		£5.00	£125.00
	D	BW	20	*War Pictures	H.122	£8.00	£160.00
	D	BW	50	*War Series (War Leaders and Warships)	H.103	£12.00	—
	A1	C	25	Wild Animals & Birds		£10.00	—
B. Post-1920 Issues							
	D	BW	25	Boxing Lessons (1935)		36p	£9.00
	—	C	25	Bridge Problems (folders) (85 × 50 mm.)		—	—
	A1	U	25	Castles† (1939)		13p	£3.00
	A1	U	25	Cathedrals† (May, 1939)		40p	£10.00

COPE BROS. & CO. LTD. *(continued)*

Illus. No.	Size	Print-ing	Number in set		Handbook ref.	Price per card	Complete set
—	C	25	Dickens' Character Series (75 × 58 mm.) (1939)			16p	£4.00
—	C	25	The Game of Poker† (75 × 58 mm.)			13p	£3.00
—	C	50	General Knowledge† (70 × 42 mm.)			£1.40	£70.00
—	BW	32	Golf Strokes (70 × 45 mm.) (1923)			£2.50	£80.00
A1	C	60	"Happy Families" (1937)			60p	£36.00
—	C	50	Household Hints† (advertisement fronts) (70 × 45 mm.)			70p	£35.00
C	BW	30	Lawn Tennis Strokes (1924)			£1.00	£30.00
—	U	50	Modern Dancing (folders) (74 × 43 mm.) (1926)			£6.00	—
A2	C	25	Pigeons			£1.20	£30.00
A2	C	25	Song Birds			£1.20	£30.00
A1	C	25	Sports & Pastimes (1925)		Ha.551	£1.20	£30.00
—	C	25	Toy Models (The Country Fair) (73 × 66 mm.)		Ha.552	13p	£2.75
146	A	C	25	The World's Police		£1.30	£32.50

†Joint Cope and Richard Lloyd issues.

C. Reprint Series by "Nostalgia"

A	C	50	Cope's Golfers (1983)			—	£6.00

E. CORONEL, London _____

Pre-1919 Issue

A	C	25	*Types of British and Colonial Troops		H.76	£35.00	—

DAVID CORRE & CO., London _____

Pre-1919 Issue

D	C	40	*Naval and Military Phrases (1900)		H.14	£45.00	—

JOHN COTTON LTD., Edinburgh _____

Post-1920 Issues

—	C	50	*Bridge Hands (folders) (82 × 66 mm.) (1934)			£2.75	—
A1	U	50	*Golf Strokes—A/B (1936)			£1.50	—
A1	U	50	*Golf Strokes—C/D (1937)			£2.00	—
A1	U	50	*Golf Strokes—E/F (1938)			£2.50	—
A1	U	50	*Golf Strokes—G/H (1939)			—	—
A1	U	50	*Golf Strokes—I/J (1939)			—	—

A. & J. COUDENS, LTD., London _____

Post-1920 Issues

A1	P	60	British Beauty Spots (1923):—		Ha.553		
			A. Printed back, numbered			80p	£50.00
			B. Printed back, unnumbered			80p	£50.00
			*C. Back rubber stamped "Cymox Cigarettes…"			£2.00	—
			*D. *Plain back*			£2.00	—
A	P	60	Holiday Resorts in East Anglia (1924)			70p	£42.00
A2	BW	25	Sports Alphabet (1924)		Ha.551	£1.80	£45.00

W. R. DANIEL & CO., London _____

Pre-1919 Issues

A2	C	30	*Colonial Troops:—		H.40		
			A. Black back			£40.00	—
			B. Brown back			£30.00	—
A2	C	25	*National Flags and Flowers—Girls		H.123	£80.00	—

W. T. DAVIES & SONS, Chester _____

A. Pre-1919 Issues

A	C	? 19	*Actresses—"DIVAN"		H.124/Ha.124	£25.00	—
A	C	25	Army Life (1915)		H.78	£7.00	—
A	BW	12	*Beauties (1903)		H.125	£20.00	—
A	C	50	Flags & Funnels of Leading Steamship Lines (1913)		H.67	£4.00	—
A	BW	? 9	Newport Football Club		H.126/Ha.126	£55.00	—
A	BW	5	Royal Welsh Fusiliers		H.127	£90.00	—

B. Post-1920 Issues

A2	U	42	Aristocrats of the Turf (1924):—		Ha.554		
			1. Nos. 1–30—"A Series of 30"			£1.20	£36.00
			2. Nos. 31–42—"A Series of 42"			£7.00	—
A2	U	36	Aristocrats of the Turf, Second Series (1924)			£1.20	£43.00
A	C	25	Boxing (1924)		H.311	£1.20	£30.00

S. H. DAWES, Luton _____

Pre-1919 Issue

D	C	30	*Army Pictures, Cartoons, Etc.		H.12	—	—

J. W. DEWHURST, Morecambe

Illus. No.	Size	Printing	Number in set		Handbook ref.	Price per card	Complete set
Pre-1919 Issue							
	D	C	30	*Army Pictures, Cartoons, Etc.	H.12	£40.00	—

R. I. DEXTER & CO., Hucknall

Pre-1919 Issue							
68	D2	U	30	*Borough Arms (1900)	H.128	55p	£16.00

A. DIMITRIOU, London

Miscellaneous Post-1920 Issue							
				Advertisement Cards (2 known)		—	—

GEORGE DOBIE & SON LTD., Paisley

A. Post-1920 Issues							
	—	—	? 22	Bridge Problems (folders) (circular 64 mm. diam.)		—	—
	A	C	25	Weapons of All Ages (1924)		£2.60	£65.00
B. Post 1940 Issues							
	—	C	32	Four Square Book (Nd. 1–32)—1963 (75 × 50 mm.)		80p	£25.00
	—	C	32	Four Square Book (Nd. 33–64)—1963 (75 × 50 mm.)		15p	£5.00
	—	C	32	Four Square Book (Nd. 65–96)—1963 (75 × 50 mm.)		15p	£5.00

DOBSON & CO. LTD.

Pre-1919 Issue							
	A	C	8	The European War Series	H.129	£11.00	—

DOBSON MOLLE & CO. LTD.—(See Anonymous)

THE DOMINION TOBACCO CO. (1929) LTD., London

Post-1920 Issues							
	A	U	25	Old Ships (1934)		90p	£22.50
	A	U	25	Old Ships (Second Series) (1935)		20p	£5.00
	A	U	25	Old Ships (Third Series) (1936)		20p	£5.00
	A	U	25	Old Ships (Fourth Series) (Oct. 1936)		80p	£20.00

JOSEPH W. DOYLE LTD., Manchester

Post-1920 Issues							
	—	P	? 18	*Beauties, Nd.X.1–X.18 (89 × 70 mm.)		£7.00	—
	D	P	? 11	*Beauties, Nd. CC.D.1–CC.D.11		—	—

MAJOR DRAPKIN & CO., London

Illus. No.	Size	Printing	Number in set		Handbook ref.	Price per card	Complete set
A. Pre-1919 Issues							
	D	BW	12	*Actresses "FRAN"	H.175	£3.50	—
	—	BW	? 1	*Army Insignia (83 × 46 mm.)	H.130	—	—
	—	—	? 86	"Bandmaster" Conundrums (58 × 29 mm.)	H.131	£2.70	—
	A	BW	? 27	*Boer War Celebrities—"JASAS" ("Sweet Alva" Cigarettes)	H.133	£55.00	—
	A1	P	36	*Celebrities of the Great War (1916)	H.135	55p	£20.00
			34	A. Plain back		70p	£24.00
	—	BW	96	Cinematograph Actors (1913) (42 × 70 mm.)	H.134	£3.20	—
	A	C	25	How to Keep Fit—Sandow Exercises:—	H.136		
				A. "Drapkin's Cigarettes"		£5.00	£125.00
				A1. "Drapkin's Cigarettes" short cards, cut officially		£5.00	—
				B. "Crayol Cigarettes"		£5.00	£125.00
	D	U	45	Photogravure Masterpieces (1915)	H.137	£3.20	—
	—	C	25	*Soldiers and Their Uniforms, cutouts:— (1914)	H.138	—	£45.00
				A. "Drapkin's Cigarettes"	From	60p	—
				B. "Crayol Cigarettes"	From	60p	—
	D	BW	12	*Views of the World	H.176	£3.50	£42.00
	D	BW	6	*Warships	H.463	£6.00	£36.00
B. Post-1920 Issues							
227	C	C	8	*Advertisement Cards:—	Ha.555		
				1. Packings (4)		£2.00	£8.00
				2. Smokers (4)		£2.00	£8.00
		BW	50	Around Britain (1929) (export):—			
	C			A. Small size		60p	£30.00
	B1			B. Large size		£1.00	—

Illus. No.	Size	Print-ing	Number in set		Handbook ref.	Price per card	Complete set
		C	50	Around the Mediterranean (1926) (export):—	Ha.610		
	C			A. Small size............................		70p	£35.00
	Bl			B. Large size............................		£1.00	—
165	A2	P	40	Australian and English Test Cricketers (export)		40p	£16.00
	A1	U	25	British Beauties (1930) (export)		90p	£22.50
		C	15	Dogs and Their Treatment (1924):—			
	A			A. Small size............................		£1.50	£22.00
	B2			B. Large size............................		£1.50	£22.00
	A	C	40	The Game of Sporting Snap (Aug. 1928)		40p	£16.00
			1	Instruction Booklet		—	£3.00
		C	50	Girls of Many Lands (Aug. 1929):—			
	D			A. Small size............................		£1.30	—
	—			B. Medium size		13p	£5.00
310	A2	BW	54	Life at Whipsnade Zoo (Dec. 1934)	Ha.556	25p	£12.50
	D2	C	50	"Limericks" (June 1929):—	Ha.557		
				A. White card		35p	£17.50
				B. Cream card		35p	£17.50
	A2	P	36	National Types of Beauty (Apr. 1928).......	Ha.558	35p	£12.50
226		C	25	Optical Illusions (June 1926):—			
	A			A. Small size, Home issue, name panel (23 × 7 mm.)		£1.00	£25.00
	A			B. Small size, Export issue, name panel (26 × 10 mm.)		44p	£11.00
	B2			C. Large size, Home issue		£1.00	£25.00
191		C	25	Palmistry:—			
	A			A. Small size (Apr. 1927)		60p	£15.00
	B			B. Large size (June 1926)		70p	£17.50
		C	25	Puzzle Pictures (July 1926):—			
	A			A. Small size		80p	£20.00
	B			B. Large size........................		£1.20	£30.00
	A2	P	36	Sporting Celebrities in Action (1930) (export)		—	£40.00
				35 different (No. 18 withdrawn).............		40p	£14.00

C. Silks

	—	C	40	Regimental Colours & Badges of the Indian Army (70 × 50 mm.) (paper-backed)— "The Buffs"	Ha.502–5	—	£90.00
				38 different		£1.80	£70.00

D. Miscellaneous

	A	C	1	"Greys" Smoking Mixture Advertisement Card (plain back)		—	£4.00

DRAPKIN & MILLHOFF, London

Pre-1919 Issues

	Size	Print	Number in set		Handbook ref.	Price	Complete
	A	U		*Beauties—"KEWA I":—	Ha.139–1		
			? 1	A. "Eldona Cigars" back		—	—
			? 1	B. "Explorer Cigars" back		—	—
	A	BW	25	*Boer War Celebrities—"PAM" ("Pick-Me-Up" Cigarettes)........................	H.140	£14.00	—
	C	C	30	*Colonial Troops ("Pick-Me-Up" Cigarettes)	H.40	£25.00	—
	—	BW	? 2	*"Pick-me-up" Paper Inserts (112 × 44 mm.)..	H.141	—	—
	—	U	? 1	*Portraits (48 × 36 mm.)	H.461	—	—

J. DUNCAN & CO. LTD., Glasgow

A. Pre-1919 Issues

	Size	Print	Number in set		Handbook ref.	Price	Complete
	D1	C	48	*Flags, Arms and Types of Nations	H.115		
				A. Back in Blue		£14.00	—
				B. Back in Green		—	—
	A	C	20	Inventors and their Inventions		£30.00	—
	A	C	30	Scottish Clans, Arms of Chiefs & Tartans:—	H.142		
				A. Back in black		—	—
				B. Back in green		£10.00	£300.00
	—	C		Scottish Gems: (58 × 84 mm.)	H.143		
	—	C	72	1st Series		£8.00	—
	—	C	50	2nd Series		£7.00	—
	—	C	50	3rd Series............................		£6.00	—
	D	C	25	*Types of British Soldiers...................	H.144	£35.00	—

B. Post-1920 Issues

	Size	Print	Number in set		Handbook ref.	Price	Complete
	D1	C	50	"Evolution of the Steamship"...............	Ha.559	—	£32.50
				47/50 ditto..............................		35p	£17.50
				"Olimpia II"		—	£10.00
				"Castalia" & "Athenia"		£2.50	—
	H1	BW	50	Scottish Gems (known as "4th Series")......	Ha.143D	40p	£20.00

G. DUNCOMBE, Buxton

Pre-1919 Issue

	Size	Print	Number in set		Handbook ref.	Price	Complete
	D	C	30	*Army Pictures, Cartoons, Etc.	H.12	—	—

EDWARDS, RINGER & BIGG, Bristol

A. Pre-1919 Issues

	Size	Print	Number in set		Handbook ref.	Price	Complete
	A	U	25	Abbeys & Castles — Photogravure series:—			
				A. Type-set back		£7.00	£175.00
				B. "Statue of Liberty" back		£7.00	£175.00
				C. "Stag Design" back		£7.00	£175.00

EDWARDS, RINGER & BIGG *(continued)*

Illus. No.	Size	Printing	Number in set		Handbook ref.	Price per card	Complete set
	A	U	25	Alpine Views — Photogravure Series:—			
				A. "Statue of Liberty" back		£7.00	£175.00
				B. "Stag Design" back		£7.00	£175.00
	A	C	12	*Beauties—"CERF" (Jun. 1905).............	H.57	£30.00	—
	A	U	25	*Beauties—"FECKSA", 1900 Calendar back	H.58	£20.00	—
	A	C	50	*Birds & Eggs (Jun. 1906)	H.60	£6.00	£300.00
	A	BW	? 1	Boer War and Boxer Rebellion Sketches.....		—	—
	A	BW	25	*Boer War Celebrities—"STEW", 1901 Calendar back	H.105	£20.00	—
	A	C	1	Calendar for 1899		—	—
	A	C	1	Calendar (1905), Exmore Hunt Stag design back		—	—
	A	C	1	Calendar (1910).........................		—	—
	A	U	25	Coast & Country—Photogravure Series:— (1911)			
				A. "Statue of Liberty" back		£7.00	£175.00
				B. "Stag Design" back		£7.00	£175.00
	A	C	23	*Dogs Series (Mar. 1908)	H.64/Ha.64	£1.30	£30.00
	A	C	3	Easter Manoeuvres of Our Volunteers (1897)	H.146	£200.00	—
	A	C	25	Flags of All Nations, 1st Series (1906)	H.37	£6.00	£150.00
	A	C	12	Flags of All Nations, 2nd Series (1907)	H.37	£11.00	£135.00
	A	C	37	*Flags of All Nations (1907):—	H.37		
				A. Globe & Grouped Flags back		£5.00	—
				B. "Exmoor Hunt" back:—			
				i. 4½d per oz.......................		£6.00	—
				ii. Altered to 5d by hand		£6.00	—
				iii. 5d label added		£8.00	—
				C. "Stag" design back		£5.00	£185.00
				D. Upright titled back		£6.00	—
	A	C	50	Life on Board a Man of War (Jul. 1905)	H.38	£6.50	—
	—	C	1	"Miners Bound for Klondyke" (1897) (41 × 81 mm.)...........................		—	£200.00
	A	C	10	Portraits of His Majesty the King in Uniforms of the British & Foreign Nations (1902).................................	H.147	£22.00	£220.00
	A	C	50	A Tour Round the World (Mar. 1909).......	H.75	£5.00	£250.00
	A	C	56	War Map of the Western Front		£4.00	£225.00
	A	U	54	War Map of the Western Front, etc. Series No. 2:—			
				A. "Exmoor Hunt" back		£4.00	£220.00
				B. "New York Mixture" back		£4.00	£220.00

B. Post-1920 Issues

Illus. No.	Size	Printing	Number in set		Handbook ref.	Price per card	Complete set
	A	C	25	British Trees & Their Uses (Mar. 1933) (see RB21/209/34)		£1.60	£40.00
	A	C	50	Celebrated Bridges (1924)	H.346	£1.20	£60.00
		U		Cinema Stars (1923):—			
	A2		50	A. Small size...........................		40p	£20.00
	—		25	B. Medium size (67 × 57 mm.)		32p	£8.00
	A	C	25	Garden Life (1934)	H.449	£1.60	£40.00
	A	C	25	How to Tell Fortunes (1929)................		£2.40	£60.00
	A	C	50	Mining (1925)...........................	H.450	£1.20	£60.00
192	A	C	25	Musical Instruments (Jan. 1924)	Ha.547	£1.20	£30.00
	A	C	25	Optical Illusions (1936)...................	Ha.560	£1.20	£30.00
58	A	C	25	Our Pets (1926)	Ha.561	£1.20	£30.00
	A	C	25	Our Pets, 2nd Series (1926)	Ha.561	£1.60	£40.00
	A	C	25	Past & Present (1928) (see W/287)...........		£1.80	£45.00
	A	C	25	Prehistoric Animals (May 1924)		£1.80	£45.00
	A	C	25	Sports & Games in Many Lands (1935) (see RB21/210/133)		£1.20	£30.00

E. EISISKI, Rhyl

Pre-1919 Issues

Illus. No.	Size	Printing	Number in set		Handbook ref.	Price per card	Complete set
	A	U	? 6	*Actresses—"COPEIS"	H.108	£90.00	—
	A	U	? 18	*Beauties—"FENA"......................	H.148	£90.00	—
	A	U	? 1	*Beauties—"KEWA I", back inscribed "Eisiski's New Gold Virginia Cigarettes"	Ha.139–1	£90.00	—
	A	U	? 1	*Beauties—"KEWA II", back inscribed "Eisiski's Rhyl Best Bird's Eye Cigarettes"	Ha.139–2	£90.00	—

ELDONS LTD.

Pre-1919 Issue

Illus. No.	Size	Printing	Number in set		Handbook ref.	Price per card	Complete set
	A1	C	30	*Colonial Troops—"Leon de Cuba" Cigars ..	H.40	£75.00	—

EMPIRE TOBACCO CO., London

Pre-1919 Issue

Illus. No.	Size	Printing	Number in set		Handbook ref.	Price per card	Complete set
	D	C	? 6	Franco-British Exhibition	Ha.471	—	—

THE EXPRESS TOBACCO CO. LTD., London

Post-1920 Issue

Illus. No.	Size	Printing	Number in set		Handbook ref.	Price per card	Complete set
	—	U	50	"How It is Made" (Motor Cars) (1931) (76 × 51 mm.).........................		£1.40	—

L. & J. FABIAN, London

FAIRWEATHER & SONS, Dundee

W. & F. FAULKNER, London

FINLAY & CO. LTD., Newcastle-on-Tyne and London

FRAENKEL BROS., London

Illus. No.	Size	Print-ing	Number in set	Handbook ref.	Price per card	Complete set
			A. Pink card		£45.00	—
			B. White card...........................		£60.00	—
	A2	C	25 *Types of British and Colonial Troops	H.76	£60.00	—

FRANKLYN, DAVEY & CO., Bristol

A. Pre-1919 Issues

Illus. No.	Size	Print-ing	Number in set	Handbook ref.	Price per card	Complete set
	A	C	12 *Beauties—"CERF" (1905)	H.57	£35.00	—
	D2	C	50 *Birds (? 1895)		£36.00	—
	A2	BW	? 12 *Boer War Generals — "FLAC" (1901)......	H.47	£80.00	—
	A	C	25 Ceremonial and Court Dress (Oct. 1915)	H.145	£5.00	—
	A	C	50 *Football Club Colours (Jan. 1909)	H.68	£6.00	£300.00
	A	C	50 Naval Dress & Badges (Nov. 1916).........	H.172	£5.00	—
	A	C	25 *Star Girls...............................	Ha.30	—	—
	A	C	10 Types of Smokers		£40.00	£400.00
	A	C	50 Wild Animals of the World	H.77	£6.00	£300.00

B. Post-1920 Issues

Illus. No.	Size	Print-ing	Number in set	Handbook ref.	Price per card	Complete set
23	A	C	25 Boxing (1924)............................	H.311	44p	£11.00
	A	C	50 Children of All Nations (1934) (see RB21/200/168)		25p	£12.50
	A	C	50 Historic Events (1924)......................	H.464	£1.20	£60.00
	A	U	25 Hunting (1925)............................		34p	£8.50
	A	U	50 Modern Dance Steps (1929)		£2.40	£120.00
	A	U	50 Modern Dance Steps, 2nd Series (1931)		22p	£11.00
	A	C	50 Overseas Dominions (Australia) (1923)......	H.451	£1.50	£75.00

C. Miscellaneous

Illus. No.	Size	Print-ing	Number in set	Handbook ref.	Price per card	Complete set
—		C	? 1 Comic Dog Folder (opens to 183 × 65 mm.)..	Ha.490	—	—

A. H. FRANKS & SONS, London

Pre-1919 Issues

Illus. No.	Size	Print-ing	Number in set	Handbook ref.	Price per card	Complete set
	D1	BW	56 *Beauties—"Beauties Cigarettes"	H.173/Ha.173	£25.00	—
	D	C	? 23 *Nautical Expressions........................	H.174	—	—
	A1	C	25 *Types of British and Colonial Troops	H.76	£45.00	—

J. J. FREEMAN, London

Pre-1919 Issues

Illus. No.	Size	Print-ing	Number in set	Handbook ref.	Price per card	Complete set
	D	BW	12 *Actresses—"FRAN"........................	H.175	£25.00	—
	D	BW	12 *Views of the World........................	H.176	£25.00	—

C. FRYER & SONS, LTD., London

A. Pre-1919 Issues

Illus. No.	Size	Print-ing	Number in set	Handbook ref.	Price per card	Complete set
	A2	C	? 25 *Boer War & General Interest:—	H.13		
			A. Brown leaf design back		—	—
			B. Green leaf design back		—	—
			C. Green daisy design back		—	—
	D	C	40 *Naval and Military Phrases..................	H.14	£25.00	—
	A2	BW	? 8 *"Vita Berlin" Series	H.177/Ha.177	—	—

B. Post-1920 Issue

Illus. No.	Size	Print-ing	Number in set	Handbook ref.	Price per card	Complete set
—		—	48 Clan Sketches (101 × 74 mm.) (paper folders with wording only)—"Pibroch Virginia"..	Ha.628	£5.00	—

FRYER & COULTMAN, London

Pre-1919 Issue

Illus. No.	Size	Print-ing	Number in set	Handbook ref.	Price per card	Complete set
—		C	12 *French Phrases, 1893 Calendar back (96 × 64 mm.)....................................	H.178	—	—

J. GABRIEL, London

Pre-1919 Issues

Illus. No.	Size	Print-ing	Number in set	Handbook ref.	Price per card	Complete set
	A	BW	10 *Actresses—"HAGG A".....................	H.24	£35.00	—
	A2	C	25 *Beauties—"GRACC"........................	H.59	—	—
	A	BW	20 Cricketers Series	H.29	£70.00	—
	A	C	40 *Home and Colonial Regiments:—	H.69		
			20. Caption in blue		£45.00	—
			20. Caption in brown		£45.00	—
	A	U	? 47 *Pretty Girl Series—"BAGG"	H.45/Ha.45	£45.00	—
	A2	C	25 *Types of British and Colonial Troops	H.76	£40.00	—

GALLAHER LTD., Belfast and London

A. Pre-1919 Issues

Illus. No.	Size	Print-ing	Number in set	Handbook ref.	Price per card	Complete set
	D	P	110 *Actors & Actresses	H.179/Ha.179	£2.60	—
	D	C	25 The Allies Flags:—(1914)		—	£90.00
			A. Toned card		£3.60	—
			B. White card............................		£3.60	—
	D	C	100 Association Football Club Colours (1910):—			
			A. Grey border		£2.50	—
			B. Brown border		£2.50	—
			C. A. and B. mixed.......................		—	£250.00
	A	C	52 *Beauties:—	H.180/Ha.180		
			A. Without inset		£11.00	—

CCC—C

Illus. No.	Size	Print-ing	Number in set		Handbook ref.	Price per card	Complete set
				B. With Playing Card inset		£11.00	—
	D	C	50	*Birds & Eggs......................	H.60	£6.50	—
	D	C	100	Birds Nests & Eggs Series (1919):—			
				A. White card........................		90p	£90.00
				B. Toned card		90p	—
	D	C		Boy Scout Series:—			
				A. Grey-green back (1911)			
			100	(a) "Belfast & London"		£1.30	£130.00
			86	(b) "London & Belfast"		£1.30	£110.00
				B. Ornamental brown back—see Post-1920 issues			
	D	U	50	British Naval Series (1914).................		£3.50	£175.00
	D	P	100	English & Scotch Views		£2.20	£220.00
	D	C	100	Fables & Their Morals, Series 1 (1912):—			
				A. Numbered in name panel		£1.10	£110.00
				B. & C. Later printings, see Post-1920 issues			
	D	C	100	The Great War Series (1915)...............		£1.75	£175.00
	D	C	100	The Great War Series—Second Series (1916)		£1.75	£175.00
	D	C		The Great War, Victoria Cross Heroes (1915–16):—			
			25	1st Series 1–25.........................		£2.00	£50.00
			25	2nd Series 26–50.......................		£2.00	£50.00
			25	3rd Series 51–75.......................		£2.00	£50.00
			25	4th Series 76–100		£2.00	£50.00
			25	5th Series 101–125		£2.00	£50.00
			25	6th Series 126–150		£2.00	£50.00
			25	7th Series 151–175		£2.00	£50.00
			25	8th Series 176–200		£2.00	£50.00
66	D	C	100	How to do it (1916)......................		£1.75	£175.00
	D			Irish View Scenery:—	H.181		
		BW	200	1–200, semi-matt, numbered on back.......		£1.50	—
		BW	200	201–400 matt: A. numbered on back		£1.50	—
				B. unnumbered, plain back		£2.00	—
		P	400	1–400 glossy—see H.181			
				A. Black photo........................		80p	£320.00
				B. Brown photo........................		£2.00	—
				C. As A, but series title and No. omitted...		£1.25	—
		P	600	1–600 glossy—see H.181			
				A. Nos 1 to 500		85p	£425.00
				B. Nos 501 to 600		£3.00	—
	D	C	100	"Kute Kiddies" Series (1916)		£1.75	£175.00
	D	P	50	Latest Actresses (1910):—			
				A. Black photo........................		£7.00	—
				B. Chocolate photo		£10.00	—
	A	C	50	*Regimental Colours and Standards (Nd. 151–200).........................		£3.20	£160.00
	A	C	50	Royalty Series (? 1902)		£3.50	£175.00
	A	C	111	The South African Series (Nd. 101–211) (1901–2):—		—	£400.00
				A. White back		£3.60	—
				B. Cream back		£3.60	—
	D	C	100	"Sports" Series (1912).....................		£2.60	£260.00
	D	U	? 75	*Stage and Variety Celebrities (collotype)	H.182/Ha.182		
				A. "Gallager" back		£40.00	—
				B. "Gallaher" back		£40.00	—
				C. as B. but larger lettering, etc.		£40.00	—
	D	C	100	Tricks & Puzzles Series, green back (1913)...		£2.00	£200.00
	A	C	50	*Types of the British Army — unnumbered:—	H.183/Ha.183		
				A. "Battle Honours" back—			
				i. white.................		£6.00	£300.00
				ii. lilac tinted........................		£6.00	£300.00
				B. "The Three Pipes ..." — green back....		£6.00	£300.00
	A	C	50	*Types of the British Army—Nd. 1–50 (1898–1900):—			
				A. "The Three Pipes ..." — brown back...		£6.00	£300.00
				B. "Now in Three ..." — brown back.....		£6.00	£300.00
	A	C	50	*Types of British and Colonial Regiments— Nd. 51–100 (1900):—			
				A. "The Three Pipes ..." — brown back...		£6.00	£300.00
				B. "Now in Three ..." — brown back.....		£6.00	£300.00
	D	C	100	Useful Hints Series (1915)		£1.80	£180.00
	D	U	25	Views in Northern Ireland.................		£36.00	—
	D	C	50	Votaries of the Weed (1916)		£2.80	£140.00
125	D	C	100	"Why is it?" Series (1915):—			
				A. Green back		£1.75	£175.00
				B. Brown back.......................		£1.75	£175.00
	D	C	100	Woodland Trees Series (1912)		£1.80	£180.00

B. Post-1920 Issues

Illus. No.	Size	Print-ing	Number in set		Handbook ref.	Price per card	Complete set
	D	C	48	Aeroplanes (1939)........................		18p	£9.00
	A2	C	25	Aesop's Fables (1931):—	Ha.518		
				A. Inscribed "A Series of 25"		24p	£6.00
				B. Inscribed "A Series of 50"		24p	£6.00
	D	C	100	Animals & Birds of Commercial Value (Nov. 1921)................................		50p	£50.00
	D	C	48	Army Badges (Jan. 1939)		35p	£17.50
	—	U	24	Art Treasures of the World (76 × 56 mm.) (1930 and 1937).......................		13p	£3.25
	—	P	48	Beautiful Scotland (77 × 52 mm.) (1939).....	Ha.564–1	18p	£9.00

Illus. No.	Size	Print-ing	Number in set		Handbook ref.	Price per card	Complete set
	D	C	100	Boy Scout Series, brown back (1922)		£1.10	£110.00
	D	C	48	British Birds (1937).........................		13p	£5.50
	D	C	100	British Birds by Rankin (Dec. 1923):—	Ha.537		
				A. "By Rankin".........................		£4.00	—
				B. "By George Rankin"		50p	£50.00
	D	C	75	British Champions of 1923 (June 1924)......		75p	£55.00
	D	C	48	Butterflies and Moths (Aug. 1938)		13p	£5.50
	D	C	25	Champion Animals & Birds of 1923 (June 1924)....................................		£1.00	£25.00
338	D	C	48	Champions (1934):—			
				A. Front without letterpress		32p	£16.00
				B. Front with captions, subjects re-drawn .		30p	£15.00
	D	C	48	Champions, 2nd Series (1935)...............		14p	£7.00
	D	C	48	Champions of Screen & Stage (1934):—			
				A. Red back		13p	£6.00
				B. Blue back, "Gallaher's Cigarettes" at base		25p	£12.00
				C. Blue back, "Gallaher Ltd." at base		25p	£12.00
	D	U	100	Cinema Stars (Aug. 1926)...................		75p	£75.00
	—	P	48	Coastwise (77 × 52 mm.) (1938)	Ha.564–2	25p	£12.50
		C	24	Dogs (1934):—			
				A. Captions in script letters (white or cream card):—			
	D			1. Small size........................		40p	£10.00
	B			2. Large size........................		40p	£10.00
				B. Captions in block Letters:—			
	D			1. Small size........................		14p	£3.50
	B			2. Large size........................		14p	£3.50
	D	C	48	Dogs (Sep. 1936).........................		13p	£5.00
335	D	C	48	Dogs, Second Series (Nov. 1938)............		13p	£4.50
	D	C	100	Fables and Their Morals:—			
				A. First printing, pre-1919 issues			
				B. Thin numerals (Mar. 1922)—			
				1. White card......................		50p	£50.00
				2. Yellow card.....................		50p	£50.00
				C. Thick numerals (Nov. 1922)		50p	£50.00
	D	U	100	Famous Cricketers (Mar. 1926).............		£1.20	£120.00
	D	C	48	Famous Film Scenes (June 1935)...........		13p	£6.50
	D	U	100	Famous Footballers, green back (1925)......		65p	£65.00
	D	C	50	Famous Footballers, brown back (1926)		80p	£40.00
	D	C	48	Famous Jockeys (Sep. 1936)		13p	£6.50
	D	C	48	Film Episodes (Mar. 1936).................		13p	£6.50
	D	C	48	Film Partners (Dec. 1935)		13p	£6.50
	—	P	48	Flying (77 × 52 mm.) (Feb. 1938)...........	Ha.564–3	60p	£30.00
	D	C	100	Footballers, red back (May 1928):—			
				1. Nos. 1–50—Action pictures...........		90p	£45.00
				2. Nos. 51–100—Portraits...............		£1.00	£50.00
	D	C	50	Footballers in Action (1928)		90p	£45.00
	D	C	48	Garden Flowers (Feb. 1938)		13p	£4.00
	D		100	Interesting Views:—			
		P		A. Uncoloured, glossy (1923)		£1.10	£110.00
		CP		B. Hand-coloured, matt (1925)		£1.10	£110.00
	B2	P	48	Island Sporting Celebrities (1938) (Channel Islands)...............................		60p	£30.00
	D	C	50	Lawn Tennis Celebrities (Apr. 1928)		£1.50	£75.00
	A	C	24	Motor Cars (1934)		£1.80	£45.00
	D	C	48	My Favourite Part (1939)...................		13p	£4.00
	D	C	48	The Navy (1937):—			
				A. "Park Drive ..." at base of back		13p	£4.50
				B. "Issued by ..." at base of back		17p	£8.50
	—	P	48	Our Countryside (72 × 52 mm.) (1938).......	Ha.564–4	50p	£24.00
	D	C	100	Plants of Commercial Value (1917 and 1923)		50p	£50.00
	D	C	48	Portraits of Famous Stars (Sep. 1935)		13p	£4.50
	D	C	48	Racing Scenes (1938).....................		13p	£4.50
367	D	C	100	The Reason Why (1924) (see RB21/345).....		50p	£50.00
	D	C	100	Robinson Crusoe (Oct. 1928)		£1.00	£100.00
	B2	P	48	Scenes from the Empire (1939) (export)......	Ha.565	13p	£5.50
	—	P	24	Shots from the Films (77 × 52 mm.) (1936)...	Ha.566	£1.40	£35.00
314	D	C	48	Shots from Famous Films (Apr. 1935).......		25p	£12.00
	D	C	48	Signed Portraits of Famous Stars (1935).....		40p	£20.00
	D	C	48	Sporting Personalities (1936)		13p	£4.00
	D	C	48	Stars of Screen & Stage (1935):—			
				A. Back in green		13p	£4.50
				B. Back in brown		30p	£15.00
62	D	C	48	Trains of the World (1937).................		35p	£17.50
291	D	C		Tricks & Puzzles Series, black back (1933):—			
				1–50		13p	£5.00
				51–100		13p	£5.00
	D	C	48	Wild Animals (1937)		13p	£4.00
	D	C	48	Wild Flowers (1939)		13p	£4.50
	D	C	100	The "Zoo" Aquarium (1924)		80p	£80.00
	D	C	50	"Zoo" Tropical Birds, 1st Series (1928)......		80p	£40.00
362	D	C	50	"Zoo" Tropical Birds, 2nd Series (1929).....		80p	£40.00

C. Silks

	—	C	24	Flags—Set 1 (68 × 48 mm.) (paper-backed) (1916)................................	Ha.501–1	£4.50	—

D. Miscellaneous

	D	C	48	Screen Lovers—"Summit" (prepared but not issued)		90p	£45.00

SAMUEL GAWITH, Kendal

Illus. No.	Size	Print-ing	Number in set		Handbook ref.	Price per card	Complete set
Post-1920 Issue							
—		BW	25	The English Lakeland (90 × 70 mm.)		£8.00	—

F. GENNARI LTD., London

Illus. No.	Size	Print-ing	Number in set		Handbook ref.	Price per card	Complete set
Pre-1919 Issue							
	A	U	50	War Portraits............................	H.86	—	—

LOUIS GERARD, LTD., London

Illus. No.	Size	Print-ing	Number in set		Handbook ref.	Price per card	Complete set
Post-1920 Issues							
	D1	U	50	Modern Armaments:—	Ha.567		
				A. Numbered...........................		13p	£6.00
				B. Unnumbered........................		15p	£7.50
	D1	U	24	Screen Favourites:—	Ha.568		
				A. Inscribed "Louis Gerard & Company" .		£1.60	—
				B. Inscribed "Louis Gerard, Limited".....		£1.60	—
	D1	C	48	Screen Favourites & Dancers	Ha.569	50p	£24.00

W. G. GLASS & CO. LTD., Bristol

Illus. No.	Size	Print-ing	Number in set		Handbook ref.	Price per card	Complete set
Pre-1919 Issues							
	A	BW	20	*Actresses—"BLARM"....................	H.23	£32.00	—
	A2	BW	10	*Actresses—"HAGG A"....................	H.24	£32.00	—
	A	U	25	*Beauties—"FECKSA".....................	H.58	£50.00	—
	D1	BW	20	*Boer War Cartoons ("Roseland Cigarettes")	H.42	£40.00	—
	A	BW	25	*Boer War Celebrities—"STEW"...........	H.105	£40.00	—
	A	BW	16	*British Royal Family (1901)	H.28	£35.00	—
	A2	BW	20	Cricketers Series	H.29	£65.00	—
	D	C	40	*Naval and Military Phrases................	H.14	£50.00	—
	A	BW	19	*Russo-Japanese Series....................	H.184	£26.00	—

R. P. GLOAG & CO., London

(Cards bear advertisements for "Citamora" and/or "The Challenge Flat Brilliantes" without maker's name)

Illus. No.	Size	Print-ing	Number in set		Handbook ref.	Price per card	Complete set
Pre-1919 Issues							
	A2	U	? 5	*Actresses	H.185/Ha.185	—	—
	D			*Beauties — Selection from "Plums":—	H.186/Ha.186		
		BW	? 24	A. "The Challenge Flat" front:			
				(a) i. front in black and white		£45.00	—
				(a) ii. smaller lettering on back........		£50.00	—
		U	? 2	(b) front in brown..................		£60.00	—
		BW	? 8	B. "Citamora" front in black and white ...		£80.00	—
	A	C	40	*Home and Colonial Regiments:—	H.69		
				20. Caption in blue		£26.00	—
				20. Caption in brown		£26.00	—
	D	C	30	*Proverbs..............................	H.15	£50.00	—
	A2	C	25	*Types of British and Colonial Troops	H.76	£32.00	—

GLOBE CIGARETTE CO.

Illus. No.	Size	Print-ing	Number in set		Handbook ref.	Price per card	Complete set
Pre-1919 issue							
	D	BW	? 3	*Actresses—French	H.1	—	—

GOLDS LTD., Birmingham

Illus. No.	Size	Print-ing	Number in set		Handbook ref.	Price per card	Complete set
Pre-1919 Issues							
	A2	BW	1	Advertisement Card (Chantecler)		—	—
	C	C	18	Motor Cycle Series:—	Ha.469		
				A. Back in blue, numbered................		£15.00	—
				B. Back in grey, numbered...............		£15.00	—
				C. Back in grey, unnumbered		£15.00	—
	—	BW	? 14	*Prints from Noted Pictures (68 × 81 mm.)....	Ha.216	—	—

T. P. & R. GOODBODY, Dublin and London

Illus. No.	Size	Print-ing	Number in set		Handbook ref.	Price per card	Complete set
A. Pre-1919 Issues							
	—	U	? 12	*Actresses—"ANGOOD" (36 × 60 mm.).....	H.187	£65.00	—
	D	BW		*Boer War Celebrities—"CAG" (1901)	H.79/Ha.79		
			? 24	See H.79—Fig. 79-B.....................		£18.00	—
			? 16	See H.79—Fig. 79-C.....................		£18.00	—
			16	See H.79—Fig. 79-D.....................		£18.00	—
	A2	C	? 39	Colonial Forces:—	H.188/Ha.188		
				A. Brown back........................		£50.00	—
				B. Black back.........................		£45.00	—
	—	U	40	*Dogs (1910) ... (36 × 60 mm.)...............	H.189/Ha.189	£40.00	—
	C	C	26	Eminent Actresses — "FROGA A".........	H.20	£17.00	£440.00
	C	C	20	Irish Scenery..............................	H.190	£28.00	—
	A2	U	? 47	*Pretty Girl Series—"BAGG":—	H.45/Ha.45		
				A. Red stamped back...................		£60.00	—

Illus. No.	Size	Printing	Number in set		Handbook ref.	Price per card	Complete set
				B. Violet stamped back..................		£60.00	—
	A	C	25	Types of Soldiers..........................	H.144	£25.00	—
	D	U	20	*War Pictures...........................	H.122	£9.00	—
	C	C	12	"With the Flag to Pretoria".................	H.191	£70.00	—

B. Post-1920 Issues

Illus. No.	Size	Printing	Number in set		Handbook ref.	Price per card	Complete set
	D	C	50	Questions & Answers in Natural History (1924)............................		£1.30	£65.00
	A	C	25	Sports & Pastimes—Series I (1925)..........	H.225	£2.00	£50.00

GORDON'S, Glasgow

Pre-1919 Issue

	A2	BW	? 4	Billiards—By George D. Gordon		—	—

GRAVESON, Mexboro'

Pre-1919 Issues

	A2	C	30	*Army Pictures, Cartoons, Etc.	H.12	—	—
	A	U	50	War Portraits.............................	H.86	—	—

FRED GRAY, Birmingham

Pre-1919 Issue

	A	C	25	*Types of British Soldiers....................	H.144	£60.00	—

W. J. HARRIS, London

Pre-1919 Issues

	A2	C	26	*Beauties—"HOL"	H.192	£13.00	—
	C	C	30	*Colonial Troops	H.40	—	—
	A1	C	25	*Star Girls................................	H.30	£80.00	—

JAS. H. HARRISON, Birmingham

Pre-1919 Issue

	C	C	18	Motor Cycle Series........................	Ha.469	—	—

HARVEY & DAVEY, Newcastle-on-Tyne

Pre-1919 Issues

	D1	C	50	*Birds & Eggs.............................	H.60	£3.00	£150.00
	A1	C	? 10	*Chinese and South African Series	H.193/Ha.193	£100.00	—
	C	C	30	*Colonial Troops	H.40	£50.00	—
	A1	C	25	*Types of British and Colonial Troops	H.76	£50.00	—

W. & H. HEATON, Birkby

Pre-1919 Issue

	—	BW	? 6	Birkby Views (70 × 39 mm.).................	H.226	£65.00	—

HENLY & WATKINS LTD., London

Post-1920 Issues

Illus. No.	Size	Printing	Number in set		Handbook ref.	Price per card	Complete set
195	A1	C	25	Ancient Egyptian Gods—"Matossin's Cigarettes" (1924)	Ha.570		
				*A. Plain back		£1.60	£40.00
				B. Back in blue........................		£1.80	£45.00

HIGNETT BROS. & CO., Liverpool

A. Pre-1919 Issues

Illus. No.	Size	Printing	Number in set		Handbook ref.	Price per card	Complete set
	C	C	26	*Actresses—"FROGA A"..................	H.20	£35.00	—
	A2	U		*Actresses—Photogravure:—	H.194/Ha.194		
			? 23	i. With "Golden Butterfly" on front......		£9.00	—
			? 1	ii. Without "Golden Butterfly" on front ..		—	—
	D1	BW	28	*Actresses—"PILPI I"....................	H.195/Ha.195	£20.00	—
	D1	P	50	*Actresses—"PILPI II"	H.196	£10.00	—
	A	U	1	Advertisement Card. Smoking mixture......		—	—
	—	C	60	Animal Pictures ... (38 × 70 mm.)..........	H.197/Ha.197	£16.00	—
	D	U	? 46	*Beauties—gravure:—	H.198		
				A. "Cavalier" back......................		£26.00	—
				B. "Golden Butterfly" back		£26.00	—
	C	C	50	*Beauties—"CHOAB".....................	H.21	£55.00	—
	A1	C	16	Cabinet, 1900...........................	H.199/Ha.199	—	—
	A	C	25	Cathedrals & Churches (Dec. 1909)		£3.20	£80.00
	A	C	25	Company Drill (Sep. 1915)		£3.20	£80.00
292	A	C	25	Greetings of the World (Jan. 1907—re-issued 1922)............................		£1.40	£35.00
	A	C	50	Interesting Buildings (Feb. 1905)...........	H.70	£3.00	£150.00

Illus. No.	Size	Print-ing	Number in set		Handbook ref.	Price per card	Complete set
—		C	40	*Medals (1901–2) (34 × 72 mm.):—	H.200		
				A. "Butterfly Cigarettes"		£13.00	—
				B. Officially cut for use in other brands		£13.00	—
	A	BW	25	Military Portraits (Dec. 1914)	H.201	£3.60	£90.00
	A	C	25	Modern Statesmen (Nov. 1906):—			
				A. "Butterfly" back		£4.00	£100.00
				B. "Pioneer" back		£4.00	£100.00
	A	C	20	*Music Hall Artistes	H.202	£24.00	—
		C	1	Oracle Butterfly (shaped))		—	£100.00
	A	C	25	Panama Canal (Mar. 1914)		£4.40	£110.00
	A2	C	12	*Pretty Girl Series—"RASH":—	H.8		
				i. 1–6 head and shoulders		£32.00	—
				ii. 7–12 full length		£32.00	—
	—	BW	25	*V.C. Heroes (1901–2) (35 × 72 mm.)	H.203	£30.00	—
	A	C	20	*Yachts (? 1902):—	H.204		
				A. Gold on black back		£50.00	—
				B. Black on white back		£50.00	—

B. Post-1920 Issues

Illus. No.	Size	Print-ing	Number in set		Handbook ref.	Price per card	Complete set
153	A	C	50	Actors—Natural & Character Studies (Feb. 1938)	Ha.571–1	16p	£8.00
	A	C	50	A.F.C. Nicknames (1933)	Ha.571–2	90p	£45.00
	A	C	50	Air-Raid Precautions (1939)	Ha.544	40p	£18.00
	A	C	50	Arms & Armour (Dec. 1924)	H.273	£1.40	£70.00
	A	C	50	British Birds & Their Eggs (1938)	Ha.571–3	60p	£30.00
	A	U	50	Broadcasting (1935)	Ha.571–4	70p	£35.00
	A	U	50	Celebrated Old Inns (June 1925)		£1.40	£70.00
	A	C	50	Champions of 1936 (June 1937)	Ha.571–5	70p	£35.00
	A	C	25	Common Objects of the Sea-Shore (Jan. 1924)		£1.40	£35.00
	A	C	50	Coronation Procession (sectional) (1937)	Ha.571–6	£1.30	—
276	A	C	50	Dogs (1936)	Ha.571–7	25p	£12.50
	A	C	50	Football Caricatures (Sep. 1935)	Ha.571–8	50p	£25.00
	A	C	50	Football Club Captains (1935)	Ha.571–9	60p	£30.00
	A	U	25	Historical London (Aug. 1926)		£1.40	£35.00
	A	C	50	How to Swim (1935)	Ha.571–10	22p	£11.00
	A	C	25	International Caps and Badges (May 1924)		£1.40	£35.00
	A	C	25	Life in Pond & Stream (Aug. 1925)		£1.40	£35.00
	A	C	50	Modern Railways (Oct. 1936)	Ha.571–11	£1.20	£60.00
260	A	C	50	Ocean Greyhounds (1938)	Ha.571–12	36p	£18.00
	A	U	25	*The Prince of Wales' Empire Tour (1924)		£1.00	£25.00
	A	U	50	Prominent Cricketers of 1938 (1938)	Ha.571–13	80p	£40.00
257	A	C	50	Prominent Racehorses of 1933 (1934)	Ha.571–14	40p	£20.00
105	A	C	50	Sea Adventure (1939)	Ha.571–15	13p	£4.50
	A	C	25	Ships Flags & Cap Badges (Nov. 1926) (see RB21/217/178)		£1.40	£35.00
	A	C	25	Ships Flags & Cap Badges, 2nd Series (July 1927) (see RB21/217/178)		£1.60	£40.00
	A	C	50	Shots from the Films (1936)	Ha.571–16	60p	£30.00
	A	C	50	Trick Billiards (1934)	Ha.571–17	£1.60	—
	A	U	25	Turnpikes (Apr. 1927)		£1.20	£30.00
	A	C	50	Zoo Studies (Aug. 1937)	Ha.571–18	32p	£16.00

R. & J. HILL LTD., London

A. Pre-1919 Issues

	Size	Print-ing	Number in set		Handbook ref.	Price per card	Complete set
	A	C	26	*Actresses—"FROGA A"	H.20	£30.00	—
	D	BW	30	*Actresses, Continental:—	H.205/Ha.205		
				A. "The Seven Wonders" back		£9.00	—
				B. "Black and White Whisky" back		£22.00	—
				C. Plain back		£7.00	—
	D	BW	? 14	*Actresses—"HAGG B":—	H.24/Ha.24		
				A. "Smoke Hill's Stockrider ..."		£22.00	—
				B. "Issued with Hill's High Class"		£20.00	—
	—	BW	25	*Actresses (Belle of New York Series) (1899):—	H.206/Ha.206		
				"The Seven Wonders ..." back:			
				A. White back (41 × 75 mm.)		£9.00	£225.00
				B. Toned back, thick card (39 × 74 mm.)		£11.00	£275.00
	D1	U	20	*Actresses, chocolate tinted (1917):—	H.207/Ha.207		
				A. "Hill's Tobaccos" etc. back		£9.00	—
				B. "Issued with Hill's ..." back		£12.50	—
				C. Plain back		£9.00	—
	C	C	20	*Animal Series (1909):—			
				A. "R. & J. Hill Ltd." back		£14.00	—
				B. "Crowfoot Cigarettes" back		£10.00	—
				C. "The Cigarettes with which ..." back		—	—
				D. Space at back		£10.00	—
				E. Plain Back		—	—
	A	BW	? 13	*Battleships:—	H.208/Ha.208		
				A. "For the Pipe Smoke Oceanic ..." back		—	—
				B. Plain back		—	—
	A	C	25	*Battleships and Crests (1901–2)		£10.00	£250.00
	D2	C	12	*Boer War Generals ("Campaigners")	H.209/Ha.209	£25.00	£300.00
	A1	C	20	Breeds of Dogs (1914):—	H.211	—	£140.00
				A. "Archer's M.F.H." back		£7.00	—
				B. "Hill's Badminton" back		£7.00	—
				C. "Hill's Verbena Mixture" back		£7.00	—
				D. "Spinet Tobacco" back		£7.00	—

Illus. No.	Size	Print-ing	Number in set		Handbook ref.	Price per card	Complete set
	D1	BW	? 44	*British Navy Series (? 1902–3).............	H.210/Ha.210	£14.00	—
	C	C		*Colonial Troops:—	H.40		
			30	A. 1–30.			
				i. "Hill's Leading Lines ..." back.....		£13.00	—
				ii. "Perfection vide Dress ..." back....		£12.00	—
			50	B. 1–50. "Sweet American" back.........		£13.00	—
	D1	U	28	Famous Cricketers Series (1912):			
				A. Red back, blue picture.................		£25.00	—
				B. Deep blue back, brown picture.........		£25.00	—
				C. Blue back, black picture...............		£25.00	—
	D1	BW	20	Famous Footballers Series (1912–13)........		£9.00	£180.00
	—	U	25	Famous Pictures:—(41 × 70 mm.)...........	H.468		
				A. "Prize Coupon" back..................		£2.60	£65.00
				B. Without "Prize Coupon" back.........		£2.60	£65.00
	C	C	30	*Flags and Flags with Soldiers	H.41	£15.00	—
	—	C	24	*Flags, Arms and Types of Nations, "Black & White" Whisky advert back (41 × 68 mm.)	H.115	£6.00	£150.00
	D	BW	20	Football Captain Series, Nd. 41–60 (1906):—			
				A. Small title.................		£10.00	—
				B. Larger title, back re-drawn............		£10.00	—
	—		10	Fragments from France (1916–17): (38 × 67 mm.):—	H.212/Ha.212		
		C		A. Coloured, caption in script............		£10.00	£100.00
		U		B. Sepia-brown on buff, caption in block ..		£14.00	£140.00
		U		C. As B, but black and white.............		£30.00	—
	—	C	10	Fragments from France, different subjects, caption in block (38 × 67 mm.)...........	H.212	£10.00	£100.00
	A1	U	25	Hill's War Series	H.35	£7.00	£175.00
182	C2	C	20	Inventors & Their Inventions Series, Nd. 1–20, (1907):—	H.213		
				A. Black back, white card................		£3.50	£70.00
				B. Black back, toned card (shorter)		£4.50	—
	C2	C	20	Inventors & Their Inventions Series, Nd. 21–40, (1907)		£5.50	£110.00
	—		15	*Japanese Series (1904–5) (40 × 66 mm.):—	H.214/Ha.214		
		C		A. "Hills" on red tablet..................		£40.00	—
		BW		B. "Hills" on black tablet................		£30.00	—
	—	C	20	Lighthouse Series—without frame lines to picture (? 1903) (42 × 68 mm.)............		£17.00	—
	—	C	30	Lighthouse Series—with frame line. Nos. 1–20 re-touched and 10 cards added.......		£17.00	—
	D	C	20	National Flag Series (1914)	Ha.473	£6.00	£120.00
				Plain back		£6.00	—
	—	BW	? 22	*Naval Series (1901–02), Unnumbered (42 × 64 mm.).........................	H.215/Ha.215	£30.00	—
	D1	BW	? 29	Naval Series (1902–3) Nd. 21–49	H.215/Ha.215	£12.00	—
	C	C	20	Prince of Wales Series (1911)...............	H.22	£9.00	£180.00
				Plain back		—	—
	—	U	? 14	*Prints from Noted Pictures (68 × 81 mm.)....	H.216/Ha.216	£45.00	—
	A	BW	20	Rhymes—black and white sketches	H.217/Ha.217	£18.00	—
	A1		? 28	*Statuary—Set 1:—	Ha.218–1		
		U		A. Brown front		—	—
		BW		B. Black and white front, matt............		—	—
		BW		C. Black and white front, varnished		£7.00	—
	A	BW	30	*Statuary—Set 2:—	Ha.218–2		
				A. Front in black and white..............		£3.50	—
				B. Front greenish-black		£3.50	—
	C1	BW	? 25	*Statuary—Set 3:—	Ha.218–3		
				A. Name panel white lettering on black background........................		£10.00	—
				B. Name panel black lettering on grey background........................		—	—
				C. Name panel black lettering on white background........................		—	—
	D	C	20	*Types of the British Army (1914):—			
				A. "Badminton" back................		£18.00	—
				B. "Verbena" back....................		£18.00	—
	A	U	25	World's Masterpieces—Photogravure, inscribed "Second Series"		£1.20	£30.00

B. Post-1920 Issues

Illus. No.	Size	Print-ing	Number in set		Handbook ref.	Price per card	Complete set
	C	U	30	The All Blacks (1924)......................		£2.00	£60.00
	A	BW	25	Aviation Series (1934):—			
				A. "Issued by R. & J. Hill ..." at base		50p	£12.50
				B. "Issued with 'Gold Flake Honeydew' ..." at base		70p	£17.50
		U	50	Caricatures of Famous Cricketers (June 1926):—			
	C			A. Small size.....................		80p	£40.00
	B1			B. Large size.....................		70p	£35.00
	D1	C	50	Celebrities of Sport (1939):—			
				A. "Issued by R. & J. Hill ..." at base		40p	£20.00
				B. "Issued with 'Gold Flake Honeydew' ..." at base		60p	£30.00
285	A2	C	35	Cinema Celebrities (1936):—	Ha.572		
				A. Inscribed "These Cigarettes are guaranteed best British Manufacture"..		20p	£7.00
				B. Inscribed "The Spinet House"		28p	£10.00
	D1	BW	40	Crystal Palace Souvenir Cards (inscribed "These Cigarettes are guaranteed best			

Illus. No.	Size	Printing	Number in set		Handbook ref.	Price per card	Complete set
				British Manufacture"):—			
				A. Front matt (1936)		50p	£20.00
				B. Front varnished (1937)		40p	£16.00
190	D1	C	48	Decorations and Medals (1940):—			
				A. "Issued by R. & J. Hill..." at base		90p	£45.00
				B. "Issued with Gold Flake Cigarettes" at base		£1.10	£55.00
		P		Famous Cinema Celebrities (1931)	Ha.573		
			? 48	Set 1:—			
—				A. Medium size (74 × 56 mm.) inscribed "Series A"................		—	—
	A			B1. Small size, inscribed "Spinet Cigarettes"		£1.50	—
	A			B2. Small size, without "Spinet Cigarettes"		£1.50	—
			50	Set 2:—			
—				C. Small size (66 × 41 mm.) inscribed "Series C":—			
				1. "Devon Cigarettes" at base of back .		—	—
				2. "Toucan Cigarettes" at base of back		£1.50	—
				3. Space at base of back blank		£1.50	£75.00
				D. Medium size (74 × 56 mm.) inscribed "Series D":—			
				1. "Kadi Cigarettes" at base of back ..		£1.50	—
				2. Space at base of back blank		£1.50	—
	C	U	40	Famous Cricketers (1923)		£1.60	£65.00
		U	50	Famous Cricketers, including the S. Africa Test Team—"Sunripe Cigarettes" (May 1924):—			
	C			A. Small size.................		£1.80	£90.00
	B1			B. Large size.................		£2.00	£100.00
—		C	30	Famous Engravings—Series XI (80 × 61 mm.)		£4.00	—
298	A2	BW	40	Famous Film Stars (1938):—			
				A. Text in English......................		45p	£18.00
				B. *Text in Arabic, caption in English (see also Modern Beauties)*		40p	£16.00
	C	U	50	Famous Footballers (Oct. 1923)		90p	£45.00
	D	C	50	Famous Footballers (1939):—	Ha.574		
				A. Shoreditch address at base............		40p	£20.00
				B. "Proprietors of Hy. Archer..." at base.		45p	£22.50
289	D	C	25	Famous Footballers, Nd. 51–75 (1939)......		60p	£15.00
	D	C	50	Famous Ships:—			
				A. Front matt (1939)		13p	£6.00
				B. Front varnished (1940)		13p	£6.00
	D	C	48	Film Stars and Celebrity Dancers (1935).....		60p	£30.00
		C	50	Historic Places from Dickens' Classics (1926 and 1934):—			
	D			A. Small size.........................		24p	£12.00
	B1			B. Large size:—			
				1. Nos. 1–26, small numerals..........		35p	—
				2. Nos. 1–50, large numerals		24p	£12.00
218		U	50	Holiday Resorts (July 1925):—			
	C			A. Small size:—			
				1. Back in grey		44p	£22.00
				2. Back in brown		80p	—
	B1			B. Large size:—			
				1. Back in grey		44p	£22.00
				2. Back in brown		80p	—
	A		20	*Inventors and Their Inventions (plain back)* (1934):—	H.213		
		BW		A. *Front in black and white*...............		35p	£7.00
		C		B. *Front in colour*		—	—
				Magical Puzzles—see "Puzzle Series"			
294	A2	BW		Modern Beauties (1939):—			
			50	A. Titled "Modern Beauties". Text in English		35p	£17.50
			40	B. *Titled "Famous Film Stars" (selection). Text in Arabic, no captions*		40p	£16.00
		C	30	Music Hall Celebrities—Past & Present (July 1930):—			
	D1			A. Small size.........................		43p	£13.00
	B1			B. Large size.........................		80p	£24.00
220	D	C	30	Nature Pictures—"The Spotlight Tobaccos"		50p	£15.00
	C2	C	30	Nautical Songs (1937)....................		23p	£7.00
		U	30	"Our Empire" (Nov. 1929):—			
	D1			A. Small size.........................		13p	£3.75
	B1			B. Large size.........................		27p	£8.00
—		BW		Popular Footballers—Season 1934–5 (68 × 49 mm.):—			
			30	"Series A"—Nd. 1–30.....................		£1.00	£30.00
			20	"Series B"—Nd. 31–50....................		70p	£14.00
		U		Public Schools and Colleges (Dec. 1923):—	Ha.575		
			50	A. "A Series of 50"....................			
	C			1. Small size		40p	£20.00
	B1			2. Large size		45p	£22.50
			75	B. "A Series of 75"—			
	C			1. Small size		40p	£30.00
	B1			2. Large size		40p	£30.00
103	A1	C	50	Puzzle Series:—			

Illus. No.	Size	Print-ing	Number in set	Number in set (description)	Handbook ref.	Price per card	Complete set
				A. Titled "Puzzle Series" (1937)...........		20p	£10.00
				B. Titled "Magical Puzzles" (1938)........		35p	£17.50
229		U	50	The Railway Centenary—"A Series of 50" (Oct. 1925):—			
	C			A. Small size............................		35p	£17.50
	B1			B. Large size—			
				1. Back in brown....................		60p	£30.00
				2. Back in grey		75p	—
		U	25	The Railway Centenary—"2nd Series—51 to 75":—			
	C			A. Small size............................		£1.00	£25.00
	B1			B. Large size............................		80p	£20.00
	C2	P	42	Real Photographs—Set 1 (Bathing Beauties):—	Ha.576–1		
				A. "London Idol Cigarettes" at base of back:—			
				1. Front black and white, glossy.......		£1.50	—
				2. Front brown, matt		90p	£37.00
				B. Space at base of back blank:—			
				1. Front black and white, glossy.......		90p	—
				2. Front brown, matt		90p	£37.00
	C2	P	42	Real Photographs—Set 2 (Beauties).........	Ha.576–2	£1.20	—
				The River Thames—see "Views of the River Thames"			
	D1	P	50	Scenes from the Films (1932):—			
				A. Front black and white		90p	—
				B. Front sepia		90p	—
34	A2	BW	40	Scenes from the Films (1938–9)		15p	£6.00
	D1		35	Scientific Inventions and Discoveries (Dec. 1929):—	Ha.213		
	C			A. Small size, "The Spinet House ..." back		35p	£12.50
	BW			B. Small size, "The Spotlight Tobaccos ..." back		35p	£12.50
	B1	C		C. Large size............................		35p	£12.50
	D1	P	50	Sports (1934):—			
				A. Titled "Sports", numbered front and back...........................		£1.20	—
				B. Titled "Sports Series", numbered front only		£1.20	—
				*C. Untitled, numbered front only		£1.20	—
	D1	C	100	*Transfers	Ha.596–2	—	—
	B2	CP	48	Views of Interest:—			
				"A First Series ..." Nd. 1–48 (1938):—			
				A. "The Spinet House ..." back		15p	£7.50
				B. "Sunripe & Spinet Ovals ..." back		13p	£4.00
			48	"Second Series ..." Nd. 49–96 (1938)		13p	£4.50
			48	"Third Series ..." Nd. 97–144 (1939)........		13p	£3.50
			48	"Fourth Series ..." Nd. 145–192 (1939)		14p	£7.00
			48	"Fifth Series ..." Nd. 193–240 (1939)		15p	£7.50
	B2	CP		Views of Interest—British Empire Series ...:—			
			48	"1st Issue—Canada—Nos. 1–48" (1940)		20p	£10.00
			48	"2nd Issue—India—Nos. 49–96" (1940).....		£1.50	£75.00
203		U	50	Views of London (1925):—	Ha.577		
	C			A. Small size............................		44p	£22.00
	B1	C		B. Large size............................		50p	£25.00
	D		50	Views of the River Thames (1924):—			
				A. Small size—			
				Nos. 1–25		£1.20	£30.00
				Nos. 26–50		32p	£8.00
	B1			B. Large size—			
				1. Back in green (thin card)		50p	£25.00
				2. Back in green and black (thick card)		50p	£25.00
		U	50	Who's Who in British Films (Nov. 1927):—			
	A2			A. Small size............................		32p	£16.00
	B2			B. Large size............................		40p	£20.00
	C	C	84	Wireless Telephony (1923):—			
				1. Nos. 1–24.........................			
				2. Nos. 25–36—Crystal Series .... }		50p	£42.00
				3. Nos. 37–84—Marconiphone Series.....			
	B1	U	20	Wireless Telephony—Broadcasting Series (1923).................................		£1.50	£30.00
		U	50	Zoological Series (1924):—	Ha.578		
	C			A. Small size—			
				1. Back in light brown		50p	£25.00
				2. Back in grey		70p	£35.00
	B1			B. Large size—			
				1. Back in light brown		50p	£25.00
				2. Back in dark brown...............		50p	£25.00

C. Post-1940 Issue

	A	U	50	Famous Dog Breeds 1954 (Admiral Cigarettes Slides)		—	—

D. Canvases. Unbacked canvases. The material is a linen fabric, glazed to give the appearance of canvas. Specimens are found rubber stamped in red on back "The Pipe Tobacco de Luxe Spinet Mixture".

	—	C	30	"Britain's Stately Homes" (78 × 61 mm.)....		£2.00	£60.00
	—	C	40	*Canvas Masterpieces—Series 1 (73 × 61 mm.):—			
				A. "Badminton Tobacco Factories ..." back:—			

R. & J. HILL LTD. *(continued)*

Illus. No.	Size	Print-ing	Number in set	Handbook ref.	Price per card	Complete set
			1. "H.T. & Co., Ltd., Leeds" at right base		£1.00	—
			2. "Cardigan Press, Leeds" at right base (Nos. 21–40)		£1.00	—
			3. Without printers' credit (Nos. 21–30)		£1.00	—
			4. As 3, but size 73 × 53 mm. (Nos. 23–25)		£1.00	—
			B. "The Spinet House ..." back		£1.00	£40.00
—	C	40	*Canvas Masterpieces—Series 2, Nd. 41–80 (73 × 61 mm.)		£1.10	£45.00
—	C	10	*Canvas Masterpieces—Series 2, Nd. 1–10:—			
			Nos. 1 to 5		£1.30	£6.50
			Nos. 6 to 10		£2.60	£13.00
—	C	5	Chinese Pottery & Porcelain—Series 1 (132 × 110 mm.)		—	£11.00
—	C	11	Chinese Pottery & Porcelain—Series 2 (107 × 62 mm.)		£2.50	—
—	C	23	*Great War Leaders—Series 10 (73 × 60 mm.)		£2.50	£57.50

J. W. HOBSON, Huddersfield

Pre-1919 Issue

C2	C	18	Motor Cycle Series	Ha.469	—	—

J. & T. HODGE, Glasgow

Pre-1919 Issues

—	C	? 2	*British Naval Crests (70 × 38 mm.)	H.219/Ha.219	—	—
A	BW	16	British Royal Family		—	—
—	U		*Scottish Views:—	Ha.220		
		? 4	A. Thick card (74 × 39 mm.)		£80.00	—
		? 6	B. Thin card (80 × 45 mm.)		£80.00	—

HUDDEN & CO. LTD., Bristol

A. Pre-1919 Issues

C	C	26	*Actresses—"FROGA A"	H.20	£45.00	—
C	C	25	*Beauties—"CHOAB"	H.21	£22.00	—
A2	U	? 19	*Beauties—"Crown Seal Cigarettes"	H.221/Ha.221	£100.00	—
A	U	? 24	*Beauties—"HUMPS":—	H.222		
			A. Blue scroll back		£50.00	—
			B. Orange scroll back		£28.00	—
			C. Typeset black in brown		—	—
D1	C	54	Comic Phrases	H.223	£60.00	—
A	C	25	*Flags of All Nations	H.37	£7.00	£175.00
—	C	50	*Flowers and Designs (55 × 34 mm.)	H.224	£65.00	—
A	C	18	*Pretty Girl Series—"RASH"	H.8	£45.00	—
A	C	25	Soldiers of the Century, Nd. 26–50 (1901)		£30.00	£750.00
A	C	25	*Star Girls	H.30	£80.00	—
A	C	25	Types of Smokers		£30.00	£750.00

B. Post-1920 Issues. All export

D	U	25	Famous Boxers (1927)	Ha.579	—	—
C	U	50	Public Schools and Colleges	Ha.575	£1.10	£55.00
A	C	25	Sports & Pastimes Series 1	H.225	£35.00	—

HUDSON

Pre-1919 Issue

C	C	? 1	*Beauties—selections from "BOCCA"	H.39/Ha.39	£110.00	—

HUNTER, Airdrie

Pre-1919 Issue

A	BW	? 11	*Footballers	H.227	—	—

J. T. ILLINGWORTH & SONS, Kendal

A. Pre-1919 Issue

A	BW	? 1	Views from the English Lakes	H.228	£130.00	—

B. Post-1920 Issues

—	P	48	Beautiful Scotland (77 × 52 mm.) (1939)	Ha.564–1	50p	£25.00
C1	C	25	*Cavalry (1924)		£2.80	£70.00
—	P	48	Coastwise (77 × 52 mm.) (1938)	Ha.564–2	30p	£15.00
A	C	25	"Comicartoons" of Sport (1927)		£2.00	£50.00
—	P	48	Flying (77 × 52 mm.) (Feb. 1938)	Ha.564–3	35p	£17.50
A	C	25	*Motor Car Bonnets (1925)		£3.00	£75.00
A	C	25	*Old Hostels (1926)		£2.60	£65.00
—	P	48	Our Countryside (77 × 52 mm.) (1938)	Ha.564–4	25p	£12.50
—	P	24	Shots from the Films (1937)	Ha.566	90p	£22.50

THE IMPERIAL TOBACCO CO. (of Great Britain & Ireland) Ltd., Bristol

Illus. No.	Size	Print-ing	Number in set		Handbook ref.	Price per card	Complete set
Pre-1919 Issues							
	A	C	50	British Birds	H.229	£3.50	£175.00
	C	C	1	Folder—Coronation of His Majesty King Edward VII (1902)		—	£45.00

INTERNATIONAL TOBACCO CO. LTD., London

Illus. No.	Size	Print-ing	Number in set		Handbook ref.	Price per card	Complete set
Post-1920 Issues							
A. Home Issues							
32	—	C	28	Domino Cards (69 × 35 mm.)		20p	£5.50
		U		Famous Buildings and Monuments of Britain (1934) (bronze metal plaques in cellophane envelopes*:—	Ha.580		
			50	"Series A":—			
	A1			1. Nos. 1–30, small size		22p	£6.50
	B2			2. Nos. 31–50, large size		45p	£9.00
			50	"Series B":—			
	A1			1. Nos. 51–80, small size		50p	£15.00
	B2			2. Nos. 81–100, large size		40p	£8.00
	A	C	50	International Code of Signals (1934)		13p	£5.50
B. Export Issues. Inscribed "International Tobacco (Overseas), Ltd."							
	A2	C	100	Film Favourites:—	Ha.581		
				A. Back in grey		75p	—
				B. Back in black		75p	—
2	—	C	100	"Gentlemen! The King!" (1937–38)—60 small, 40 large:—	Ha.582		
				A. Back in blue		13p	£12.00
				B. Back in black		13p	£6.50

*The same plaques were also used for an export issue, with envelopes inscribed "International Tobacco (Overseas), Ltd."

J. L. S. TOBACCO CO., London

Illus. No.	Size	Print-ing	Number in set		Handbook ref.	Price per card	Complete set
Pre-1919 Issues							
				("Star of the World" Cigarettes)			
	D	BW	20	*Boer War Cartoons	H.42	£45.00	—
	B2	BW	? 27	*Boer War Celebrities—"JASAS"	H.133	—	—
	A2	C	30	*Colonial Troops	H.40	£45.00	—

PETER JACKSON, London

Illus. No.	Size	Print-ing	Number in set		Handbook ref.	Price per card	Complete set
Post-1920 Issues							
A. Home Issues							
69		P		Beautiful Scotland (1939):—	Ha.564–1		
	D		28	A. Small size		50p	£14.00
	—		48	B. Medium size, 77 × 52 mm.		25p	£12.50
293		P		Coastwise (1938):—	Ha.564–2		
	D		28	A. Small size		40p	£11.00
	—		48	B. Medium size, 77 × 52 mm.		40p	£20.00
37	D	P	27	Famous Films (1934–35)		£1.10	£30.00
	D	P	28	Famous Film Stars (1935)		£1.10	£30.00
	D	P	28	Film Scenes (Sep. 1936)		60p	£17.00
	B	P	28	Film Scenes (Sep. 1936)		90p	£25.00
		P		Flying (Feb. 1938):—	Ha.564–3		
	D		28	A. Small size		£1.00	—
	—		48	B. Medium size (77 × 52 mm.)		50p	£25.00
41	D	P	28	Life in the Navy (Mar. 1937)		50p	£14.00
	B	P	28	Life in the Navy (March 1937)		£1.10	£30.00
		P		Our Countryside (1938):—	Ha.564–4		
	D		28	A. Small size		36p	£10.00
	—		48	B. Medium size (77 × 52 mm.)		50p	£25.00
		P		Shots from the Films (Aug. 1937):—	Ha.566		
	D		28	A. Small size		40p	£11.00
	—		24	B. Medium size (77 × 52 mm.)		60p	£15.00
	D	P	28	Stars in Famous Films		60p	£17.00
B. Export Issues. Inscribed "Peter Jackson (Overseas), Ltd."							
	—	C	100	"Gentlemen! The King!" (1937–38)—60 small, 40 large:—	Ha.582		
				A. Overprinted on International black back		40p	£40.00
				B. Overprinted on International blue back		55p	—
				C. Reprinted with Jackson's name at base:—			
				i. Back in black		50p	£50.00
				ii. Back in blue		50p	—
197	—	C	150	The Pageant of Kingship—90 small, 60 large:—			
				A. Inscribed "Issued by Peter Jackson"		50p	£75.00
				B. Inscribed "Issued by Peter Jackson (Overseas), Ltd.":			
				1. Printed on board		50p	£75.00
				2. Printed on paper		20p	£30.00
208	—	C	250	Speed—Through the Ages (1937–38)—171 small, 79 large	Ha.583	13p	£32.50

JACOBI BROS. & CO. LTD., London

Illus. No.	Size	Print-ing	Number in set	Handbook ref.	Price per card	Complete set
Pre-1919 Issue						
	A	BW	? 27 *Boer War Celebrities—"JASAS"	H.133		
			A. Black and white front..................		—	—
			B. As A, but mauve tinted		£95.00	—

JAMES & CO. (Birmingham) LTD.

Illus. No.	Size	Print-ing	Number in set	Handbook ref.	Price per card	Complete set
Pre-1919 Issue						
	—	C	20 Arms of Countries (70 × 49 mm.)...........		£65.00	—

JAMES'S (GOLD LEAF NAVY CUT)

Illus. No.	Size	Print-ing	Number in set	Handbook ref.	Price per card	Complete set
Pre-1919 Issue						
	A	U	? 10 Pretty Girl Series "BAGG".................		—	—

J. B. JOHNSON & CO., London

Illus. No.	Size	Print-ing	Number in set	Handbook ref.	Price per card	Complete set
Pre-1919 Issue						
	A	C	25 *National Flags and Flowers—Girls	H.123	£95.00	—

JONES BROS., Tottenham

Illus. No.	Size	Print-ing	Number in set	Handbook ref.	Price per card	Complete set
Pre-1919 Issues						
250	A	BW	18 *Spurs Footballers:—	H.230		
			A. 12 small titles		From £2.50	—
			10/12 small titles		—	£25.00
			B. 5 large titles.........................		From £2.50	—
			C. 1 Group—Tottenham Hotspur Football Club 1911–12 (group of 34)........		—	—

A. I. JONES & CO. LTD., London

Illus. No.	Size	Print-ing	Number in set	Handbook ref.	Price per card	Complete set
Pre-1919 Issue						
	D	C	12 Nautical Terms	H.231	£20.00	£240.00

A. S. JONES, Grantham

Illus. No.	Size	Print-ing	Number in set	Handbook ref.	Price per card	Complete set
Pre-1919 Issue						
	D	C	30 Army Pictures, Cartoons, etc...............	H.12	—	—

ALEX. JONES & CO., London

Illus. No.	Size	Print-ing	Number in set	Handbook ref.	Price per card	Complete set
Pre-1919 Issues						
	D2	U	? 13 *Actresses—"ANGOOD"....................	Ha.187	—	—
	A	BW	1 Portrait of Queen Victoria 1897.............		—	£85.00

T. E. JONES & CO., Aberavon

Illus. No.	Size	Print-ing	Number in set	Handbook ref.	Price per card	Complete set
Pre-1919 Issues						
	D	C	? 4 *Conundrums	H.232/Ha.232	—	—
	—	C	48 *Flags of All Nations (35 × 60 mm.)..........	H.233	£60.00	—
	—	BW	? 4 *Footballers (34 × 63 mm.)	H.234/Ha.234	£60.00	—
	D	C	? 7 Well-known Proverbs	H.235	£60.00	—

C. H. JORDEN LTD., London

Illus. No.	Size	Print-ing	Number in set	Handbook ref.	Price per card	Complete set
Pre-1919 Issue						
	—	P	? 10 *Celebrities of the Great War, 1914–18 (35 × 64 mm.)...........................	H.236/Ha.236	£60.00	—

J. & E. KENNEDY, Dublin

Illus. No.	Size	Print-ing	Number in set	Handbook ref.	Price per card	Complete set
Pre-1919 Issue						
	A	U	25 *Beauties—"FECKSA".....................	H.58	£16.00	£400.00

RICHARD KENNEDY, Dundee

Illus. No.	Size	Print-ing	Number in set	Handbook ref.	Price per card	Complete set
Pre-1919 Issue						
	A	U	50 War Portraits.............................	H.86	—	—

KINNEAR LTD., Liverpool

Illus. No.	Size	Print-ing	Number in set	Handbook ref.	Price per card	Complete set
Pre-1919 Issues						
	A	C	? 13 *Actresses	H.237	£45.00	—
	D1	BW	? 14 *Australian Cricketers (1897).................	H.238	£80.00	—
	A2	C	25 *Footballers and Club Colours	H.239/Ha.239	£60.00	—

KINNEAR LTD. *(continued)*

Illus. No.	Size	Print- ing	Number in set		Handbook ref.	Price per card	Complete set
—	U		1	The Four Generations (Royal Family) (1897) (65 × 70 mm.)		—	£275.00
—	BW		1	"A Gentleman in Kharki" (1900) (44 × 64 mm.)		—	£28.00
A	C		? 33	*Jockeys (1896):—	H.240/Ha.240		
				12—see H.240-A		£20.00	£240.00
				1—see H.240-B		£38.00	—
				1—see H.240-C		£38.00	—
				3—see H.240-D		£38.00	—
				16—see H.240-E		£38.00	—
A	C		? 2	*Prominent Personages	Ha.479	—	—
D1	U		13	*Royalty (1897)	H.241	£30.00	—
—	U		? 2	Views (49 × 35 mm.)		£130.00	

B. KRIEGSFELD & CO., Manchester

Pre-1919 Issues

Illus. No.	Size	Print- ing	Number in set		Handbook ref.	Price per card	Complete set
	A2	U	? 40	*Beauties—"KEWA":—	H.139/Ha.139		
				A. Matt surface		£50.00	—
				B. Glossy surface		—	—
	A	C	? 6	Celebrities	H.242/Ha.242	£90.00	—
	A	C	48	*Flags of All Nations	H.233	£30.00	—
	A	C	50	*Phrases and Advertisements	H.243	£35.00	—

A. KUIT LTD., Manchester

Pre-1919 Issues

Illus. No.	Size	Print- ing	Number in set		Handbook ref.	Price per card	Complete set
	—	C	? 12	*Arms of Cambridge Colleges* (17 × 25 mm.)	H.458	—	—
	—	C	? 12	*Arms of Companies* (30 × 33 mm.)	H.459	£30.00	—
	—	C	30	British Beauties—oval card (36 × 60 mm.)	H.244	£20.00	—
	—	P	? 2	*"Crosmedo" Bijou cards* (55 × 37 mm.)	H.245	—	—
	A	U	25	Principal Streets of British Cities & Towns (1916)		£50.00	—
	A	CP	? 4	Types of Beauty	H.246	£85.00	—

LAMBERT & BUTLER, London

A. Pre-1919 Issues

Illus. No.	Size	Print- ing	Number in set		Handbook ref.	Price per card	Complete set
	A1	BW	20	*Actresses—"BLARM"	H.23	£8.00	£160.00
	—	C	10	*Actresses and Their Autographs:	H.247		
				A. Wide card (70 × 38 mm.):—			
				"Tobacco"		£55.00	—
				"Cigarettes"		—	—
				B. Narrow card (70 × 34 mm.):—			
				"Tobacco"		—	—
				"Cigarettes"		£55.00	—
	A2	BW	50	*Admirals (1900–1 ?):—	H.248		
				A. "Flaked Gold Leaf Honeydew" back		£8.00	—
				B. "May Blossom" back		£8.00	—
				C. "Prize Medal Bird's Eye" back		£8.00	—
				D. "Viking" back		£8.00	—
	C	C	1	*Advertisement Card—Spanish Dancer	H.249	—	£250.00
	A	C	40	Arms of Kings & Queens of England (1906–8)		£2.50	£100.00
67	A	C	25	Aviation (1915–16)		£1.60	£40.00
	A2	C	26	*Beauties—"HOL":	H.192		
				A. "Flaked Gold Leaf Honey Dew" back		£14.00	—
				B. "Log Cabin" back		£14.00	—
				C. "May Blossom" back		£14.00	—
				D. "Viking Navy Cut" back		£14.00	—
179	A	C	50	Birds & Eggs (1906 and 1917)	H.60	£1.80	£90.00
	C	BW	? 22	*Boer War and Boxer Rebellion—Sketches (1904)	H.46	£14.00	—
	C	BW	? 12	*Boer War Generals—"FLAC" (1901–2)	H.47	£14.00	—
	C	U	20	*Boer War Generals "CLAM" (1900–1)	H.61		
				I. 10. No frame lines to back:—			
				A. Brown back		£14.00	—
				B. Black back		£14.00	—
				II. 10. With frame lines to back:—			
				A. Brown back		£14.00	—
				B. Black back		£14.00	—
	C	U	1	*Boer War Series—"The King of Scouts" (Col. R. S. S. Baden-Powell)		—	£175.00
	—	C	50	*Conundrums (1901) (38 × 57 mm.):—	H.250		
				A. Blue back—thick card		£9.00	—
				B. Green back		£7.00	—
	A2	C	12	Coronation Robes (1901–2)	H.251	£10.00	£120.00
	A	C	20	International Yachts (1902)		£35.00	—
	A	C	25	Japanese Series (1904–5):—			
				A. Thick toned card		£4.00	£100.00
				B. Thin white card		£4.00	£100.00
	—	C	4	*Jockeys, no frame lines (35 × 70 mm.)	H.252	£17.00	£70.00
	—	C	10	*Jockeys, with frames lines (35 × 70 mm.)	H.252	£18.00	£180.00
	A	C	1	*Mayblossom Calendar, 1900		—	—
	A	C	25	Motors (Nov. 1908):—			
				A. Green back		£11.00	£275.00
				B. Plain back		£11.00	—

Illus. No.	Size	Print- ing	Number in set		Handbook ref.	Price per card	Complete set
	A	BW	25	Naval Portraits (1914)	H.253	£2.50	£62.50
	A	BW	50	Naval Portraits, incl. above 25 (1915)	H.253	£2.50	£125.00
	A	C	50	The Thames from Lechlade to London:—			
				A. Small numerals (1907)		£3.50	£175.00
				B. Large numerals (Sep. 1908)		£3.60	£180.00
				C. Plain back		£3.60	—
	—	C	4	*Types of the British Army & Navy (? 1897) (35 × 70 mm.):	H.254		
				A. "Specialities" back in brown		£32.00	—
				B. "Specialities" back in black		£32.00	—
				C. "Viking" back in black		£35.00	—
	A	C	25	*Waverley Series (1904)	H.255	£5.00	£125.00
	A	C	25	Winter Sports (1914)		£2.20	£55.00
	A	C	25	Wireless Telegraphy (1909)		£2.80	£70.00
	A	C	25	World's Locomotives, Nd. 1–25 (1912)		£2.60	£65.00
64	A	C	50	World's Locomotives (1913)		£3.20	£160.00
	A	C	25	World's Locomotives, Nd. 1A–25A, additional series		£3.20	£80.00

B. Post-1920 Issues

Illus. No.	Size	Print- ing	Number in set		Handbook ref.	Price per card	Complete set
	A	C	50	Aeroplane Markings (Mar. 1937)		25p	£15.00
	A	C	25	British Trees & Their Uses (Aug. 1937) (see RB21/209/34)		£1.00	£25.00
	A	C	25	Common Fallacies (Feb. 1928)		80p	£20.00
	A	C	25	Dance Band Leaders (1936)		£1.00	£25.00
	A	C	50	Empire Air Routes (Sep. 1936)		32p	£16.00
	A	BW	25	Famous British Airmen & Airwomen (1935)		34p	£8.50
59	A	U	25	Fauna of Rhodesia (Mar. 1929)		70p	£17.50
	A	C	51	Find Your Way (Set of 50 and Joker):—			
				A. Address "Box No. 152, London" (1932)		30p	£15.00
				B. Address "Box No. 152, Drury Lane, London" (1932)		30p	£15.00
				C. Overprinted in red (1933)		30p	£15.00
	A	C	50	Footballers 1930–1 (Jan. 1931)		£1.10	—
	A	C	25	Garden Life (Apr. 1930)	H.449	32p	£8.00
	A	C	25	Hints & Tips for Motorists (May 1929) (see RB21/209/50)		£1.20	£30.00
	A	U	25	A History of Aviation:—			
				A. Front in green (Apr. 1932)		40p	£10.00
				B. Front in brown (Dec. 1933)		50p	£12.50
	A	C	50	Horsemanship (June 1938)		40p	£20.00
	A	C	25	How Motor Cars Work (June 1931)		50p	£12.50
	A	C	50	Interesting Customs & Traditions of the Navy, Army & Air Force (Jan. 1939)		26p	£13.00
26	A	C	25	Interesting Musical Instruments (1929)		£1.00	£25.00
	A	C	50	Interesting Sidelights on the Work of the G.P.O. (Oct. 1939)		36p	£18.00
342	A.	C	50	Keep Fit (Nov. 1937) (see RB21/209/63)		13p	£6.50
188	A	C	25	London Characters (1934):—			
				A. With Album Clause		70p	£17.50
				B. Without Album Clause		£6.00	—
	A	C	25	Motor Car Radiators (Aug. 1928)		£1.80	£45.00
73	A	C	25	Motor Cars—"A Series of 25", green back (Oct. 1922)		£1.20	£30.00
	A	C	25	Motor Cars—"2nd Series of 25' (June 1923)		£1.20	£30.00
	A	C	50	Motor Cars—"3rd Series 50" (Feb. 1926)		£1.80	£90.00
	A	C	25	Motor Cars—"A Series of 25", grey back (Feb. 1934)		70p	£17.50
	A	C	50	Motor Cycles (Nov. 1923)		£1.80	£90.00
	A	C	50	Motor Index Marks (Dec. 1926)		£1.00	£50.00
	A	C	25	Pirates & Highwaymen (Aug. 1926 and Oct. 1932)	Ha.584	30p	£7.50
147	A	U	25	Rhodesian Series (Apr. 1928)		60p	£15.00
	A	U	25	Third Rhodesian Series (Aug. 1930)		24p	£6.00
	A	C	25	Wonders of Nature (Sep. 1924)		44p	£11.00

C. Miscellaneous

Illus. No.	Size	Print- ing	Number in set		Handbook ref.	Price per card	Complete set
	A	C	50	Travellers Tales (Prepared but not issued)		—	—

LAMBKIN BROS., Cork

Post-1920 Issues

Illus. No.	Size	Print- ing	Number in set		Handbook ref.	Price per card	Complete set
	A	C	36	*Country Scenes—Small size (1924) (6 sets of 6):—			
				Series 1—Yachting		£2.50	—
				Series 2—Country		£2.50	—
				Series 3—Far East		£2.50	—
				Series 4—Sailing		£2.50	—
				Series 5—Country		£2.50	—
				Series 6—Country		£2.50	—
	C	C	36	*Country Scenes—Large size (1924) (6 sets of 6):—			
				Series 7—Yachting		£2.50	—
				Series 8—Country		£2.50	—
				Series 9—Far East		£2.50	—
				Series 10—Sailing		£2.50	—
				Series 11—Country		£2.50	—
				Series 12—Windmill Scenes		£2.50	—
	—	C	? 9	*Irish Views, anonymous, inscribed "Eagle, Cork" (68 × 67 mm.)	Ha.585	—	—
	—	C	? 5	*"Lily of Killarney" Views (73 × 68 mm.)	Ha.586	—	—

LANCS & YORKS TOBACCO MANUFACTURING CO. LTD., Burnley (L. & Y. Tob. Mfg. Co.)

Illus. No.	Size	Printing	Number in set		Handbook ref.	Price per card	Complete set
Pre-1919 Issue							
	C	C	26	*Actresses—"FROGA A"	H.20	—	—

C. & J. LAW, Hertford

Pre-1919 Issues							
	A	C	25	*Types of British Soldiers	H.144	£13.00	—
	A	U	50	War Portraits	H.86	—	—

R. & J. LEA, LTD., Manchester

A. Pre-1919 Issues							
	A1	C	50	Chairman Miniatures 1–50 (1912):—			
				A. No border		£2.00	£100.00
				B. Gilt border		£2.00	£100.00
	A1	C	50	Chairman & Vice Chair Miniatures, 51–100 (1912)		£1.60	£80.00
	A1	BW	25	Chairman War Portraits (marked "War Series" on front) (1915)		£4.00	£100.00
	A	C	70	Cigarette Transfers (Locomotives) (1916)		£2.50	—
	A	BW	25	Civilians of Countries Fighting with the Allies (1914–15)		£6.00	£150.00
	A1	C	50	Flowers to Grow (The Best Perennials) (1913)		£2.20	£110.00
126	A1	C	50	Modern Miniatures (1913)		—	£300.00
				46 different, less 1, 8, 12, 32		80p	£40.00
	A1	C	? 13	More Lea's Smokers (1906–7):	H.256/Ha.256		
				A. Green borders		£50.00	—
				B. Red borders		£50.00	—
	A1	C	50	Old English Pottery & Porcelain, 1–50 (1912)		£1.60	£80.00
181	A1	C	50	Old Pottery & Porcelain, 51–100 (1912):—			
				A. "Chairman Cigarettes"		£1.20	£60.00
				B. "Recorder Cigarettes"		£3.50	—
	A1	C	50	Old Pottery & Porcelain, 101–150 (1912–13):—			
				A. "Chairman Cigarettes"		£1.20	£60.00
				B. "Recorder Cigarettes"		£3.50	—
	A1	C	50	Old Pottery & Porcelain, 151–200 (1913)		£1.20	£60.00
	A1	C	50	Old Pottery & Porcelain, 201–250		£1.20	£60.00
	A	BW	25	War Pictures (1915–16)		£2.40	£60.00
B. Post-1920 Issues							
			48	Coronation Souvenir (1937):—			
	A2	P		A. Small size, glossy—			
				1. Lea's name		20p	£10.00
				2. "Successors to …"		13p	£6.00
	A2	BW		B. Small size, matt—			
				1. Lea's name		32p	£16.00
				2. "Successors to …"		17p	£8.50
	—	P		C. Medium size (77 × 51 mm.)		20p	£10.00
	A2	C	50	Dogs (1923):—			
				1. Nos. 1–25–A. White card		£1.60	—
				B. Cream card		£1.60	—
				2. Nos. 26–50		£3.40	£85.00
217	A2	C	25	English Birds (1922):—			
				A. Glossy front		£1.60	£40.00
				B. Matt front		£2.00	£50.00
	A2	C	25	The Evolution of the Royal Navy (1925)		80p	£20.00
	A2	P	54	Famous Film Stars (1939)		30p	£15.00
		CP	48	Famous Racehorses of 1926 (1927):—			
	A2			A. Small size		90p	£45.00
	—			B. Medium size (75 × 50 mm.)		£1.30	£65.00
347			48	Famous Views (1936):—			
	A2	P		A. Small size—1. Glossy		13p	£6.00
		BW		2. Matt		50p	£25.00
	—	P		B. Medium size (76 × 51 mm.)		13p	£6.00
	A2	P	36	Film Stars—"A First Series …" (1934)		£1.10	£40.00
	A2	P	36	Film Stars—"A Second Series …" (1934)		80p	£30.00
	A2	C	25	Fish (1926)		40p	£10.00
25	A2		48	Girls from the Shows (1935):—			
		P		A. Glossy front		40p	£20.00
		BW		B. Matt front		60p	£30.00
	A2		54	Radio Stars (1935):—			
		P		A. Glossy front		60p	£32.00
		BW		B. Matt front		60p	£32.00
158	A2	C	50	Roses (1924)		50p	£25.00
204	A2	C	50	Ships of the World (1925)		90p	£45.00
287			48	Wonders of the World (1938):—			
	A2	P		A. Small size—1. Glossy		25p	£12.50
		BW		2. Matt		25p	£12.50
		P		B. Medium size (76 × 50 mm.)		16p	£8.00
C. Silks. All paper-backed.							
	—	C		*Butterflies and Moths III:—	Ha.505–7		
			12	1. Small size (70 × 44 mm.)		50p	£6.00
			12	2. Large size (70 × 88 mm.)		50p	£6.00

Illus. No.	Size	Print-ing	Number in set		Handbook ref.	Price per card	Complete set
			6	3. Extra-large size (143 × 70 mm.).........		70p	£4.00
—		C	54	*Old Pottery—Set 1 (68 × 38 mm.)	Ha.505–14	70p	£37.50
—		C	72	*Old Pottery—Set 2 (61 × 37 mm.)	Ha.505–14	70p	£50.00
—		C	50	Regimental Crests and Badges—Series I (48 mm. sq.).................	Ha.502–4	90p	£45.00
—		C	50	Regimental Crests and Badges—Series II (48 mm. sq.).................	Ha.502–4	£1.80	£90.00

D. Miscellaneous

Illus. No.	Size	Print-ing	Number in set		Handbook ref.	Price per card	Complete set
—		C	24	Old English Pottery & Porcelain (Post Card Size) .... (Inscribed Chairman Cigarette Series or other firms' names)	Ha.257	£5.00	—

J. LEES, Northampton

Pre-1919 Issue

Illus. No.	Size	Print-ing	Number in set		Handbook ref.	Price per card	Complete set
A		C	? 21	Northampton Town Football Club (No. 301–321).................		£22.00	—

A. LEWIS & CO. (WESTMINSTER) LTD., London

A. Pre-1919 Issue

Illus. No.	Size	Print-ing	Number in set		Handbook ref.	Price per card	Complete set
A		U	50	War Portraits...........................	H.86	£25.00	—

B. Post-1920 Issue

Illus. No.	Size	Print-ing	Number in set		Handbook ref.	Price per card	Complete set
A2		C	52	Horoscopes (1938).......................	Ha.587	25p	£13.00

H. C. LLOYD & SON, Exeter

Pre-1919 Issues

Illus. No.	Size	Print-ing	Number in set		Handbook ref.	Price per card	Complete set
A		U	28	Academy Gems:—	H.258		
				A. Red-brown tint		£35.00	—
				B. Purple tint		£30.00	—
				C. Green tint............................		£35.00	—
D		BW	? 25	*Actresses and Boer War Celebrities	H.260/Ha.260	£30.00	—
—		BW		*Devon Footballers and Boer War Celebrities:—	H.259/Ha.259		
			? 25	Set 1—Without framelines (70 × 41 mm.)...		£35.00	—
			? 1	Set 2—With framelines (70 × 45 mm.)		—	—
A1		C	25	*Star Girls—"Tipsy Loo Cigarettes".........	H.30	£130.00	—
—		BW	36	War Pictures (73 × 69 mm.)................		—	—

RICHARD LLOYD & SONS, London

A. Pre-1919 Issues

Illus. No.	Size	Print-ing	Number in set		Handbook ref.	Price per card	Complete set
—		BW	25	*Boer War Celebrities (1899) (35 × 61 mm.)...	H.261	£16.00	—
—		U	? 20	*General Interest—Actresses, Celebrities and Yachts (62 × 39 mm.)	H.262/ Ha.262–1	£85.00	—
A1		C	96	*National Types, Costumes and Flags........	H.263	£22.00	—
A		C	10	*Scenes fron San Toy	H.462	£7.50	£75.00

B. Post-1920 Issues. Most cards inscribed "Branch of Cope Bros. & Co., Ltd.". See also under "Cope Bros."

Illus. No.	Size	Print-ing	Number in set		Handbook ref.	Price per card	Complete set
70	A	C	25	Atlantic Records (1936)		80p	£20.00
	A2	P	27	Cinema Stars, glossy—"A Series of 27", Nd. 1–27		£2.00	—
	A2	P	27	Cinema Stars, glossy—"A Series of 27", Nd. 28–54		20p	£5.00
	A2	P	27	Cinema Stars, glossy—"Third Series of 27", Nd. 55–81		£2.00	—
	A2	U	25	Cinema Stars, matt—"A Series of 25".......		34p	£8.50
	A	BW	25	*Famous Cricketers (Puzzle Series)) (1930) ...		£2.40	£60.00
	D	C		Old Inns:—			
			25	A1. Titled "Old English Inns" (1923).......		40p	£10.00
			25	A2. Titled "Old Inns—Series 2" (1924)		£1.20	£30.00
			50	B. Titled "Old Inns" (1925)..............		40p	£20.00
	A	BW	25	Tricks & Puzzles (1935)...................		14p	£3.50
	A2	U	25	Types of Horses (1926):—			
				A. Back in light brown		£1.00	£25.00
				B. Back in dark brown		£1.00	£25.00
	A2	U	25	"Zoo" Series (1926)	Ha.588	32p	£8.00

LUSBY LTD., London

Pre-1919 Issue

Illus. No.	Size	Print-ing	Number in set		Handbook ref.	Price per card	Complete set
D		C	25	Scenes from Circus Life	H.264	£85.00	—

HUGH McCALL, Edinburgh, Glasgow and Aberdeen

Post-1920 Issue

Illus. No.	Size	Print-ing	Number in set		Handbook ref.	Price per card	Complete set
C	C	C	? 1	*R.A.F. Advertisement Card	Ha.594	—	—

D. & J. MACDONALD, Glasgow

Illus. No.	Size	Printing	Number in set		Handbook ref.	Price per card	Complete set
Pre-1919 Issues							
	A	C	? 9	*Actresses—"MUTA"	H.265	£70.00	—
	A	BW	25	*Cricketers	H.266	£85.00	—
		BW	? 7	*Cricket & Football Teams	Ha.267	£100.00	—
		C	? 1	County Cricket Team		£500.00	—

MACKENZIE & CO., Glasgow

Pre-1919 Issues							
	—	P	50	*Actors & Actresses (32 × 58 mm.)	H.268	£7.00	—
	—	U	50	Victorian Art Pictures—Photogravure (32 × 58 mm.)		£7.00	—
	A	BW	50	The Zoo		£7.00	—

WM. M'KINNELL, Edinburgh

Pre-1919 Issue							
	A	C	20	European War Series	H.129	£75.00	—
	A	U	50	War Portraits	H.86	—	—

MACNAUGHTON, JENKINS & CO., LTD., Dublin

Post-1920 Issues							
	—	C	50	Castles of Ireland (1924):—			
				A. Size 76 × 45 mm.		£1.40	£70.00
				B. Size 74 × 44 mm.		£1.60	—
	D	C	50	Various Uses of Rubber (1924)		£1.00	£50.00

McWATTIE & SONS, Arbroath

Pre-1919 Issue							
	D	C	30	Army Pictures, Cartoons, etc.	H.12	—	—

THE MANXLAND TOBACCO CO., Isle of Man

Pre-1919 Issues							
	D	BW	? 1	*Views in the Isle of Man	Ha.491	—	—

MARCOVITCH & CO., London

A. Post-1920 Issue							
	A2	P	18	*Beauties (anonymous with plain backs, numbered left base of front) (1932)	Ha.627	13p	£2.25
B. Post-1940 Issue							
	—	U	7	The Story in Red and White (1955) (75 × 66 mm.)		30p	£2.00

MARCUS & CO., Manchester

Pre-1919 Issues							
	A	C	? 5	*Cricketers, "Marcus Handicap Cigarettes" (1895)	H.269/Ha.269	£150.00	—
	A	C	25	*Footballers and Club Colours (1896)	H.239/Ha.239	£70.00	—

T. W. MARKHAM, Bridgwater

Pre-1919 Issue							
	—	BW	? 14	Somerset Views and scenes (68 × 42 mm.)		—	—

MARSUMA LTD., Congleton

Pre-1919 Issue							
	A	BW	50	*Famous Golfers & Their Strokes		£6.00	£300.00

MARTINS LTD., London

Pre-1919 Issues							
	A	C	1	"Arf a 'Mo Kaiser!"		—	£25.00
		U	? 4	Carlyle Series—folding card (39 × 84 mm.)	H.270/Ha.270	£80.00	—
	D	U	25	*V.C. Heroes		£10.00	£250.00

R. MASON & CO., London

Pre-1919 Issues							
	C	C	30	*Colonial Troops	H.40	£40.00	—
	D2	C	40	*Naval and Military Phrases	H.14	£25.00	—

JUSTUS VAN MAURIK

Illus. No.	Size	Printing	Number in set		Handbook ref.	Price per card	Complete set
Post-1920 Issue							
—		C	12	*Dutch Scenes (108 × 70 mm.)	Ha.622	—	—

MAY QUEEN CIGARETTES

Post 1940 Issue					
—	C	12	Interesting Pictures (68 × 48 mm.)..........	80p	£10.00

MENTORS LTD., London

Pre-1919 Issue					
—	C	32	Views of Ireland (42 × 67 mm.).............	H.271	£5.00	—

J. MILLHOFF & CO. LTD., London

Illus. No.	Size	Printing	Number in set		Handbook ref.	Price per card	Complete set
A. Pre-1919 Issue							
—		BW	? 2	*Theatre Advertisement Cards...............	H.272	—	—
B. Post-1920 Issues		CP		Antique Pottery (1927):—			
	A2		54	A. Small size....................		50p	£27.00
	—		56	B. Medium size (74 × 50 mm.)		60p	£34.00
		C		Art Treasures:—			
	D		30	A. Small size (1927)		40p	£12.00
	B		50	B. Large size (1926)		30p	£15.00
	B	C	25	Art Treasures—"2nd Series of 50", Nd. 51–75 (1928)...........................		60p	£15.00
	B	C	25	England, historic & picturesque—"Series of 25" (1928)		40p	£10.00
	B	C	25	England, historic & picturesque—"Second Series ..." (1928)		28p	£7.00
	A2	P	27	Famous Golfers (1928)		£2.20	£60.00
		P	27	Famous "Test" Cricketers (1928):—			
	A2			A. Small size........................		£2.00	£55.00
	—			B. Medium size (76 × 51 mm.)		£2.00	£55.00
	—	C	25	Gallery Pictures (76 × 51 mm.).............		50p	£12.50
	A2	C	50	"Geographia" Map Series (sectional) (1931).		80p	£40.00
94		CP		The Homeland Series (Dec. 1933):—	Ha.539		
	A2		54	A. Small size........................		13p	£6.00
	—		56	B. Medium size (76 × 51 mm.)		15p	£7.50
245	A2	P	36	In the Public Eye (1930)		30p	£11.00
	D	C	25	Men of Genius (1924)		£2.20	£55.00
	B	C	25	Picturesque Old England (1931).............		40p	£10.00
	A2	P		Real Photographs:—	Ha.538		
			27	"A Series of 27"—A. Matt front		30p	£7.50
				B. Glossy front		20p	£5.00
			27	"2nd Series of 27"......................		20p	£5.00
			27	"3rd Series of 27"		20p	£5.00
			27	"4th Series of 27"		24p	£6.00
			27	"5th Series of 27"		20p	£5.00
			27	"6th Series of 27"		30p	£7.50
101	C	C	25	Reproductions of Celebrated Oil Paintings (1928).................................	Ha.542	70p	£17.50
	B	C	25	Roses (1927).............................		90p	£22.50
	A2	C	50	Things to Make—"De Reszke Cigarettes" (1935).................................		13p	£4.00
	A2	C	50	What the Stars Say—"De Reszke Cigarettes" (1934).................................		13p	£6.50
	A2	P	36	Zoological Studies (1929)...................		20p	£7.00
C. Miscellaneous							
—		U	74	"RILETTE" Miniature Pictures (60 × 45 mm.).................................		From £1.00	—

MIRANDA LTD., London

Illus. No.	Size	Printing	Number in set		Handbook ref.	Price per card	Complete set
Post-1920 Issues							
	A	C	20	Dogs...........................	H.211	£2.00	£40.00
	A	C	25	Sports & Pastimes—Series I	H.225	£1.60	£40.00

STEPHEN MITCHELL & SON, Glasgow

Illus. No.	Size	Printing	Number in set		Handbook ref.	Price per card	Complete set
A. Pre-1919 Issues							
	C	C	50	*Actors and Actresses—Selection from "FROGA B and C".....................	H.20	£11.00	—
	C	U	25	*Actors and Actresses—"FROGA C"	H.20	£11.00	—
	C	U	50	*Actors and Actresses—"FROGA D"	H.20	£11.00	—
	C	U	26	*Actresses—"FROGA B".................	H.20	£11.00	—
	A	U	1	Advertisement Card "Maid of Honour".....		—	—
	A	C	50	Arms & Armour (Jul. 1916)...............	H.273	£2.20	£110.00
13	A	C	25	Army Ribbons & Buttons (Oct. 1916 & 1917)		£2.20	£55.00
	C	BW	25	*Boxer Rebellion—Sketches................	H.46	£14.00	—
	D1	BW	25	British Warships, 1—25 (Mar. 1915)		£3.00	£75.00

STEPHEN MITCHELL & SON (continued)

Illus. No.	Size	Print-ing	Number in set		Handbook ref.	Price per card	Complete set
	D1	BW	25	British Warships, Second Series 26–50 (Sep. 1915).............		£3.00	£75.00
	A	C	50	Interesting Buildings (1905).................	H.70	£3.50	£175.00
	A	C	25	Medals (Jan. 1916)........................	H.71	£3.20	£80.00
	A	C	25	Money (1913)............................		£2.80	£70.00
	A	C	25	*Regimental Crests, Nicknames and Collar Badges (1900).........................	H.274	£7.00	£175.00
	A	C	25	Scottish Clan Series No. 1 (1903–4)........	H.33	£6.00	£150.00
	A	C	25	Seals (1911).............................		£2.60	£65.00
	A	C	25	Sports (1907)...........................	H.275	£4.00	£100.00
	A	C	25	Statues & Monuments (1914).............		£2.60	£65.00

B. Post-1920 Issues

Illus. No.	Size	Print-ing	Number in set		Handbook ref.	Price per card	Complete set
	A	C	50	Air Raid Precautions (1938).............	Ha.544	40p	£20.00
	A	C	25	Angling (1928) (see RB21/449)...........		£1.20	£30.00
	A	C	50	Clan Tartans—"A Series of 50" (1927).....		80p	£40.00
	A	C	25	Clan Tartans—"2nd Series, 25" (1927).....		22p	£5.50
	A	C	25	Empire Exhibition, Scotland, 1938 (1938)...		18p	£4.50
	A2	C	25	Famous Crosses (1923)....................		22p	£5.50
344	A	C	50	Famous Scots (1933).....................		25p	£12.50
	A	U	50	First Aid (1938).........................		18p	£9.00
	A	U	50	A Gallery of 1934 (1935).................		50p	£25.00
	A	U	50	A Gallery of 1935 (1936).................		25p	£12.50
	A	C	50	Humorous Drawings (1924)...............	Ha.590	£1.00	£50.00
	A	C	40	London Ceremonials (1928) (RB21/462)....		60p	£24.00
341	A	C	30	A Model Army (cut-outs) (1932)...........		30p	£9.00
348	A	C	25	Old Sporting Prints (1930)...............	Ha.563	20p	£5.00
	A	U	50	Our Empire (Feb. 1937)...................	Ha.522	13p	£6.00
	A	C	70	River & Coastal Steamers (1925)..........		£1.40	£100.00
	A	C		A Road Map of Scotland (1933):—			
			50	A. Small numerals..................		90p	£45.00
			50	B. Large numerals in circles..............		90p	£45.00
			50	C. Overprinted in red..................		£1.30	£65.00
			1	D. Substitute Card......................		—	£1.50
	A	C	50	Scotland's Story (1929)...................		£1.00	£50.00
	A	U	50	Scottish Footballers (1934)................		50p	£25.00
	A	U	50	Scottish Football Snaps (1935).............		50p	£25.00
	A	C	25	Stars of Screen & History (1939)...........		34p	£8.50
	—	C	25	Village Models Series (Apr. 1925):—	Ha.591		
	A			A. Small size......................		80p	£20.00
	—			B. Medium size (68 × 62 mm.)...........		£1.40	£35.00
	—	C	25	Village Models Series—"Second" (May 1925):—			
	A			A. Small size......................		£1.00	£25.00
	—			B. Medium size, 68 × 62 mm.		£1.40	£35.00
	A	U	50	Wonderful Century (Oct. 1937)...........		13p	£6.50
	A	U	50	The World of Tomorrow (Dec. 1936) (see RB21/315).............................		30p	£15.00

MOORGATE TOBACCO CO., London

Post-1940 Issue

Illus. No.	Size	Print-ing	Number in set		Handbook ref.	Price per card	Complete set
	—	BW	30	The New Elizabethan Age (20 small, 10 large) (1953)			
				A. Matt Front.........................		£1.00	—
				B. Varnished Front.....................		£1.00	—

B. MORRIS & SONS LTD., London

A. Pre-1919 Issues

Illus. No.	Size	Print-ing	Number in set		Handbook ref.	Price per card	Complete set
	—	BW	30	*Actresses (1898) (41 × 68 mm.).............	H.276	£1.00	£30.00
	C	U	26	*Actresses—"FROGA A"..................	H.20	£16.00	—
	—	C	? 4	*Actresses—selection from "FROGA B"—"Morris's High Class Cigarettes" on front	H.20	—	—
	A1	P	1	*Advertisement Card (Soldier & Girl) collotype, chocolate brown..................		—	—
	A	U	21	*Beauties—"MOM"......................	H.277/Ha.277	£16.00	—
	A	C	50	*Beauties—"CHOAB".....................	H.21/Ha.21	£17.00	—
	A	U	? 17	*Beauties—Collotype....................	H.278/Ha.278	£90.00	—
	A	C	20	Boer War, 1900 (V.C. Heroes)............	H.279	£17.00	—
	A	BW	25	*Boer War Celebrities—"PAM"............	H.140	£15.00	—
	A	C	30	*General Interest—composite series, six cards each entitled:—	H.280		
				i. Agriculture in the Orient................		£4.00	£24.00
				ii. Architectural Monuments..............		£4.00	£24.00
				iii. The Ice Breaker.......................		£4.00	£24.00
				iv. Schools in Foreign Countries...........		£4.00	£24.00
				v. Strange Vessels........................		£4.00	£24.00
	D	BW	20	London Views...........................	H.34	£15.00	—
	A	C	25	Marvels of the Universe Series.............	H.281	£2.00	£50.00
	D	C	50	National & Colonial Arms (1917)..........		£4.00	£200.00
	C	U	25	War Celebrities (1915)...................	H.279	£3.60	£90.00
	D	C	25	War Pictures............................	H.51	£3.60	£90.00

B. Post-1920 Issues

Illus. No.	Size	Print-ing	Number in set		Handbook ref.	Price per card	Complete set
	A1	C	50	Animals at the Zoo (1924):—	Ha.520		
				A. Back in blue........................		25p	£12.50
				B. Back in grey........................		20p	£10.00
	A1	C	35	At the London Zoo Aquarium (1928).......		13p	£3.50

B. MORRIS & SONS LTD. *(continued)*

Illus. No.	Size	Print-ing	Number in set		Handbook ref.	Price per card	Complete set
	A1	BW	25	Australian Cricketers (1925)		£1.20	£30.00
	A2	C	25	Captain Blood (1937)		20p	£5.00
	D	U	50	Film Star Series (1923)		£1.20	£60.00
	D	U	25	Golf Strokes Series (1923) (see RB21/309) ...		80p	£20.00
	A1	—	12	Horoscopes (wording only) (1936):—			
				A. White card...........................		50p	—
				B. Cream card		15p	£1.75
	A2	C	25	How Films are Made (1934):—			
				A. White card...........................		16p	£4.00
				B. Cream Card		17p	£4.25
271	A1	BW	50	How to Sketch (1929)		35p	£17.50
	A1	C	25	Measurement of Time (1924)		22p	£5.50
77	D	U	25	Motor Series (Motor parts) (Oct. 1922).....		£1.40	£35.00
261	A1	C	25	The Queen's Dolls' House (1925)..........		£1.00	£25.00
	D	U	25	Racing Greyhounds—"Issued by Forecasta" (1939)		16p	£4.00
305	A1	BW	24	Shadowgraphs (1925)		£1.00	£24.00
	A1	C	13	Treasure Island (1924)...................		50p	£6.50
	A1	C	50	Victory Signs (1928).....................		13p	£6.50
	A	C	25	Wax Art Series (1931)		13p	£3.50
273	A	C	25	Whipsnade Zoo (1932)		18p	£4.50
	D	C	25	Wireless Series (1923)		£1.40	£35.00

C. Silks

Illus. No.	Size	Print-ing	Number in set		Handbook ref.	Price per card	Complete set
	—	C	? 24	Battleship Crests (70 × 50 mm.) (paper-backed)	Ha.504–3	£13.00	—
	—	C		English Flowers (78 × 56 mm.) (paper-backed):—	Ha.505–4		
			25	A. Series of 25............................		£1.80	£45.00
			50	B. Series of 50...........................		£2.50	—
	—	C	25	English & Foreign Birds (78 × 56 mm.) (paper-backed)	Ha.505–1	£1.60	£40.00
	—	C	25	*Regimental Colours IV (75 × 55 mm.) (un-backed and anonymous)...................	Ha.502–9	£1.20	£30.00

PHILIP MORRIS & CO. LTD., London

Post-1920 Issues

Illus. No.	Size	Print-ing	Number in set		Handbook ref.	Price per card	Complete set
	—	U	50	British Views:—			
	C			A. Small size............................		£1.50	—
	—			B. Large size (79 × 67 mm.)		£1.50	—

P. MOUAT & CO., Newcastle-on-Tyne

Pre-1919 Issue

Illus. No.	Size	Print-ing	Number in set		Handbook ref.	Price per card	Complete set
	C	C	30	*Colonial Troops	H.40	£60.00	—

MOUSTAFA LTD., London

Post-1920 Issues

Illus. No.	Size	Print-ing	Number in set		Handbook ref.	Price per card	Complete set
	D2	CP	50	Camera Studies (1923–4):—			
				A. Front with number and caption, back in black		£1.20	—
				*B. Front without letterpress, plain back		£1.20	—
	D2	C	25	Cinema Stars—Set 8 (1924).................	Ha.515–8	£1.20	£30.00
193	A2	C	40	Leo Chambers Dogs Heads (1924)		80p	£32.00
	D2	C	25	Pictures of World Interest (1923)		£1.20	—
57	A2	P	25	Real Photos (Views).......................		13p	£2.75

B. MURATTI SONS & CO. LTD., Manchester and London

A. Pre-1919 Issues

Illus. No.	Size	Print-ing	Number in set		Handbook ref.	Price per card	Complete set
	EL	U	? 9	*Actresses, cabinet size, collotype	H.282/Ha.282	£110.00	
	C	C	26	*Actresses—"FROGA A"....................	H.20		
				A. "To the Cigarette Connoisseur" back ..		£12.00	—
				B. "Muratti's Zinnia Cigarettes" back		£18.00	—
	EL	C		*Actresses and Beauties—Green Corinthian column, framework—"Neb-Ka" vertical backs:—			
			? 7	Actresses—selection from "FROGA C".....	H.20	£125.00	—
			? 3	Beauties—selection from "MOM"	H.277	£125.00	—
	EL	C		*Actresses and Beauties—brown and yellow ornamental framework:—			
				I. "Neb-Ka" horizontal backs—			
			? 16	i. Actresses—selection from "FROGA A"......................	H.20	£125.00	
			? 19	ii. Beauties—selection from "CHOAB"	H.21	£125.00	—
			? 6	II. Rubber stamped back. Beauties—selection from "CHOAB"	H.21	£125.00	
			? 10	III. Plain back—Beauties—selection from CHAOB"................................	H.21	£125.00	—
	EL	C		*Advertisement Cards, Globe design back:—	H.283/Ha.283		
			? 5	i. Brown borders to front		£150.00	—
			? 12	ii. White borders to front.................		£150.00	—

B. MURATTI SONS & CO. LTD. (continued)

Illus. No.	Size	Print-ing	Number in set		Handbook ref.	Price per card	Complete set
	C	C	50	*Beauties—"CHOAB" (Zinnia back)	H.21		
				A. Black printing on back		£20.00	—
				B. Olive green printing on back		£35.00	—
	—	C	? 41	*Beautiful Women, Globe design back (54 × 75 mm.)............................	H.284	£26.00	—
	—	BW	20	*Boer War Generals "CLAM" (35 × 61 mm.).	H.61	£13.00	—
	—	C	15	*Caricatures (42 × 62 mm.):—	H.285	—	£150.00
				A. "Sole Manufacturers of ..." brown back.................................		£10.00	—
				B. "Muratti's Zinnia Cigarettes" brown back.................................		£10.00	—
				C. "Muratti's Zinnia Cigarettes" black back.................................		£10.00	—
				D. "Muratti's Vassos Cigarettes" (not seen)................................		—	—
				E. As D, but "Vassos" blocked out, brown back.................................		£30.00	—
	—	C	35	Crowned Heads (53 × 83 mm.)..............		£6.00	—
	C	C	52	*Japanese Series, Playing Card inset (? 1904)..		£6.00	£310.00
				Plain back		£6.00	
	—	P		Midget Post Card Series:—	H.286/Ha.286		
			? 12	I. Matt front (90 × 70 mm.) — Miscellaneous subjects....................		£8.00	—
				II. Glossy front (85 × 65 mm.):—			
			? 53	i. Named—English Views............		—	—
			? 6	ii. Named — Miscellaneous subjects...		£7.00	—
			? —	iii. Unnamed — Miscellaneous subjects		£7.00	—
	—	P	? 36	"Queens" Post Card Series:—(90 × 70 mm.) .	H.287		
				A. Front in black/sepia		£14.00	—
				B. Front in reddish-brown...............		—	—
	A1	BW	19	*Russo-Japanese Series (1904)	H.184	£8.00	£150.00
	A1	C	25	*Star Girls..............................	H.30	—	—
	A	U	? 47	*Views of Jersey:—	H.288/Ha.288		
				A. Plain back		£9.00	—
				B. "Opera House, Jersey" back		£15.00	—
	A	U	24	*War Series—"MURATTI I", white card (1916)................................	H.289	£12.00	—
	A	U	40	*War Series—"MURATTI II", toned card (1917/18) Nos. 1–25 and alternative cards)	H.290/Ha.290	£7.00	—

B. Post-1920 Issues

| 99 | A2 | P | 24 | Australian Race Horses (export)............ | | 16p | £4.00 |

C. Silks. For summary of paper-backed issues, see Ha.497.

	—	C		*Flags—Set 2 (70 × 52 mm.) (unbacked and anonymous):—	Ha.501–2		
			?	A. Numbered...........................		£2.00	—
				B. Unnumbered:—			
			? 23	1. Caption in red.....................		£6.00	—
			? 24	2. Caption in myrtle-green.............		£3.50	—
			? 18	3. Caption in bright green		£3.50	—
			? 17	4. Caption in blue....................		£6.00	—
			? 2	5. Caption in black...................		£7.00	—
	—	C		*Flags—Set 3 (70 × 52 mm.) (paper-backed):—	Ha.501–3		
			25	1st Series—Series C, Nd. 20–44..........		£2.20	—
			25	2nd Series:			
				Series A, Nd. 26–50....................		£2.00	—
				Series E, Nd. 48–72, paper backing in grey		£2.00	—
				Series E, Nd. 48–72, paper backing in green		£2.00	—
	—	C		*Flags—Set 8 (paper backed):—	Ha.501–8		
			3	Series A, Nd. 1–3 (89 × 115 mm.)		£6.50	—
			1	Series B, Nd. 19 (70 × 76 mm.)............		£4.00	—
			18	Series C, Nd. 1–18 (89 × 115 mm.)		£5.50	—
			3	Series D, Nd. 45–47 (89 × 115 mm.)		£6.00	—
			6	Series F, Nd. 73–78 (89 × 115 mm.)		£5.00	—
	—	C	18	*Great War Leaders—Series P (89 × 115 mm.) (paper backed)........................	Ha.504–6	£6.00	—
	—	C		*Regimental Badges I (paper backed):—	Ha.502–1		
			25	Series A, Nd. 1–25 (70 × 52 mm.)		£2.25	—
			48	Series B, Nd. 1–48 (76 × 70 mm.).........		£4.00	—
			15	Series B, Nd. 4–18 (76 × 70 mm.).........		£3.25	—
			16	Series G, Nd. 79–94 (76 × 70 mm.)		£5.00	—
	—	C	25	*Regimental Colours I—Series CB (76 × 70 mm.) (paper backed).....................	Ha.502–6	£4.50	—
	—	C	72	*Regimental Colours V—Series RB (70 × 52 mm.) (paper backed).....................	Ha.502–10	£3.00	—

D. Canvases. Unbacked canvases. The material is not strictly canvas, but a linen fabric glazed to give the appearance of canvas.

	—	C	40	Canvas Masterpieces—Series M (71 × 60 mm.):—			
				A. Shaded back design, globe 12 mm. diam.		£4.00	—
				B. Unshaded back design, globe 6 mm. diam...............................		£1.50	£60.00
	—	C	? 16	Canvas Masterpieces—Series P (114 × 90 mm.)................................		£6.00	—

MURRAY, SONS & CO. LTD., Belfast

Illus. No.	Size	Printing	Number in set		Handbook ref.	Price per card	Complete set
A. Pre-1919 Issues							
	A	BW	20	*Actresses—"BLARM":—	H.23		
				A. "Pineapple Cigarettes" back		£28.00	—
				B. "Special Crown Cigarettes" back		£45.00	—
	C	C	? 14	Chess & Draughts Problems—Series F (1912)	H.291	£25.00	—
	A	BW	52	*Cricketers and Footballers—Series H:—	H.292/Ha.292		
				20 Cricketers, A. Thick card		£25.00	—
				B. Thin card		£25.00	—
				C. Brown Printing		£35.00	—
				32 Footballers, A. Thick card		£11.00	—
				B. Thin card		£11.00	—
	—	C	? 17	Football Flags (Shaped) (60 × 32 mm.)			
				A. Maple Cigarettes......................		£30.00	—
				B. Murray's Cigarettes		£30.00	—
	C	C	25	*Football Rules:—			
				1–12 Rugby Football.....................		£13.00	—
				13–25 Association Football.................		£13.00	—
	A	BW	104	*Footballers—Series J.....................	H.293	£7.00	—
	C	U	25	*Irish Scenery (1905) Nd. 101–125:—			
				A. "Hall Mark Cigarettes"		£14.00	—
				B. "Pine Apple Cigarettes"		£14.00	—
				C. "Special Crown Cigarettes"............		£12.00	—
				D. "Straight Cut Cigarettes"..............		£12.00	—
				E. "Yachtsman Cigarettes"................		£12.00	—
	C	BW	25	Polo Pictures—E Series (1911)	H.294	£9.00	£225.00
	—	U		Prominent Politicians—B Series (1909) (41 × 70 mm.):—	H.295/Ha.295		
			? 16	A. Without "... in two strengths" in centre of back		£13.00	—
			50	B. With "... in two strengths" in centre of back:		£1.40	£70.00
	C	U	25	Reproduction of Famous Works of Art—D Series (1910)............................	H.296	£12.00	£300.00
	C	U	25	Reproductions of High Class Works of Art— C Series (1910).........................	H.297	£14.00	£350.00
	A1	C	35	*War Series—Series K......................	H.298/Ha.298	£14.00	—
	C2	U	25	*War Series—Series L, Nd. 100–124:—			
				A. Sepia		£1.80	£45.00
				B. Grey-brown		£2.00	—
				C. Purple-brown		£2.20	—
B. Post-1920 Issues							
	D1	P	22	Bathing Beauties (1929)		£1.70	—
	A1	BW	40	Bathing Belles	Ha.592	13p	£2.50
	D1	P	22	Cinema Scenes (1929)		£1.70	—
	A1	BW	25	Crossword Puzzles		£40.00	÷
	D1	P	26	Dancers (1929)...........................		£1.70	—
	D	P		Dancing Girls (1929):—			
			25	A. "Belfast–Ireland" at base		£1.50	£37.50
			25	B. "London & Belfast" at base...........		90p	£22.50
			26	C. Inscribed "Series of 26"...............		£1.50	—
	A	C	20	Holidays by the L.M.S. (1927)	Ha.593	£5.00	£100.00
	A1	C	20	Inventors Series (1924)	H.213	£1.80	£36.00
	—	C	50	Puzzle Series (1925):—			
	A1			A. With coupon attached at top..........		£6.00	—
	—			B. Without coupon		£1.20	—
	D2	C	50	Stage and Film Stars—"Erinmore Cigarettes" (see RB21/200/172)...........		£1.10	£55.00
	A1	BW	25	Steam Ships (1939).......................		28p	£7.00
	A1	C	50	The Story of Ships (1940).................		13p	£2.75
	A2	C	25	Types of Aeroplanes (1929)................		24p	£6.00
78	C	C	20	Types of Dogs (1924):—	Ha.211		
				A. Normal back....................		£1.25	£25.00
				B. Normal back, with firm's name rubber stamped in red		£1.25	£25.00
C. Silks							
	—	C	? 15	*Flags, small (70 × 42 mm.)—"Polo Mild Cigarettes" (plain paper backing).........	Ha.498-1	£8.00	—
	—	C	? 3	*Flags and Arms, large (102 × 71 mm.)— "Polo Mild Cigarettes" (plain paper backing)................................	Ha.498-2	—	—
	—	C	? 31	*Orders of Chivalry II, "Series M" (70 × 42 mm.) (paper-backed). Nd. 35–65..........	Ha.504-15	£7.00	—
	—	C	? 22	*Regimental Badges (70 × 42 mm.)—"Polo Mild Cigarettes" (plain paper backing)....	Ha.498-3	£8.00	—

N. J. NATHAN, London

Illus. No.	Size	Printing	Number in set		Handbook ref.	Price per card	Complete set
Pre-1919 Issue							
	D	C	40	Comical Military & Naval Pictures..........	H.14	£40.00	—

JAMES NELSON, London

Illus. No.	Size	Printing	Number in set		Handbook ref.	Price per card	Complete set
Pre-1919 Issue							
	A	P	? 18	*Beauties—"FENA".......................	H.148/Ha.148	—	—

THE NEW MOSLEM CIGARETTE CO., London

Pre-1919 Issue

	D	C	30 *Proverbs	H.15	£60.00	—

E. J. NEWBEGIN, Sunderland

Pre-1919 Issues

	Size	Print	Number in set	Handbook ref.	Price	Complete
	—	P	? 46 *Actors and Actresses, Etc. (39 × 60 mm.)	H.299/Ha.299	£20.00	—
	A	BW	? 10 *Actresses—"HAGG A"	Ha.24	—	—
	D	C	? 4 Advertisement Cards		—	—
	A	BW	20 Cricketers Series	H.29	£70.00	—
	A	BW	19 *Russo-Japanese Series		—	—
	D	C	? 6 Well-Known Proverbs	H.235	£55.00	—
	D	C	? 18 Well-Known Songs	H.300	£55.00	—

W. H. NEWMAN, Birmingham

Pre-1919 Issues

	C	C	18 Motor Cycle Series	Ha.469	—	—

THOS. NICHOLLS & CO., Chester

Pre-1919 Issue

	A	C	50 Orders of Chivalry	H.301	£3.50	£175.00

THE NILMA TOBACCO COY., London

Pre-1919 Issues

(All Cards marked "Series of 70")

	A	C	40 *Home and Colonial Regiments:—	H.69		—
			20. Caption in blue		£60.00	—
			20. Caption in brown		£60.00	—
	D	C	30 *Proverbs	H.15	£60.00	—

M. E. NOTARAS LTD., London

Post-1920 Issues

35	A2	P	36 National Types of Beauty	Ha.558	28p	£10.00
	—	U	24 *Views of China (68 × 43 mm.)		13p	£2.00

OGDENS LTD., Liverpool

A. Pre-1919 Issues

Home Issues (*excluding "Guinea Gold" and "Tabs", but including some early issues abroad*).

	C	C	? 24 *Actresses—coloured, "Ogden's Cigarettes contain no glycerine" back:—	H.302/Ha.302		
			A. Titled in black		£45.00	—
			B. Titled in brown		£45.00	—
	D2	U	? 1 *Actresses—green, green borders	H.303	—	—
	D1	U	50 *Actresses—green photogravure	H.304	£4.50	—
	D	P	?533 *Actresses—"Ogden's Cigarettes" at foot	H.305/Ha.305	£2.00	—
	D	P	*Actresses and Beauties—collotype:—	H.306		
			? 75 i. named.			
			A. *Plain back*		—	—
			B."Midnight Flake" back		£17.00	—
			? 19 ii. unnamed.			
			A. *Plain back*		—	—
			B."Midnight Flake back			
			(blue)		£20.00	—
			(red)		—	—
	D	P	*Actresses and Beauties—collotype, "Ogden's Cigarettes" back:—	H.306		
			? 39 i. named		£24.00	—
			? 32 ii. unnamed		£24.00	—
	A	P	*Actresses and Beauties—woodbury-type:—	H.307/Ha.307		
			?184 i. named		£22.00	—
			? 9 ii. unnamed		£22.00	—
	—	C	192 Army Crests and Mottoes (1902) (39 × 59 mm.)		£1.70	—
	A	C	? 29 *Beauties—"BOCCA"	H.39/Ha.39	£14.00	—
	—	C	50 *Beauties—"CHOAB":—	H.21		
			1–25 (size 65 × 36 mm.)		£17.00	—
			26–50 (size 67 × 37 mm.)		£17.00	—
	A	C	26 *Beauties—"HOL":—	H.192		
			A. "Guinea Gold" red rubber stamp back .		—	—
			B. Blue Castle design back		£10.00	£260.00
	A2	C	52 *Beauties — "Playing Card" series:—	H.308		
			A. 52 with playing card inset		£16.00	—
			B. 26 without playing card inset		£18.00	—
	A2	C	52 *Beauties and Military—P.C. inset		£24.00	—

Illus. No.	Size	Print-ing	Number in set		Handbook ref.	Price per card	Complete set
—		P	50	Beauty Series, numbered, "St. Julien Tobacco" (36 × 54 mm.)		£1.60	£80.00
	D	P	? 21	Beauty Series, unnumbered, issued Australia	H.309/Ha.309	£30.00	
	A	C	50	Birds Eggs (Dec. 1904):—		—	£65.00
				A. White back		£1.40	£70.00
				B. Toned back		£1.30	£65.00
	D	P	?111	*Boer War and General Interest—"Ogden's Cigarettes" at foot	H.310/Ha.310	£2.00	—
	A	C	50	Boxers (Oct. 1915)		£3.40	£170.00
	A	C	25	Boxing (Jul. 1914)	H.311	£2.40	£60.00
—		C	? 4	*Boxing Girls (165 × 94 mm.)		—	
	A	C	50	Boy Scouts (Jan. 1911):—	H.62		
				A. Blue back		£1.50	£75.00
				B. Green back		£2.20	£110.00
	A	C	50	Boy Scouts, 2nd Series (Feb. 1912):—	H.62		
				A. Blue back		£1.50	£75.00
				B. Green back		£2.20	£110.00
	A	C	50	Boy Scouts, 3rd Series (Oct. 1912):—	H.62		
				A. Blue back		£1.50	£75.00
				B. Green back		£2.20	£110.00
	A	C	50	Boy Scouts, 4th Series, green back (Nov. 1913)		£2.00	£100.00
	A	C	25	Boy Scouts, 5th Series, green back (Sep. 1914)		£2.00	£50.00
	A	C	50	British Birds:—	H.229		
				A. White back (May 1905)		£1.20	£60.00
				B. Toned back (1906)		£1.10	£55.00
	A	C	50	British Birds, Second Series (Jan. 1908)		£1.40	£70.00
	A	C	50	British Costumes from 100 B.C. to 1904 (Apr. 1905)	H.312	£3.00	£150.00
	A	C	50	Club Badges (Jul. 1914)		£3.00	£150.00
—		C	? 21	*Comic Pictures (1890–95) (size varies)	H.313	£180.00	—
	A2	C	12	*Cricket and Football Terms—Women, "Ogden's Gold Medal Cigarettes" back	H.314/Ha.314	£140.00	—
	A	U	? 32	*Cricketers and Sportsmen	H.315/Ha.315	£25.00	—
	A	U	28	*Dominoes—Actresses "FROGA A" back:—	H.20		
				A. Mitred corners (7 backs)		£14.00	—
				B. Unmitred corners (7 backs)		£14.00	—
	A	U	28	*Dominoes—Beauties "MOM" back	H.277	£14.00	—
	A2	BW	55	*Dominoes—black back (Apr. 1909)		£1.10	£60.00
	A	C	50	Famous Footballers (Jan. 1908)		£1.60	£80.00
	A	C	50	Flags & Funnels of Leading Steamship Lines (Feb. 1906)	H.67	£2.20	£110.00
—		C	43	*Football Club Badges (shaped for buttonhole)	H.316	£4.00	
	A	C	51	Football Club Colours (May 1906):—	H.68		
				Nos. 1–50		£1.60	£80.00
				No. 51		—	£5.00
	A	C	50	Fowls, Pigeons & Dogs (May 1904)	H.64	£1.50	£75.00
—		C	1	*History of the Union Jack (threefold card) (1901) (51 × 37 mm. closed)		—	£140.00
	A	BW	50	Infantry Training (Apr. 1915)	H.317	£1.80	£90.00
	A	C	? 1	Lady Cricket and Football Team	H.318	—	—
	K2	C	52	*Miniature Playing Cards — Actresses & Beauties Back:	H.319/Ha.319		
				I. Unnamed, no numeral (76 backs known)		£2.00	—
				II. Unnamed, "numeral 40" (26 backs known)		£2.00	—
				III. Named, "numeral 46" (26 backs known)	H.20	£2.25	—
				IV. Named, no numeral (26 backs known).	H.20	£2.00	—
	K2	C	52	*Miniature Playing Cards, blue Tabs "Shield and Flower" design back (Apr. 1909)		£1.50	£75.00
	K2	C	52	*Miniature Playing Cards, yellow "Coolie Plug" design back:—			
				A. Yellow back (May 1904)		£1.50	£75.00
				B. Yellow back with white border (Nov. 1904)		£1.50	£75.00
	A	BW	50	Modern War Weapons (Nov. 1915):—	H.320		
				A. Original numbering		£1.80	£90.00
				B. Numbering re-arranged		£6.00	—
	A	C	50	Orders of Chivalry (Jan. 1907)		£2.00	£100.00
	A	C	25	Owners, Racing Colours & Jockeys (May 1914)		£2.00	£50.00
	A	C	50	Owners, Racing Colours & Jockeys (Jan. 1906)		£1.50	£75.00
	A	C	25	Poultry (Aug. 1915):—			
				A. "Ogden's Cigarettes" on front		£1.60	£40.00
				B. Without "Ogden's Cigarettes" on front		£1.60	£40.00
	A	C	25	Poultry, 2nd Series, as "B" above (Apr. 1916)		£1.60	£40.00
	A	C	25	Pugilists & Wrestlers, Nd. 1–25 (Oct. 1908)		£2.20	£55.00
	A	C	25	Pugilists & Wrestlers, Nd. 26–50:—			
				A. White back (Aug. 1909)		£2.40	£60.00
				B. Toned back (Oct. 1908)		£2.20	£55.00
	A	C	25	Pugilists & Wrestlers, 2nd Series, Nd. 51–75 (Aug. 1909)		£2.50	£62.50
	A	C	50	Racehorses (Sep. 1907)		£1.20	£60.00
	A	C	25	Records of the World (Jan. 1908)		£2.00	£50.00
	A	C	50	Royal Mail (Sep. 1909)	H.82	£2.80	£140.00
	A	C	50	Sectional Cycling Map (Oct. 1910)	H.74	£2.20	£110.00

OGDENS LTD. *(continued)*

Illus. No.	Size	Print- ing	Number in set		Handbook ref.	Price per card	Complete set
	A	C	50	*Shakespeare Series:—	H.321		
				A. Unnumbered..........................		£12.00	£600.00
				B. Numbered		£12.00	£600.00
	A	C	50	Soldiers of the King (Oct. 1909):			
				A. Grey printing on front.................		£4.00	£200.00
				B. Brown printing on front		£4.00	—
	D	C	25	*Swiss Views, Nd. 1–25...................		£2.20	£60.00
	D	C	25	*Swiss Views, Nd. 26–50.................		£3.40	£85.00
	D	C	48	Victoria Cross Heroes (1901–02)............	H.322/Ha.322	£10.00	£500.00

B. "Guinea Gold" Series (The S and X numbers represent the reference numbers quoted in Cartophilic Society Booklet No. 24).

	Size	Print-ing	Number in set		Handbook ref.	Price per card	Complete set
	D	P	1148	1–1148 Series:—			
				Nos. 1–200		35p	£70.00
				Nos. 201–500............................		70p	—
				Nos. 501–900, excl. 523 & 765		65p	—
				Nos. 901–1000, excl. 940, 943, 947 and 1000		90p	—
				Nos. 1001–1148, excl. 1003, 1006–8, 1024, 1030. 1033, 1034, 1037, 1040, 1042, 1048, 1066, 1081, 1082, 1088		£1.00	—
				Scarce Nos:— 523, 940, 943, 947, 1000, 1003, 1007, 1008, 1024, 1030, 1033, 1034, 1037, 1040, 1042, 1048, 1066, 1088.............		£22.00	—
				Very scarce Nos. 765, 1006, 1081, 1082.....		—	—
	D	CP	?	Selected numbers from 1–1148 series		£1.50	—
	D	P		400 New Series I		75p	£300.00
	D	P		400 New Series B..........................		75p	£300.00
	D	P		300 New Series C..........................		75p	£225.00
	D	P	312	Set 73S Base B Actresses...................		£1.10	—
				Set 75S Base D:—			
	D	P	?320	List DA—White Panel Group		60p	—
	D	P	? 57	List DB—The Denumbered Group		80p	—
	D	P	? 62	List DC—The Political Group		60p	—
	D	P	?185	List DD—Boer War Etc....................		50p	—
	D	P	? 46	List DE—Pantomime & Theatre Group.....		£1.50	—
	D	P	?374	List DF—Actors & Actresses		60p	—
	D	P	? 40	Set 76S Base E Actors & Actresses		£1.50	—
	D	P	? 58	Set 77S Base F Boer War Etc...............		60p	—
				Set 78S Base I:—			
				List IA—The small Machette Group:—			
	D	P	83	I. Actors & Actresses		80p	—
	D	P	14	II. London Street Scenes..................		£1.50	—
	D	P	32	III. Turner Pictures		£1.00	—
	D	P	11	IV. Cricketers...........................		£6.50	—
	D	P	18	V. Golf.................................		£6.50	—
	D	P	10	VI. Views & Scenes Abroad		80p	—
	D	P	30	VII. Miscellaneous........................		80p	—
	D	P	656	List IB—The Large Machette Group........		50p	—
	D	P	5	List IC—The White Panel Group		—	—
	D	P	30	Set 79S Base J Actresses		£2.50	—
	D	P	237	Set 80S Base K Actors & Actresses		80p	—
	D	P	215	Set 81S Base L Actors & Actresses		80p	—
				Set 82S Base M:—			
	D	P	3	List Ma Royalty		£1.00	£3.00
	D	P	77	List Mb Cricketers		£6.50	—
	D	P	50	List Mc Cyclists..........................		£3.50	—
	D	P	149	List Md Footballers.......................		£3.50	—
	D	P	50	List Me Pantomime & Theatre Group.......		£1.50	—
	D	P	33	List Mf Footballers & Cyclists.............		£3.50	—
	D	P	27	List Mg Boer War & Miscellaneous		60p	—
				List Mh Actors and Actresses:—			
	D	P	60	a. Subjects with white framelines		75p	—
	D	P	33	b. Subjects without names or nicknames ..		75p	—
	D	P	2846	c. Other subjects........................		50p	—

Ba. Guinea Gold Series, Large & Medium

		Print-ing	Number in set			Price per card	Complete set
		P	63	Set 73X Actresses Base B		£8.00	—
		P	1	Set 74X Actress Base C.....................		—	£8.00
		P	571	Set 75X Actors, Actresses, Boer War Etc. Base D		£1.00	—
		P	17	Set 78X Actresses Base I....................		£22.00	—
		P	403	Set 82X Actors, Actresses, Boer War Etc. Base M.................................		£1.00	—

C. *"Tabs" Series*

(Numbers in parentheses following word "item" represent the reference numbers quoted in Cartophilic Society Booklet No. 15. The listing includes both home and overseas "Tabs" issues.)

	Size	Print-ing	Number in set			Price per card	Complete set
	D	BW	?136	*Actresses (item 7)		£1.50	—
	D	BW	?199	*Actresses and Foreign Views (item 14).......		£1.00	—
	D	BW	?330	*Composite Tabs Series, with "Labour Clause" (item 63):—			
				1. General de Wet		—	£1.00
				1. General Interest......................		—	£3.00
				17. Heroes of the Ring		£3.00	—
				1. H.M. The Queen		—	£1.50
				2. H.R.H. The Prince of Wales		£1.25	£2.50
				14. Imperial Interest		65p	£9.00
				105. Imperial and International Interest.....		50p	—
				3. International Interest..................		65p	£2.00
				14. International Interest or a Prominent British Officer........................		65p	£9.00

Illus. No.	Size	Print- ing	Number in set		Handbook ref.	Price per card	Complete set
			22.	Leading Athletes......................		£1.10	£25.00
			15.	Leading Favourites of the Turf.........		£1.40	—
			54.	Leading Generals at the War..........		60p	£32.50
			2.	Members of Parliament...............		£1.25	£2.50
			11.	Notable Coursing Dogs		£1.80	£20.00
			12.	Our Leading Cricketers...............		£6.50	—
			17.	Our Leading Footballers		£1.75	£30.00
			37.	Prominent British Officers		60p	£23.00
			1.	The Yacht "Columbia"...............		—	£2.50
			1.	The Yacht "Shamrock"		—	£2.50
D	BW	? 10		*Composite Tabs Series, without "Labour Clause" (item 64):—			
			8.	General Interest......................		£3.00	—
			2.	Leading Artistes of the Day............		£3.00	—
D	BW	? 65		*Composite Tabs Series, Sydney issue (item 65):—			
			15.	English Cricketer Series		£25.00	—
			1.	Christian de Wet		—	—
			1.	Corporal G. E. Nurse, V.C.............		—	—
			13.	Imperial or International Interest		—	—
			3.	International Interest.................		—	—
			1.	Lady Sarah Wilson...................		—	—
			25.	Leading Generals of the War..........		—	—
			6.	Prominent British Officers		—	—
D	BW	150		General Interest, Series "A"		40p	£60.00
D	BW	200		General Interest, Series "B"		40p	£80.00
D	BW	470		General Interest, Series "C":—			
				C.1–200		40p	£80.00
				C.201–300		£1.20	—
				C.301–350		70p	£35.00
				No. Letter, Nd. 1–120		70p	£85.00
D	BW	200		General Interest, Series "D"		40p	£80.00
D	BW	120		General Interest, Series "E"		60p	£72.00
D	BW	420		General Interest, Series "F":—			
				F.1–200		80p	—
				F.201–320		80p	—
				F.321–420		£1.30	—
D	BW	?500		General Interest, Sydney issue:			
				Nd. 1–100 on front.......................		£1.50	—
				101–400 on back....................		£1.50	—
				Unnumbered, mostly similar numbered cards 101–200 (item 99-a)		£2.50	—
D	BW	?196		*General Interest, unnumbered, similar style C.201–300 (item 95).......................		60p	—
D	BW	100		*General Interest, unnumbered, similar style C.301–350 (item 96).......................		60p	£60.00
D	BW	300		*General Interest, unnumbered, similar style (F.321–420) (item 97):—			
				A. 100 with full stop after caption		75p	£75.00
				B. Without full stop after caption:—			
			79	I Stage Artistes...................		70p	£56.00
			21	II Cricketers		£6.50	—
			25	III Football.......................		£3.00	—
			15	IV Golf...........................		£6.50	—
			10	V Cyclists........................		£3.50	—
			9	VI Fire Brigades		£3.50	—
			5	VII Aldershot Gymnasium...........		£1.60	£8.00
			36	VIII Miscellaneous		60p	—
D	BW	? 26		*General Interest, "oblong" back (item 98)...		£3.00	—
D	BW	? 75		*Leading Artistes of the Day, numbered 126–200, plain backs (item 109) (see H.1)..		£4.00	—
D	BW	? 71		Leading Artistes of the Day with "Labour Clause" (item 110):—			
				A. Type-set back		65p	£46.00
				B. Plain back		£1.50	—
D	BW	? 22		Leading Artistes of the Day, without "Labour Clause" (item 111–1):—			
				A. With caption, type-set back		£3.00	—
				B. With caption, plain back..............		£3.00	—
				C. Without caption, type-set back.........		£3.00	—
D	BW	? 73		Leading Artistes of the Day. without "Labour Clause" (item 111–2):—			
				A. Type-set back		£3.00	—
				B. Plain back		£3.00	—
D	BW	25		Leading Generals at the War, with descriptive text (item 112):—			
				A. "Ogden's Cigarettes" back.............		£1.50	—
				B. "Ogden's Tab Cigarettes" back........		80p	£20.00
D	BW	? 47		Leading Generals at the War, without descriptive text (item 113):—			
				A. "Ogden's Tab Cigarettes" back (47 known)		60p	£30.00
				B. "Ogden's Lucky Star" back (25 known)		£2.50	—
D	BW	50		*Stage Artistes and Celebrities (item 157).....		£1.00	£50.00

D. Post-1920 Issues

	Size	Print- ing	Number in set		Handbook ref.	Price per card	Complete set
	A	C	25	ABC of Sport (1927)		£1.20	£30.00
	A	C	50	Actors—Natural & Character Studies (1938)	Ha.571–1	13p	£5.00
	A	C	50	A.F.C. Nicknames (1933)...................	Ha.571–2	80p	£40.00

OGDENS LTD. *(continued)*

Illus. No.	Size	Printing	Number in set		Handbook ref.	Price per card	Complete set
	A	C	50	Air-Raid Precautions (1938)	Ha.544	18p	£9.00
	A	C	50	Applied Electricity (1928).		70p	£35.00
	A	U	36	Australian Test Cricketers, 1928–29 (see RB15/21).		£1.65	£60.00
	A	C	50	Billiards, by Tom Newman (1928) (see RB21/215/33)		80p	£40.00
	A	C	50	Bird's Eggs (cut-outs) (1923).		40p	£20.00
	A	C	50	The Blue Riband of the Atlantic (1929)......		£1.30	£65.00
	A	C	50	Boy Scouts (1929) (see RB21/215/46).		80p	£40.00
	A	C	50	British Birds (cut-outs) (1923) (see RB15/49).		35p	£17.50
	A	C	50	British Birds & Their Eggs (1939)	Ha.571–3	50p	£25.00
	A	U	50	Broadcasting (1935).	Ha.571–4	35p	£17.50
	A	C	50	By the Roadside (1932).		50p	£25.00
	A	C	44	Captains of Association Football Clubs & Colours (1926).		90p	£40.00
	A	U	50	Cathedrals & Abbeys (1936):—			
				A. Cream card		40p	£20.00
				B. White card.		40p	£20.00
	A	C	50	Champions of 1936 (1937)	Ha.571–5	20p	£10.00
	A	C	50	Children of All Nations (cut-outs) (see RB21/200/168)		35p	£17.50
	A	C	50	Colour in Nature (1932)		70p	£35.00
	A	C	50	Construction of Railway Trains (1930)		£1.30	£65.00
	A	C	50	Coronation Procession (sectional) (1937)....	Ha.571–6	45p	£22.50
	A	U	50	Cricket, 1926		£1.30	£65.00
	A	C	25	Derby Entrants, 1926 (see RB21/215/71)		90p	£22.50
	A	C	50	Derby Entrants, 1928		70p	£35.00
	A	U	50	Derby Entrants, 1929		90p	£45.00
	A	C	50	Dogs (1936).	Ha.571–7	35p	£17.50
	A	C	25	Famous Dirt-Track Riders (1929).		£1.60	£40.00
	A	U	50	Famous Rugby Players (1926–27).		60p	£30.00
242	A	C	50	Football Caricatures (1935).	Ha.571–8	50p	£25.00
	A	C	50	Football Club Captains (1935).	Ha.571–9	50p	£25.00
	A	C	50	Foreign Birds (1924) (see RB21/215/87)		40p	£20.00
	A	U	25	Greyhound Racing—"1st Series ..." (1927–28).		£1.60	£40.00
72	A	U	25	Greyhound Racing—"2nd Series ..." (1928)		£1.60	£40.00
	A	C	50	How to Swim (1935).	Ha.571–10	13p	£6.50
	A	C	50	Jockeys, and Owners' Colours (1927).		70p	£35.00
	A	C	50	Jockeys, 1930		80p	£40.00
	A	C	50	Leaders of Men (1924–25) (see RB21/215/108)		90p	£45.00
	A	C	25	Marvels of Motion (1928–29)		£1.00	£25.00
	A	C	50	Modern British Pottery (1925)		50p	£25.00
	A	C	50	Modern Railways (1936)	Ha.571–11	80p	£40.00
	A	C	25	Modes of Conveyance (1927) (see W/264) ...		£1.20	£30.00
	A	C	50	Motor Races (1931)		£1.00	£50.00
	A	C	50	Ocean Greyhounds (1938)	Ha.571–12	30p	£15.00
	A	C	25	Optical Illusions (1923).	Ha.560	£1.20	£30.00
	A	C	25	Picturesque People of the Empire (1927) (see RB21/200/288)		60p	£15.00
	A	U	50	Picturesque Villages (1936)		50p	£25.00
	A	C	25	Poultry Alphabet (1924) (see RB15/135).....		£1.40	£35.00
	A	C	25	Poultry Rearing & Management—"1st Series ..." (1922).		80p	£20.00
	A	C	25	Poultry Rearing & Management—"2nd Series ..." (1923)		80p	£20.00
	A	U	50	Prominent Cricketers of 1938 (1938)	Ha.571–13	60p	£30.00
	A	C	50	Prominent Racehorses of 1933 (1934)	Ha.571–14	50p	£25.00
	A	U	50	Pugilists in Action (1928) (see RB17/156)....		70p	£35.00
	A	C	50	Racing Pigeons (1931).		70p	£35.00
	A	C	50	Sea Adventure (1939)	Ha.571–15	13p	£3.50
	A	C	50	Shots from the Films (1936)	Ha.571–16	45p	£22.50
	A	U	25	Sights of London (1923)		90p	£22.50
	A	C	50	Smugglers and Smuggling (1932–33)		50p	£25.00
	A	U	50	Steeplechase Celebrities (1931).		40p	£20.00
	A	C	50	Steeplechase Trainers, and Owners' Colours (1927).		70p	£35.00
	A	C	50	The Story of Sand (1934) (see RB15/160)		30p	£15.00
	A	C	50	Swimming, Diving and Life-Saving (1931)...	Ha.523	35p	£17.50
	A	C	25	Trainers, and Owners' Colours—"1st Series ..." (1925).		70p	£17.50
	A	C	25	Trainers, and Owners' Colours—"2nd Series ..." (1926).		£1.00	£25.00
	A	C	50	Trick Billiards (1934).	Ha.571–17	35p	£17.50
	A	C	50	Turf Personalities (1929)		60p	£30.00
	A	C	25	Whaling (1927) (see RB21/215/169)		90p	£22.50
	A	C	50	Yachts & Motor Boats (1930).		90p	£45.00
71	A	C	50	Zoo Studies (1937)	Ha.571–18	20p	£10.00

OSBORNE TOBACCO CO. LTD., Portsmouth & London ———

Post-1940 Issues

	Size	Printing	Number in set		Price per card	Complete set
	A	U	50	Modern Aircraft (1953):—		
				A. Dark Blue back	10p	£2.00
				B. Light Blue back	10p	£4.00
				C. Brown back.	10p	£4.00

Illus. No.	Size	Print-ing	Number in set	Handbook ref.	Price per card	Complete set
Pre-1919 Issue						
	D	C	40 *Naval and Military Phrases.................	H.14	£20.00	—

J. A. PATTREIOUEX, Manchester

A. 1920's Photographic Series. Listed in order of letters and/or numbers quoted on cards. References after word "back" refer to the nine backs illustrated in Handbook Part II under Ha.595.

	Size	Print-ing	Number in set	Handbook ref.	Price per card	Complete set
	H2	P	50 *Animals and Scenes—Unnumbered ("Junior Member"). Back 4	Ha.595–1	55p	—
	H2	P	50 Animals and Scenes, Nd. 1–50. Back 1		55p	—
	H2	P	50 *Scenes, Nd. 201–250 ("Junior Member"). Back 4		55p	—
	C	P	96 Animals and Scenes, Nd. 250–345:—			
			A. Back in style 2 in (i) grey		60p	—
			(ii) brown		70p	—
			*B. "Junior Member" back 9		60p	—
	C	P	96 Animals and Scenes, Nd. 346–441:—			
			A. Back 2.............................		70p	—
			B. Back style 1 and back 3		60p	—
			*C. "Junior Member" back 9		60p	—
	H	P	50 *Animal Studies, Nd. A42–A91 ("Junior Member"). Back 4		55p	—
	H	P	50 *Animal Studies, Nd. A92–A141 ("Junior Member"). Back 4		70p	—
	H	P	50 *Animal Studies, Nd. A151–A200 ("Junior Member"). Back 4		60p	—
	C	P	*Natives and Scenes:—			
			36 A. "Series 1/36 B" on front, Nd. 1–36 ("Junior Member"). Back 9...........		55p	—
			96 B. "Series 1/96 B" on front, Nd. 1–96. Back 6		60p	—
	C	P	96 *Foreign Scenes, Nd. 1/96C–96/96C. Back 6..		55p	—
	C	P	96 Cricketers, Nd. C1–C96, "Casket Cigarettes" on front:—			
			A. Back 5.............................		£10.00	—
			*B. Plain back		£10.00	—
	C	P	96 *Animals—"Series Nos. C.A.1 to 96". Back 7		55p	—
	C	P	96 *Natives and Scenes:—			
			A. "C.B.1 to 96" on front. Back 7			
			1. Nd. 1–96		55p	—
			2. Nd. C.B.1–C.B.96		60p	—
			B. "J.S.1 to 96" on front. "Junior Member", back 9		60p	—
	C	P	96 *Animals and Scenes—"CC1 to 96" on front. Back 7		55p	—
	H2	P	50 *British Scenes—"Series C.M.1–50.A" on front. Back style 7......................		80p	—
	H2	P	50 *Foreign Scenes:—			
			A. "Series C.M. 1/50 B" on front. Backstyle 7		80p	—
			B. "J.M. Series 1/50" on front. "Junior Member", back 9		60p	—
	H2	P	50 *Foreign Scenes:—			
			A. "Series C.M. 101–150.S" on front. Back style 7		60p	—
			B. Nd. S.101–S.150 on front. Back 4		60p	—
	C	P	96 *Foreign Scenes, Nd. 1/96D–96/96D. Back 6 .		80p	—
	H2	P	50 *Foreign Scenes, Nd. 1/50E–50/50E. Back 6..		60p	£30.00
	H2	P	50 *Foreign Scenes, Nd. 1/50F–50/50F. Back 6..		65p	—
	C	P	96 Footballers, Nd. F.1–F.96. "Casket" and "Critic" back style 5...................		£1.50	—
	C	P	96 Footballers, Nd. F.97–F.192. "Casket" and Critic" back style 5....................		£1.50	—
	H	P	50 Football Teams, Nd. F.193–F.242. ("Casket" and "Critic")................		£3.00	—
	C	P	96 *Footballers—"Series F.A. 1/96" on front. Back 8		£1.50	—
	C	P	96 *Footballers—"Series F.B. 1–96" on front. Back 8		£1.50	—
	C	P	96 *Footballers—"Series F.C. 1/96" on front. Back 8...............................		£1.50	—
	H2	P	50 *Scenes—"G. 1/50" on front. "Junior Member", back 9		80p	—
	H2	P	50 *Scenes—"1/50. H" on front. "Junior Member", back 9		70p	—
	H2	P	50 *Animals and Scenes, Nd. I.1–I.50. Back style 6....................................		80p	—
	H2	P	50 Famous Statues—"J.C.M. 1 to 50 C" on front. Back style 6....................		80p	—
	H2	P	50 *Scenes, Nd. JCM 1/50D–JCM 50/50D—			
			A. Back style 6.........................		55p	—

Illus. No.	Size	Print-ing	Number in set		Handbook ref.	Price per card	Complete set
				B. Back style 9 ("Junior Member")		60p	—
	B1	P	30	Child Studies, Nd. J.M. No. 1–J.M. No. 30. "Junior Member", back style 9		£1.20	—
	B1	P	30	*Beauties, Nd. J.M.1–J.M.30. "Junior Member", back style 9		£1.20	—
	H2	P	50	*Foreign Scenes—"J.M. 1 to 50 A" on front. "Junior Member", back style 9		55p	—
	H2	P	50	British Empire Exhibition "J.M. 1 to 50 B" on front		£1.00	—
	C	P	96	*Animals and Scenes—"J.S. 1/96 A" on front. "Junior Member", back style 9		60p	—
	H2	P	50	*Scenes, Nd. S.1–S.50. "Junior Member", back 4		90p	—
	H2	P	50	*Scenes, Nd. S.51–S.100. "Junior Member", back 4		70p	—
	B1	P	50	*Cathedrals and Abbeys, Nd. S.J. 1–S.J. 50. Plain back	Ha.595–3	£1.00	—
	B1	P	50	*British Castles, Nd. S.J. 51–S.J. 100. Plain back	Ha.595–3	£1.00	—
	H2	P	? 4	*Scenes, Nd. V.1–V.4. "Junior Member", back 4		—	—

B. Coloured and Letterpress Series

Illus. No.	Size	Print-ing	Number in set		Handbook ref.	Price per card	Complete set
76	A	C	50	British Empire Exhibition Series		£1.30	£65.00
	A	C	50	Builders of the British Empire...............		£1.30	£65.00
	A	C	50	Celebrities in Sport........................		£1.10	£55.00
	A	C	75	Cricketers Series		£3.00	—
	A	C	50	Dirt Track Riders		£2.50	—
	A	C	30	Drawing Made Easy		£1.20	£36.00
	A	C	52	The English & Welsh Counties...............		£1.20	£65.00
	A	C		Footballers Series:—			
			50	A. Captions in blue.....................		£2.00	—
			100	B. Captions in brown		£2.00	—
	A	C	25	"King Lud" Problems......................		£10.00	—
	A	C	26	Maritime Flags		£6.00	—
	A	U	25	Photos of Football Stars...................		£14.00	—
	D	C	50	Railway Posters by Famous Artists		£3.40	—
	A	C	50	Sports Trophies...........................		£1.30	£65.00
	A2	CP	51	*Views...................................	Ha.597	90p	£45.00

C. 1930's Photographic Series

Illus. No.	Size	Print-ing	Number in set		Handbook ref.	Price per card	Complete set
		P		Beautiful Scotland (1939):—	Ha.564–1		
	D		28	A. Small size......................		18p	£5.00
	—		48	B. Medium size (77 × 52 mm.)		13p	£5.00
	—	P	48	The Bridges of Britain (Apr. 1938) (77 × 52 mm.)................................		13p	£4.25
	—	P	48	Britain from the Air (77 × 52 mm.) (1939)....		13p	£4.00
	—	P	48	British Railways (77 × 52 mm.) (Nov. 1938)..		13p	£6.50
		P		Coastwise (Jan. 1939):—	Ha.564–2		
	D		28	A. Small size......................		22p	£6.00
	—		48	B. Medium size (77 × 52 mm.)		13p	£3.50
	D	P	54	Dirt Track Riders (1930). Front black and white or sepia:—			
				A. Descriptive back		£3.00	—
				*B. Non-descriptive back.................		£3.00	—
	—	P	48	Dogs (1939):—			
				A. Size 76 × 51 mm.		13p	£3.50
				B. Size 74 × 48 mm.		—	—
		P		Flying (1938):—	Ha.564–3		
	D		28	A. Small size...........................		£1.00	£28.00
	—		48	B. Medium size (77 × 52 mm.)		32p	£16.00
	A2	P	78	Footballers in Action (1934)		£1.40	—
	—	P	48	Holiday Haunts by the Sea (77 × 52 mm.) (Aug. 1937)................................		13p	£4.00
	—	P	48	The Navy (May 1937):—			
				A. Large captions		13p	£5.50
				B. Smaller captions		15p	£7.50
345		P		Our Countryside (1938):—	Ha.564–4		
	D		28	A. Small size.....................		28p	£8.00
	—		48	B. Medium size (77 × 52 mm.)		13p	£3.50
	A2	P	54	Real Photographs of London (1936)		£1.00	£54.00
	D	P	28	Shots from the Films (1938)		75p	£21.00
	—	P	48	Sights of Britain—"Series of 48" (76 × 51 mm.) (1936)		13p	£4.25
	—	P	48	Sights of Britain—"Second Series ..." (76 × 51 mm.) (1936):—			
				A. Large captions		13p	£3.25
				B. Smaller captions		13p	£4.00
	—	P	48	Sights of Britain—"Third Series ..." (76 × 51 mm.) (1937)............................		13p	£4.25
	—	P	48	Sights of London—"First Series ..." (76 × 51 mm.) (1935)		35p	£17.50
	—	P	12	Sights of London—"Supplementary Series of 12 Jubilee Pictures" (76 × 51 mm.) (1935)..		50p	£6.00
	A2	P	54	Sporting Celebrities (1935)		£1.40	£75.00
	—	P	96	Sporting Events and Stars (76 × 50 mm.) (1935)...............................		33p	£32.00
	A2	P	54	Views of Britain (1937)		£1.10	£60.00
	—	P	48	Winter Scenes (76 × 52 mm.) (1937)		13p	£3.25

J. A. PATTRIEOUEX (continued)

D. Miscellaneous

Illus. No.	Size	Printing	Number in set		Handbook ref.	Price per card	Complete set
—		C	1	Advertisement Card (70 × 40 mm.)		—	—
—		C	24	Cadet's Jackpot Jigsaws (90 × 65 mm.) (1969)		—	—
—		C	24	Treasure Island (65 × 45 mm.) (1968)........		—	—

W. PEPPERDY

Pre-1919 Issues

	A	C	30	*Army Pictures, Cartoons, etc...............	H.12	—	—

M. PEZARO & SON, London

Pre-1919 Issues

	D	C	25	*Armies of the World	H.43	£85.00	—
	D	C	? 14	Song Titles Illustrated	H.323	£95.00	—

GODFREY PHILLIPS LTD., London

A. Pre-1919 Issues

Size	Printing	Number in set		Handbook ref.	Price per card	Complete set
D1	C	25	*Actresses "C" Series, Nd. 101–125:—			
			A. Blue Horseshoe design back		£11.00	—
			B. Green back, "Carriage" Cigarettes.....		£20.00	—
			C. Blue back, "Teapot" Cigarettes		£80.00	—
			D. Blue back, "Volunteer" Cigarettes		£70.00	—
			E. Blue back, "Derby" Cigarettes.........		£80.00	—
			F. Blue back, "Ball of Beauty" Cigarettes .		£80.00	—
—	C	50	*Actresses—oval card (1916–1917) (38 × 62 mm.):—	H.324/Ha.324		
			A. With name.........................		£5.00	—
			B. *Without Maker's and Actress's Name* ...		£2.50	£125.00
D	C	40	Animal Series (pre-1908)		£4.00	£160.00
D1	C	25	*Beauties, Nd. B.801–825 (pre-1908)	H.325	£7.00	£175.00
A1	U	? 24	*Beauties, collotype—"HUMPS" (? 1895)....	H.222	£40.00	—
A	C	30	*Beauties, "Nymphs" (? 1896)	H.326	£40.00	—
D			*Beauties—"Plums" (1897–8):—	H.186		
	BW	? 9	A. Front in black and white...............		—	—
	C	50	B. Plum-coloured background............		£20.00	—
	C	50	C. Green background		£20.00	—
A1	C	50	Beautiful Women (? 1908):—	H.284		
			A. Inscribed "W.I. Series"		£5.00	—
			B. Inscribed "I.F. Series".................		£5.00	—
—	C	50	Beautiful Women, Nd. W.501–550 (55 × 75 mm.)...............................	H.284	£7.00	—
D1	C	25	*Boxer Rebellion—Sketches (1904)	H.46	£14.00	—
—	C	30	*British Beauties—Oval Card (36 × 60 mm.) Plain back..............................	H.244	£2.00	£60.00
D	U	50	"British Beauties" (? 1916) photogravure....	H.327	£2.60	£130.00
—	PC	76	British Beauties (? 1916) (37 × 55 mm.)		£2.00	£150.00
A	C	54	British Beauties (1914–15), Nd. 1–54	H.328		
			(a) Blue back, grey-black, glossy front		£2.00	£110.00
			(b) *Plain back, grey-black, glossy front*		—	—
			(c) *Plain back, sepia, matt front*...........		£2.00	—
A	C	54	British Beauties (1914–15), Nd. 55–108:—	H.328		
			A. Blue back, grey-black, semi-glossy front		£2.00	£110.00
			B. Blue back, grey-black matt front		£2.00	£110.00
			C. *Plain back, grey-black matt front*		£2.00	—
D1	C	30	British Butterflies, No. 1 issue (1911)		£3.00	£90.00
D1	U	25	British Warships, green photo style (1915)...		£4.00	£100.00
L	U	25	British Warships, green photo style (1915)...		—	—
A1	P	80	British Warships, "real photographic"	H.329	£8.00	—
D1	C	50	*Busts of Famous People (1906–7):—			
			A. Pale green back, caption in black		£7.00	—
			B. Brown back, caption in black		£13.00	—
			C. Green back, caption in white, "Patent No. 20736"		£3.50	£175.00
D1	C	25	*Chinese Series (? 1910):—	H.330		
			A. Back in English		£3.00	£75.00
			B. "Volunteer" Cigarettes back...........		£3.60	£90.00
A	C	50	*Colonial Troops (1904)...................	H.40	£15.00	→
D1	C	30	Eggs Nests & Birds, No. 1 issue (1912–13):—	H.331		
			A. Unnumbered.........................		£3.30	£100.00
			B. Numbered		£3.30	£100.00
D	C	25	First Aid Series, green back (1914–15).......		£3.40	£85.00
A	C	13	*General Interest (? 1895)....................	H.332	£25.00	£325.00
—	BW	100	*Guinea Gold Series, unnumbered (1899–1901) (64 × 38 mm.) Inscribed "Phillips' Guinea Gold", matt	H.333/Ha.333	£2.25	—
—	BW	90	*Guinea Gold Series, numbered 101–190 (68 × 41 mm.) Inscribed "Smoke Phillips' ...":—			
			A. Glossy.............................		£2.25	—
			B. Matt...............................		£2.25	—
		160	*Guinea Gold Series, unnumbered (63 × 41 mm.)...........................	H.333		
		134	Actresses:—			
	BW		A. Black front...........................		£2.00	—

Illus. No.	Size	Print-ing	Number in set		Handbook ref.	Price per card	Complete set
		U		B. Brown front		£4.00	—
		BW	26	Celebrities, Boer War		£3.50	—
	D1	C	25	How to do it Series (1913–14)		£4.40	£110.00
	D	C	25	Indian Series (1908–9)		£7.00	£175.00
	K1	C	52	*Miniature Playing Cards	H.334	—	—
	D1	C	30	Morse and Semaphore Signalling (1916):—	H.335		
				"Morse Signalling" back		£3.70	£110.00
				"Semaphore Signalling" back		£3.70	£110.00
	—	P	27	Real Photo Series—Admirals and Generals of the Great War. Cut-outs for buttonhole—20 × 40 mm.		£7.00	—
	A	C	20	Russo-Japanese War Series	H.100	£120.00	—
	D1	C	30	Semaphore Signalling—See "Morse & Semaphore Signalling"			
	D1	C	25	Sporting Series		£8.00	—
	D1	C	25	*Statues & Monuments (cut-outs) (1907):—			
				A. Provisional Patent No. 20736		£4.00	£100.00
				B. Patent No. 20736		£4.00	£100.00
	D	C	25	*Territorial Series (Nd. 51–75) (1908)		£13.00	—
	A1	C	25	*Types of British and Colonial Troops (1899–1900)	H.76	£30.00	—
	D1	C	25	*Types of British Soldiers (Nd. M.651–675) (1900)	H.144	£10.00	£250.00
	A	C	63	*War Photos (1916)	H.336	£3.50	—

B. Post-1920 Issues

Illus. No.	Size	Print-ing	Number in set		Handbook ref.	Price per card	Complete set
	A2	C	1	*Advertisement Card—"Grand Cut" (1934)		—	£14.00
	A2	C	1	*Advertisement Card—"La Galbana Fours" (1934)		—	£14.00
	A	C	50	Aircraft (1938)	Ha.598	70p	£35.00
	A2	C	54	Aircraft—Series No. 1 (1938):—			
				A. Millhoff and Phillips names at base of back		£3.50	—
				B. Phillips and Associated Companies at base of back:—			
				1. Front varnished		£1.00	£54.00
				2. Front matt		32p	£17.00
	A2	U	50	*Animal Studies (Australia)	Ha.538	£2.00	—
187	—	C	30	Animal Studies (61 × 53 mm.) (1936)		13p	£3.25
	A2	C	50	Annuals (1939):—			
				A. Home issue		13p	£3.50
				B. New Zealand issue (dates for planting 4–6 months later)		45p	£22.50
	D	BW	50	Australian Sporting Celebrities (1932) (Australia)		£1.30	—
	B	C	25	Arms of the English Sees (1924)		£2.60	£65.00
	A	C	44	Beauties of To-Day, small—"A Series of 44 …" (1937)		45p	£20.00
169	A	C	50	Beauties of To-Day, small—"A Series of 50 …" (1938)	Ha.514	15p	£7.50
	A2	P	54	Beauties of To-Day, small—"A Series of Real Photographs …" (1939)		32p	£17.50
	A	C	36	Beauties of To-Day, small—"A Series of 36 … Second Series" (1940)		14p	£5.00
	—	P		Beauties of To-Day, large (83 × 66 mm.) (see RB13/21–22):—			
			36	First arrangement, known as "Series A"		£1.60	—
			36	Second arrangement, known as "Series B"		£1.60	—
	J2	P	36	Beauties of To-Day, extra-large, unnumbered (1937) (see RB13/23)		75p	£27.00
	J2	P	36	Beauties of To-Day, extra large—"Second Series" (1938)		50p	£18.00
	J2	P	36	Beauties of To-Day, extra-large—"Third Series" (1938)		36p	£13.00
	J2	P	36	Beauties of To-Day, extra-large—"Fourth Series" (1938)		50p	£18.00
	J2	P	36	Beauties of To-Day, extra-large—"Fifth Series" (1938)		21p	£7.50
	J2	P	36	Beauties of To-Day, extra-large—"Sixth Series" (1939)		21p	£7.50
	J2	P	36	Beauties of To-Day, extra-large—Unmarked (1939):—			
				A. Back "Godfrey Phillips Ltd. and Associated Companies"		21p	£7.50
				B. Back "Issued with B.D.V. Medium Cigarettes …"		13p	£3.50
	A2	BW	36	Beauties of the World—Stage, Cinema, Dancing Celebrities (1931)		60p	£22.00
	A2	C	36	Beauties of the World—Series No. 2—Stars of Stage and Screen (1933)		90p	£32.00
	—	C	30	Beauty Spots of the Homeland (126 × 89 mm.) (1938)		40p	£12.00
	A	C	50	Bird Painting (1938)		17p	£8.50
	A	C	50	British Birds and Their Eggs (1936)		32p	£16.00
95	A	C	25	British Butterflies:—	Ha.517–1		
				A. Back in pale blue (1923)		40p	£10.00
				B. Back in dark blue (1927)		24p	£6.00
				C. "Permacal" transfers (1936)		15p	£3.75
	A2	C	25	British Orders of Chivalry & Valour (1939):—	Ha.599		

Illus. No.	Size	Print-ing	Number in set		Handbook ref.	Price per card	Complete set
				A. Back "Godfrey Phillips Ltd. and Associated Companies"		£1.20	£30.00
				B. Back "De Reszke Cigarettes" (no maker's name)		£1.20	£30.00
—		C	36	Characters Come to Life (61 × 53 mm.) (1938)		13p	£3.25
—		P	25	*Cinema Stars—Circular cards (57 mm. diam.) (1924) (see RB13/49)		50p	£12.50
A		P	52	Cinema Stars—Set 1	Ha.515–1A	£1.10	—
A2		U	30	Cinema Stars—Set 2	Ha.515–2	£1.20	—
A2		U	30	Cinema Stars—Set 3 (cream, yellow or orange tint)	Ha.515–3	90p	£27.00
A2		C	32	Cinema Stars—Set 4	Ha.515–4	60p	£19.00
A2		BW	32	Cinema Stars—Set 5	Ha.515–5	60p	£19.00
				Come to Life Series—see "Zoo Studies"			
		C		Coronation of Their Majesties (1937):—			
A2			50	A. Small size		13p	£3.75
—			36	B. Medium size (61 × 53 mm.)		13p	£3.00
—			24	C. Postcard size (127 × 89 mm.)		60p	£15.00
		P		Cricketers (1924):—			
K2			210	*A. Miniature size, "Pinnace" photos (Nd. 16c–225c)		£2.20	—
D			192	B. Small size, brown back (selected Nos., see RB13/58)		£2.20	—
B1			?	*C. Large size, "Pinnance" photos (number unknown)		£5.00	—
B1			25	D. Large size, brown back (selected Nos., see RB13/58)		£4.50	—
—			?	E. *Cabinet size*		£10.00	—
D	C		25	Derby Winners & Jockeys (1923)		£1.20	£30.00
D1	C		25	Empire Industries (1927)	Ha.600	50p	£12.50
A2	C		50	*Evolution of the British Navy* (1930)		—	£60.00
			49/50	Ditto (No. 40 missing)		50p	£25.00
D	C		25	Famous Boys (1924)		£1.00	£25.00
D	C		32	Famous Cricketers (1926)		£1.70	£55.00
A	C		25	Famous Crowns (1938)		13p	£3.50
A2	C		50	*Famous Footballers* (1936) (see RB13/66)		50p	£25.00
—	C		36	Famous Love Scenes (60 × 53 mm.) (1939)		13p	£4.25
A2	C		50	Famous Minors (1936)		13p	£4.00
—	C		26	Famous Paintings (128 × 89 mm.) (1938)		90p	£23.00
D	C		25	Feathered Friends (1928)	Ha.516	70p	£17.50
246	A2	C	50	Film Favourites (1934)	Ha.517–2	13p	£5.50
	D	BW	50	Film Stars (Australia) (1934)		£1.00	—
129	A2	C	50	Film Stars (1934)		30p	£15.00
—		C	24	*Film Stars—"... No. ... of a series of 24 cards ..." (128 × 89 mm.) (1934):—			
				A. Postcard format back		50p	£12.00
				B. Back without postcard format		£1.00	£24.00
—		C	24	*Film Stars—"... No. ... of a series of cards", Nd. 25–48 (128 × 89 mm.) (1935):—			
				A. Postcard format back		£1.00	—
				B. Back without postcard format		—	—
—		C	24	*Film Stars—"... No. ... of a series of cards", vivid backgrounds (128 × 89 mm.) (1936):—			
				A. Postcard format back	Ha.517–3	50p	£12.00
				B. Back without postcard format		£1.00	—
D	C		50	First Aid (1923)		60p	£30.00
D	C		25	*Fish (1924)		90p	£22.50
	C		30	Flower Studies (1937):—			
				A. Medium size (61 × 53 mm.)		13p	£2.75
				*B. Postcard size (128 × 89 mm.)		40p	£12.00
	P			Footballers—"Pinnace" photos (1922–24):—			
K2				A. Miniature size:—			

(Prices shown apply to numbers 1 to 940, for numbers above 940 prices are doubled)

Illus. No.	Size	Print-ing	Number in set		Handbook ref.	Price per card	Complete set
			112	1a. "Oval" design back, in brown		40p	—
			400	1b. "Oval" design back, in black		40p	—
			517	2. Double-lined oblong back		40p	—
			1109	3. Single-lined oblong back, address "Photo"		40p	—
				4. Single-lined oblong back, address "Pinnace" photos:—			
			2463	a. Name at head, team at base		40p	—
			?1651	b. Name at base, no team shown		40p	—
			?217	c. Team at head, name at base		40p	—
—			?	B. Large size (83 × 59 mm.):—			
				1. "Oval" design back		£1.00	—
				2. Double-lined oblong back:—			
				a. Address "Photo"		£1.00	—
				b. Address "Pinnace" photos		£1.00	—
				3. Single-lined oblong back:—			
				a. Name at head, team at base		£1.00	—
				b. Name at base, no team shown		£1.00	—
				c. Team and name at base		£1.00	—
				C. *Cabinet size*		£3.00	—
—	C		30	Garden Studies (128 × 89 mm.) (1938)		25p	£7.50
A2	C		25	Home Pets (1924)	Ha.540	£1.00	£25.00
A2	U		25	How to Build a Two Valve Set (1929)		50p	£12.50

1 (Page 72)

2 (Page 43)

3 (Page 69)

4 (Page 25)

5 (Page 70)

6 (Page 88)

7 (Page 89)

8 (Page 69)

9 (Page 90)

10 (Page 22)

11 (Page 69)

12 (Page 24)

13 (Page 50)

14 (Page 66)

15 (Page 69)

16 (Page 89)

17 (Page 88)

18 (Page 88)

19 (Page 76)

20 (Page 18)

21 (Page 89)

22 (Page 89)

23 (Page 33)

24 (Page 131)

25 (Page 47)

26 (Page 46)   27 (Page 88)   28 (Page 80)   29 (Page 18)   30 (Page 71)

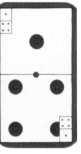
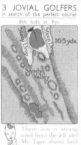

31 (Page 86)   32 (Page 43)   33 (Page 24)   34 (Page 41)   35 (Page 55)

36 (Page 90)   37 (Page 43)   38 (Page 18)   39 (Page 65)   40 (Page 71)

41 (Page 43)   42 (Page 89)   43 (Page 69)   44 (Page 19)   45 (Page 69)

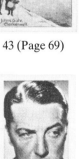

46 (Page 91)   47 (Page 84)   48 (Page 72)

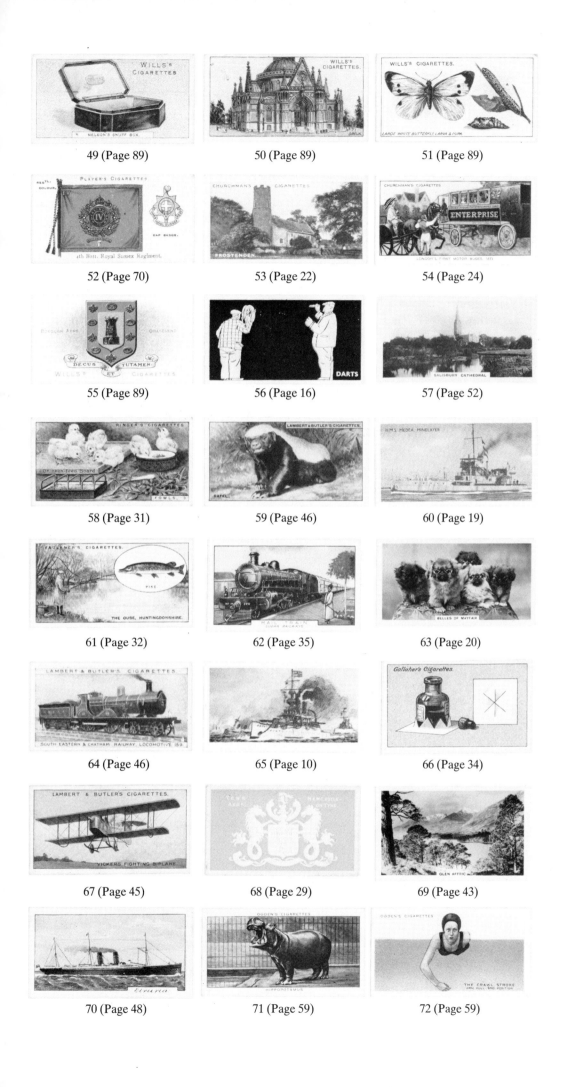

49 (Page 89)

50 (Page 89)

51 (Page 89)

52 (Page 70)

53 (Page 22)

54 (Page 24)

55 (Page 89)

56 (Page 16)

57 (Page 52)

58 (Page 31)

59 (Page 46)

60 (Page 19)

61 (Page 32)

62 (Page 35)

63 (Page 20)

64 (Page 46)

65 (Page 10)

66 (Page 34)

67 (Page 45)

68 (Page 29)

69 (Page 43)

70 (Page 48)

71 (Page 59)

72 (Page 59)

73 (Page 46)   74 (Page 124)   75 (Page 24)

76 (Page 61)   77 (Page 52)   78 (Page 54)

79 (Page 79)   80 (Page 116)   81 (Page 23)

82 (Page 68)   83 (Page 89)   84 (Page 68)

85 (Page 108)   86 (Page 70)   87 (Page 70)

88 (Page 124)   89 (Page 124)   90 (Page 123)

91 (Page 73)

92 (Page 73)

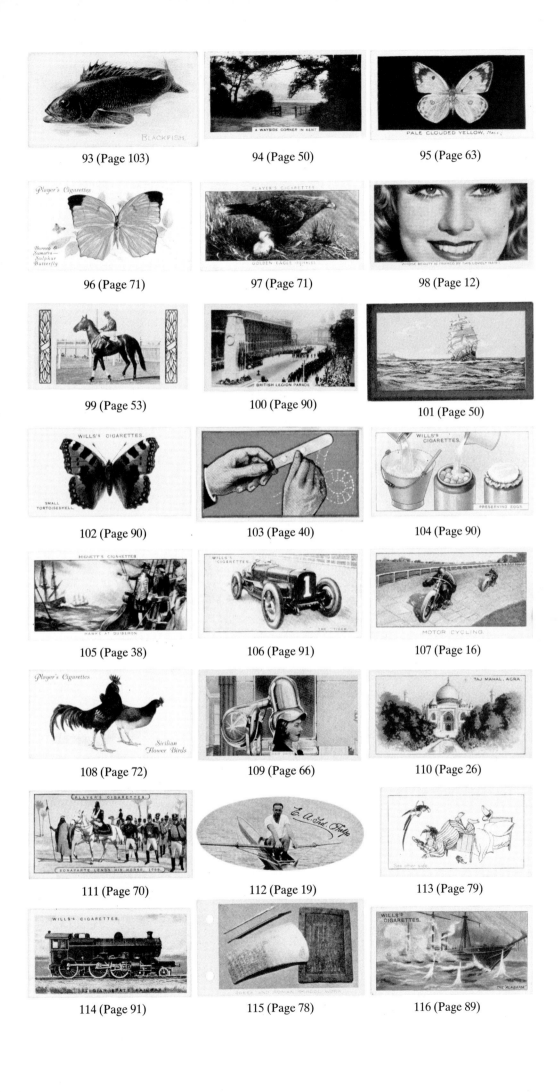

93 (Page 103)

94 (Page 50)

95 (Page 63)

96 (Page 71)

97 (Page 71)

98 (Page 12)

99 (Page 53)

100 (Page 90)

101 (Page 50)

102 (Page 90)

103 (Page 40)

104 (Page 90)

105 (Page 38)

106 (Page 91)

107 (Page 16)

108 (Page 72)

109 (Page 66)

110 (Page 26)

111 (Page 70)

112 (Page 19)

113 (Page 79)

114 (Page 91)

115 (Page 78)

116 (Page 89)

117 (Page 70)

118 (Page 90)

119 (Page 11)

120 (Page 90)

121 (Page 70)

122 (Page 12)

123 (Page 91)

124 (Page 86)

125 (Page 34)

126 (Page 47)

127 (Page 89)

128 (Page 116)

129 (Page 64)

130 (Page 17)

131 (Page 70)

132 (Page 89)

133 (Page 84)

134 (Page 88)

135 (Page 12)

136 (Page 71)

137 (Page 90)

138 (Page 90)

139 (Page 72)

140 (Page 121)   141 (Page 109)   142 (Page 88)   143 (Page 68)   144 (Page 72)

145 (Page 90)   146 (Page 28)   147 (Page 46)   148 (Page 10)   149 (Page 18)

150 (Page 65)   151 (Page 89)   152 (Page 89)   153 (Page 38)   154 (Page 76)

155 (Page 68)   156 (Page 19)   157 (Page 92)   158 (Page 47)   159 (Page 19)

160 (Page 69)   161 (Page 9)   162 (Page 72)   163 (Page 91)   164 (Page 90)

165 (Page 30)   166 (Page 69)   167 (Page 120)   168 (Page 89)   169 (Page 63)

170 (Page 69)   171 (Page 69)   172 (Page 104)   173 (Page 23)   174 (Page 69)

175 (Page 17)   176 (Page 70)   177 (Page 69)   178 (Page 127)   179 (Page 45)

180 (Page 65)   181 (Page 47)   182 (Page 39)   183 (Page 17)   184 (Page 73)

185 (Page 65)   186 (Page 82)   187 (Page 63)

188 (Page 46)   189 (Page 124)   190 (Page 40)   191 (Page 30)   192 (Page 31)

193 (Page 52)   194 (Page 16)   195 (Page 37)   196 (Page 85)   197 (Page 43)

198 (Page 32)   199 (Page 27)   200 (Page 24)   201 (Page 24)   202 (Page 23)

203 (Page 41)   204 (Page 47)   205 (Page 26)   206 (Page 92)   207 (Page 11)

208 (Page 43)   209 (Page 122)   210 (Page 112)

211 (Page 89)

212 (Page 107)

213 (Page 69)

214 (Page 77)

215 (Page 92)

216 (Page 69)

217 (Page 47)

218 (Page 40)

219 (Page 109)

220 (Page 40)

221 (Page 11)

222 (Page 79)

223 (Page 11)

224 (Page 12)

225 (Page 78)

226 (Page 30)

227 (Page 29)

228 (Page 9)

229 (Page 41)

230 (Page 80)

231 (Page 15)

232 (Page 70)   233 (Page 72)   234 (Page 85)   235 (Page 23)   236 (Page 108)

237 (Page 112)   238 (Page 90)   239 (Page 105)   240 (Page 91)   241 (Page 72)

 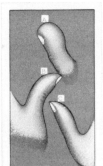  

242 (Page 59)   243 (Page 19)   244 (Page 85)   245 (Page 50)   246 (Page 64)

247 (Page 109)   248 (Page 10)   249 (Page 79)   250 (Page 44)   251 (Page 128)

252 (Page 18)   253 (Page 89)   254 (Page 17)   255 (Page 118)   256 (Page 69)

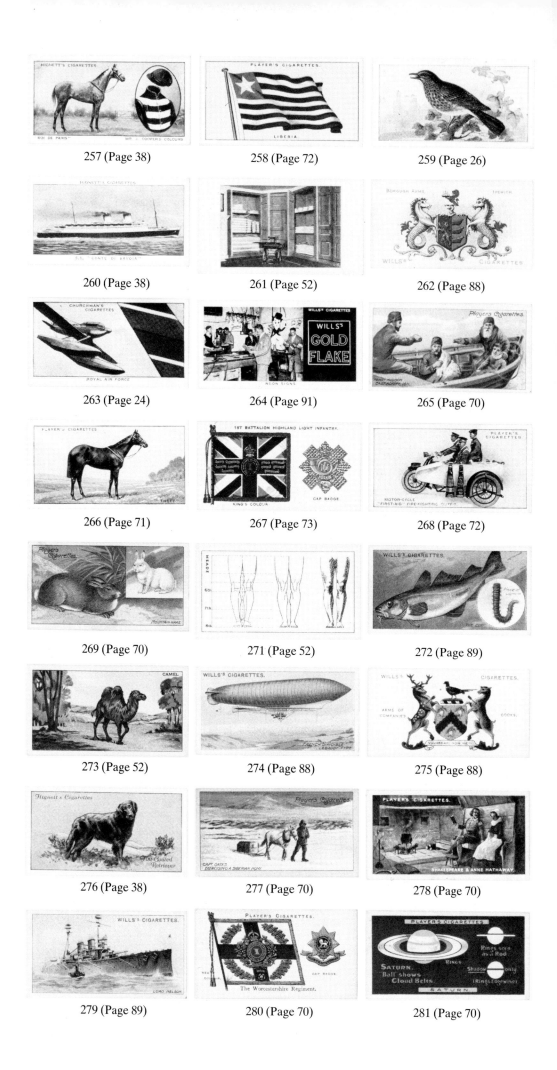

257 (Page 38)

258 (Page 72)

259 (Page 26)

260 (Page 38)

261 (Page 52)

262 (Page 88)

263 (Page 24)

264 (Page 91)

265 (Page 70)

266 (Page 71)

267 (Page 73)

268 (Page 72)

269 (Page 70)

271 (Page 52)

272 (Page 89)

273 (Page 52)

274 (Page 88)

275 (Page 88)

276 (Page 38)

277 (Page 70)

278 (Page 70)

279 (Page 89)

280 (Page 70)

281 (Page 70)

282 (Page 107) 283 (Page 69) 284 (Page 17) 285 (Page 39) 286 (Page 70)

   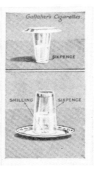

287 (Page 47) 288 (Page 21) 289 (Page 40) 290 (Page 85) 291 (Page 35)

292 (Page 37) 293 (Page 43) 294 (Page 40) 295 (Page 121) 296 (Page 127)

297 (Page 12) 298 (Page 40) 299 (Page 78) 300 (Page 10) 301 (Page 23)

302 (Page 12) 303 (Page 110) 304 (Page 89) 305 (Page 52) 306 (Page 18)

307 (Page 89)

308 (Page 16)

309 (Page 72)

310 (Page 30)

311 (Page 101)

312 (Page 90)

313 (Page 89)

314 (Page 35)

315 (Page 89)

316 (Page 71)

317 (Page 23)

318 (Page 18)

319 (Page 17)

320 (Page 70)

321 (Page 88)

322 (Page 11)

323 (Page 89)

324 (Page 88)

325 (Page 89)

326 (Page 107)

327 (Page 18)

328 (Page 80)

329 (Page 18)

330 (Page 89)

331 (Page 76)

332 (Page 121)

333 (Page 126)

334 (Page 130)

335 (Page 35)

336 (Page 129)

337 (Page 129)

338 (Page 35)

339 (Page 130)

340 (Page 129)

341 (Page 51)

342 (Page 46)

343 (Page 91)

344 (Page 51)

345 (Page 61)

346 (Page 72)

347 (Page 47)

348 (Page 51)

349 (Page 90)

350 (Page 91)

351 (Page 73)

352 (Page 91)

353 (Page 17) 354 (Page 17) 355 (Page 20) 356 (Page 10) 357 (Page 19)

358 (Page 19) 359 (Page 10) 360 (Page 17) 361 (Page 20) 362 (Page 35)

363 (Page 90) 364 (Page 21) 365 (Page 89)

366 (Page 73) 367 (Page 35)

368 (Page 13)

369 (Page 72) 370 (Page 21) 371 (Page 72)

Illus. No.	Size	Print-ing	Number in set		Handbook ref.	Price per card	Complete set
	D	C	25	How to Make a Valve Amplifier ..., Nd. 26–50 (1924)		£1.00	£25.00
	A	C	25	How to Make Your Own Wireless Set (1923)		£1.00	£25.00
180	A2	C	54	In the Public Eye (1935)		13p	£4.50
39	A2	C	50	International Caps (1936) (see RB13/66)		30p	£15.00
	A2	C	37	Kings & Queens of England (1925):—			
				Nos. 1 and 4		£20.00	–
				Other numbers		90p	£32.00
	A2	U	25	Lawn Tennis (1930)		60p	£15.00
	K2	C	53	*Miniature Playing Cards (1932–34):—			
				A. Back with exchange scheme:—			
				1. Buff. Offer for "pack of playing cards"		30p	–
				2. Buff. Offer for "playing cards, dominoes or chess"		30p	£16.00
				3. Buff. Offer for "playing cards, dominoes or draughts"		30p	£16.00
				4. Lemon		30p	–
				5. White, with red over-printing		30p	–
				B. Blue scroll back, see Fig. 30, Plate 5, RB13		30p	£16.00
	A2	C	25	Model Railways (1927) (see RB13/101)		£1.00	£25.00
	D	C	50	Motor Cars at a Glance (1924)		£1.50	£75.00
	D	C	20	Novelty Series (1924)		£4.50	–
	A2	C	48	The "Old Country" (1935)		35p	£17.50
	A	C	25	Old Favourites (1924)	Ha.517–4	80p	£20.00
	—	C	36	Old Masters (60 × 53 mm.) (1939)		25p	£9.00
	A	U	36	Olympic Champions Amsterdam, 1928		60p	£22.00
	A	C	25	Optical Illusions (1927)		70p	£17.50
		C		"Our Dogs" (1939):—			
	A2		36	A. Small size (export)		40p	£14.00
	—		30	B. Medium size (60 × 53 mm.)		13p	£3.75
	—		30	*C. Postcard size (128 × 89 mm.)		£1.50	£45.00
	—	BW	48	"Our Favourites" (60 × 53 mm.) (1935)		13p	£3.50
	—	C	30	Our Glorious Empire (128 × 89 mm.) (1939)		60p	£18.00
185		C	30	"Our Puppies" (1936):—			
	—			A. Medium size (60 × 53 mm.)		20p	£6.00
	—			*B. Postcard size (128 × 89 mm.)		25p	£7.50
	A2	C	25	Personalities of To-Day (Caricatures) (1932)		40p	£10.00
	A2	C	25	Popular Superstitions (1930)		50p	£12.50
	A	C	25	Prizes for Needlework (1925) (see RB13/116)		90p	£22.50
	D	C	25	Railway Engines (1924)		£1.20	£30.00
	D	C	25	Red Indians (1927)	Ha.601	£1.00	£25.00
	A	C	25	School Badges (1927)	Ha.543	50p	£12.50
	A	C		Screen Stars (1936–37):—			
			48	First arrangement, known as "Series A" (see RB13/121):—			
				A. Frame embossed		17p	£8.50
				B. Frame not embossed		17p	£8.50
			48	Second arrangement, known as "Series B" (see RB13/122)		14p	£7.00
	A2	C		A Selection of B.D.V. Wonderful Gifts:—			
			48	"... based on 1930 Budget" (1930) (see RB13/84)		30p	£15.00
			48	"... based on 1931 Budget" (1931) (see RB13/85)		25p	£12.50
			48	"... based on 1932 Budget" (1932) (see RB13/86)		20p	£10.00
	D	C	25	Ships and Their Flags (1924)	Ha.602	£1.60	£40.00
	—	C	36	Ships that have Made History (60 × 53 mm.) (1938)		13p	£3.50
	—	C	48	Shots from the Films (60 × 53 mm.) (1934)		13p	£5.00
	A2	C	50	Soccer Stars (1936) (see RB13/66)		25p	£12.50
	A2	C	36	Soldiers of the King (1939):—	Ha.603		
				A. Inscribed "This surface is adhesive"		50p	£18.00
				B. Without the above:—			
				1. Thin card		25p	£9.00
				2. Thick card		33p	£12.00
		C		Special Jubilee Year Series (1935):—			
	—		20	A. Medium size (60 × 53 mm.)		15p	£3.00
	—		12	B. Postcard size (128 × 89 mm.)		£1.00	£12.00
	A2	U	30	Speed Champions (1930)		50p	£15.00
	A2	U	36	Sporting Champions (1929)		50p	£18.00
	D	C	25	Sports (1923):—			
				A. White card		£2.00	–
				B. Grey card		£2.00	–
	A2	C	50	*Sportsmen—"Spot the Winner" (1937):—			
				A. Inverted back		13p	£5.00
				B. Normal back		13p	£6.50
	A2	C		Stage and Cinema Beauties (1933–34):—	Ha.572		
150			35	First arrangement—known as "Series A"		23p	£8.00
			35	Second arrangement—known as "Series B"		29p	£10.00
	A2	C	50	Stage and Cinema Beauties (1935)	Ha.517–5	50p	£25.00
	D	C	50	Stars of British Films (Australia) (1934):—			
				A. Back "B.D.V. Cigarettes ..."		£1.00	–
				B. Back "Grey's Cigarettes ..."		£1.00	–
				C. Back "De Reszke Cigarettes ..."		£1.00	–
				D. Back "Godfrey Phillips (Aust.) ..."		£1.00	–
	A2	CP	54	Stars of the Screen—"A Series of 54" (1934)		50p	£27.00

65

Illus. No.	Size	Print- ing	Number in set		Handbook ref.	Price per card	Complete set
14	A2	C	48	Stars of the Screen—"A Series of 48" (1936):—			
				A. Frame not embossed		13p	£6.50
				B. Frame embossed		13p	£6.50
				C. In strips of three, per strip		30p	£5.00
	D	BW	38	Test Cricketers, 1932–1933 (Australia):—			
				A. "Issued with Grey's Cigarettes...".....		£1.60	—
				B. "Issued with B.D.V. Cigarettes..."		£1.60	—
				C. Back "Godfrey Phillips (Aust.)"		£1.60	—
	A	U	25	The 1924 Cabinet (1924)....................		£1.00	£25.00
	A	C	50	This Mechanized Age—First Series (1936):—			
				A. Inscribed "This surface is adhesive"		13p	£3.50
				B. Without the above		13p	£5.00
109	A	C	50	This Mechanized Age—Second Series (1937)		25p	£12.50
	A2	C	100	*Who's Who in Australian Sport (Australia) (1933) (see RB13/147)...................		£1.00	—
	D2	C		Victorian Footballers (Australia) (1933):—			
			50	1. "Series of 50":—			
				A. "Godfrey Phillips (Aust.)..."		£1.00	—
				B. "B.D.V. Cigarettes..."		£1.00	—
				C. "Grey's Cigarettes..."............		£1.00	—
			75	2. "Series of 75":—			
				D. "B.D.V. Cigarettes..."		£1.00	—
	D	BW	50	Victorian League and Association Foot- ballers (Australia) (1934)................		£1.00	—
	—	C	30	Zoo Studies—Come to Life Series (1939) (101 × 76 mm.)..........................		60p	£18.00
				Spectacles for use with the above..........		—	£0.65

C. Silks. Known as "the B.D.V. Silks". All unbacked. Inscribed "B.D.V. Cigarettes" or "G.P." (Godfrey Phillips), or anonymous. Issued about 1910–25.

Illus. No.	Size	Print- ing	Number in set		Handbook ref.	Price per card	Complete set
	—	C	? 61	*Arms of Countries and Territories (73 × 50 mm.)—Anonymous.....................	Ha.504–12	£1.40	—
	—	C	32	*Beauties—Modern Paintings (B.D.V.):—	Ha.505–13		
				A. Small size (70 × 46 mm.)		£3.50	—
				B. Extra-large size (143 × 100 mm.)		£14.00	—
	—	C	100	*Birds II (68 × 42 mm.)—B.D.V.	Ha.505–2	£1.00	—
	—	C	12	*Birds of the Tropics III—B.D.V.:—	Ha.505–3		
				A. Small size (71 × 47 mm.)		£4.00	—
				B. Medium size (71 × 63 mm.)		£4.50	—
				C. Extra-large size (150 × 100 mm.)		£8.00	—
	—	U	24	*British Admirals (83 × 76 mm.)—Anonymous.	Ha.504–5	£2.60	£65.00
	—	C		*British Butterflies and Moths II— Anonymous:—	Ha.505–6		
			40	Nos. 1–40. Large size, 76 × 61 mm.		£1.10	—
			10	Nos. 41–50. Medium size, 70 × 51 mm.		£1.10	—
	—	C	108	*British Naval Crests II:—	Ha.504–4		
				A. B.D.V., size 70 × 47 mm................		70p	—
				B. Anonymous, size 70 × 51 mm............		80p	—
	—	C	25	*Butterflies I (70 × 48 mm.)—Anonymous	Ha.505–5	£5.00	—
	—	C	47	Ceramic Art—B.D.V.:—	Ha.505–16		
				A. Small size (70 × 43 mm.)		55p	£27.50
				B. Medium size (70 × 61 mm.)		70p	£35.00
	—	C		*Clan Tartans:—	Ha.505–15		
				A. Small size (71 × 48 mm.):—			
			49	1. Anonymous........................		60p	£30.00
			65	2. B.D.V............................		60p	£40.00
			65	B. Medium size (70 × 60 mm. –B.D.V.) ...		£2.25	—
			12	C. Extra-large size (150 × 100 mm.)— B.D.V. (selected Nos.).................		£2.25	£27.00
	—	C	108	*Colonial Army Badges (71 × 50 mm.) — Anonymous....................	Ha.502–3	£1.25	—
	—	C	17	County Cricket Badges (69 × 48 mm.):—	Ha.505–8		
				A. Anonymous		£7.00	—
				B. B.D.V...........................		£7.00	—
	—	C	108	*Crests and Badges of the British Army II:—	Ha.502–2		
				A1. Small size (70 × 48 mm.)— Anonymous:—			
				(a) Numbered.......................		50p	£54.00
				(b) Unnumbered....................		60p	£65.00
				A2. Small size (70 × 48 mm.)—B.D.V.......		45p	£48.00
				A3. Medium size (70 × 60 mm.):—			
				(a) Anonymous......................		80p	—
				(b) B.D.V...........................		70p	—
	—	C		*Flags—Set 4—Anonymous:—	Ha.501–4		
			?143	A. "Long" size (82 × 53) mm..............		£3.00	—
				B. "Short" size, (70 × 48) mm.:—			
			?143	1. First numbering arrangement (as A) .		£1.20	—
			?119	2. Second numbering arrangement		50p	—
			?115	3. Third numbering arrangement.......		50p	—
	—	C		*Flags—Set 5—Anonymous:—	Ha.501–5		
				A. Small size, (70 × 50 mm.):—			
			20	1. With caption......................		70p	—
			6	2. Without caption, flag 40 × 29 mm. ...		70p	—
			? 6	3. Without caption, flag 60 × 41 mm. ...		70p	—
			? 2	B. Extra-large size (155 × 108) mm........		£7.00	—
	—	C	18	*Flags—Set 6—Anonymous:—	Ha.501–6		
				A. Size (69 × 47) mm....................		55p	£10.00
				B. Size (71 × 51) mm....................		55p	£10.00

Illus. No.	Size	Print-ing	Number in set		Handbook ref.	Price per card	Complete set
—		C	20	*Flags—Set 7 (70 × 50 mm.)—Anonymous	Ha.501–7	70p	—
—		C	50	*Flags—Set 9 ("5th Series") (70 × 48 mm.)—Anonymous	Ha.501–9	80p	£40.00
—		C		*Flags—Set 10:—	Ha.501–10		
			120	"7th Series" (70 × 48 mm.)—Anonymous ...		40p	—
			120	"10th Series" (70 × 62 mm.)—Anonymous ..		50p	—
			120	"12th Series" (70 × 48 mm.)—Anonymous ..		80p	—
			75	"15th Series" (70 × 62 mm.) (selected Nos.)—B.D.V.		90p	—
			75	"16th Series" (70 × 62 mm.) (selected Nos.)—B.D.V.		90p	—
			132	"20th Series" (70 × 48 mm.)—B.D.V., in brown or red		80p	—
			126	"25th Series" (70 × 48 mm.)—B.D.V., in brown or black		50p	—
			75	"25th Series" (70 × 62 mm.) (selected Nos.), B.D.V.		£2.50	—
			120	"26th Series" (70 × 48 mm.)—B.D.V., in brown or blue		40p	—
			75	"28th Series" (70 × 48 mm.) (selected Nos.), B.D.V.		40p	—
—		C		*Flags—Set 12:—	Ha.501–12		
			1	A. "Let 'em all come" (70 × 46 mm.)—Anonymous		—	£3.00
				B. Allied Flags (grouped):—			
			1	Four Flags—Anonymous:—			
				1. Small size, (70 × 46 mm.)		—	£7.00
				2. Extra-large size, (163 × 120 mm.)....		—	—
			1	Seven Flags (165 × 116 mm.):—			
				1. Anonymous		—	£5.00
				2 B.D.V., in brown or orange........		—	£6.00
			1	Eight Flags (165 × 116 mm.)—B.D.V. ...		—	—
—		C		*Flags—Set 13:—	Ha.501–13		
			? 23	A. Size 163 × 114 mm.—Anonymous.......		80p	£18.00
			? 27	B. Size 163 × 114 mm.—B.D.V., in brown, orange, blue, green or black...........		80p	—
			? 23	C. Size 150 × 100 mm.—B.D.V.		80p	£18.00
—		C	? 26	*Flags—Set 14 ("House Flags") (68 × 47 mm.)—Anonymous......................	Ha.501–14	£3.50	—
—		C	25	*Flags—Set 15 (Pilot and Signal Flags) (70 × 50 mm.):—	Ha.501–15		
				A. Numbered 601–625—Anonymous.......		£1.00	£25.00
				B. Inscribed "Series 11"—B.D.V..........		90p	£22.50
—		C	90	*Football Colours:—	Ha.505–9		
				A. Anonymous, size 68 × 49 mm............		£1.75	—
				B. B.D.V., size 68 × 49 mm................		£1.00	—
				C. B.D.V., size 150 × 100 mm.		£1.00	—
—		C	126	G.P. Territorial Badges (70 × 48 mm.).......	Ha.502–12	60p	£75.00
—		U	25	*Great War Leaders II (81 × 68 mm.)—Anonymous..............................	Ha.504–7	£1.60	£40.00
—		U	? 51	*Great War Leaders III and Warships, sepia, black or blue on white or pink material (70 × 50 mm.)—Anonymous...............	Ha.504–10	£2.75	—
—		C		*Great War Leaders IV and Celebrities:—	Ha.504–11		
			3	A. Small size, (70 × 48 mm.)—Anonymous .		£2.75	—
			4	B. Small size (70 × 48 mm.)—B.D.V.......		£2.75	—
			3	C. Medium size, 70 × 63 mm.—Anonymous.		£2.75	—
			2	D. Medium size (70 × 63 mm.)—B.D.V. ...		£2.75	—
			? 18	E. Extra-large size (150 × 100 mm.)—B.D.V................................		£1.70	£30.00
			? 4	F. Extra-large size, (150 × 110 mm.)—Anonymous		£2.50	£10.00
			? 1	G. Extra-large size (150 × 110 mm.)—B.D.V................................		—	£7.00
			? 26	H. Extra-large size (163 × 117 mm.)—Anonymous		£2.00	—
			? 46	I. Extra-large size (163 × 117 mm.)—B.D.V................................		£1.70	—
—		C		Heraldic Series—B.D.V.:—	Ha.504–17		
			25	A. Small size (68 × 47 mm.)		60p	£15.00
			25	B. Small size (68 × 43 mm.)		60p	£15.00
			25	C. Medium size (68 × 60 mm.)		£2.00	—
			12	D. Extra-large size (150 × 100 mm.) (selected Nos.).......................		£2.25	£27.00
—		C	10	*Irish Patriots—Anonymous:—	Ha.505–11		
				A. Small size (67 × 50 mm.).		£4.50	—
				B. Large size (83 × 76 mm.)		£5.50	—
				C. Extra-large size (152 × 110 mm.)........		£5.50	—
—		C	1	*Irish Republican Stamp (70 × 50 mm.)......	Ha.505–12	—	£1.25
—		C	54	*Naval Badges of Rank and Military Headdress (70 × 47 mm.)—Anonymous	Ha.504–9	£2.50	—
—		C	? 40	*Old Masters—Set 1 (155 × 115 mm.)—B.D.V.	Ha.503–1	£12.00	—
—		C	20	*Old Masters—Set 2 (150 × 105 mm.):—	Ha.503–2		
				A. Anonymous...........................		£2.50	£50.00
				B. B.D.V. wording above picture		£2.25	£45.00
				C. B.D.V. wording below picture		£2.50	—
—		C		*Old Masters—Set 3A (70 × 50 mm.):—	Ha.503–3A		

GODFREY PHILLIPS LTD. (continued)

Illus. No.	Size	Printing	Number in set		Handbook ref.	Price per card	Complete set
			40	A. B.D.V.		£1.25	—
			? 55	B. Anonymous		£1.25	—
—		C	30	*Old Masters—Set 3B (70 × 50 mm.)—Anonymous	Ha.503–3B	£1.25	—
—		C	120	*Old Masters—Set 4 (70 × 50 mm.)—Anonymous:—	Ha.503–4		
				Nos. 1–60		80p	£50.00
				Nos. 61–120		£1.40	—
—		C		*Old Masters—Set 5 (70 × 50 mm.):—	Ha.503–5		
			20	A. Unnumbered—Anonymous		£1.75	—
			60	B. Nd. 1–60—B.D.V.		40p	£24.00
			20	C. Nd. 101–120—Anonymous:—			
				1. Numerals normal size		80p	—
				2. Numerals very small size		60p	£12.00
			20	D. Nd. 101–120—B.D.V.		60p	£12.00
—		C	50	*Old Masters—Set 6 (67 × 42 mm.)—B.D.V.	Ha.503–6	60p	£30.00
—		C	50	*Old Masters—Set 7, Nd. 301–350 (67 × 47 mm.)—Anonymous	Ha.503–7	£1.50	£75.00
—		C	50	*Orders of Chivalry I (70 × 48 mm.)—Anonymous	Ha.504–14	£1.10	—
—		C	24	*Orders of Chivalry—Series 10 (70 × 50 mm.):—	Ha.504–16		
				A. Nd. 1–24—B.D.V.		80p	£20.00
				B. Nd. 401–424—G.P.		£1.00	£25.00
—		C	? 67	*Regimental Colours II (76 × 70 mm.)—Anonymous	Ha.502–7	£2.00	—
—		C		*Regimental Colours and Crests III:—	Ha.502–8		
				A. Small size (70 × 51 mm.):—			
			40	1. Colours with faint backgrounds—Anonymous		70p	—
			120	2. Colours without backgrounds—Anonymous		80p	—
			120	3. Colours without backgrounds—B.D.V.		80p	—
			120	B. Extra-large size (165 × 120 mm.):—			
				1. Anonymous—Unnumbered		£4.00	—
				2. B.D.V.—Numbered		£3.00	—
—		C	50	*Regimental Colours—Series 12 (70 × 50 mm.)—B.D.V.	Ha.502–11	80p	£40.00
—		C	10	*Religious Pictures—Anonymous:—	Ha.505–10		
				A. Small size (67 × 50 mm.)		£6.00	—
				B. Large size (83 × 76 mm.)		£6.00	—
				C. Extra-large size (155 × 110 mm.)		£8.00	—
—		C	75	*Town and City Arms—Series 30 (48 unnumbered, 27 numbered 49–75)—B.D.V.:—	Ha.504–13		
				A. Small size (70 × 50 mm.)		50p	—
				B. Medium size (70 × 65 mm.)		70p	—
—		C	25	*Victoria Cross Heroes I (70 × 50 mm.)—Anonymous	Ha.504–1	£4.00	—
—		C	? 24	*Victoria Cross Heroes II (70 × 50 mm.)—Anonymous	Ha.504–2	£6.00	—
—		C	90	*War Pictures (70 × 48 mm.)—Anonymous	Ha.504–8	£2.75	—

D. Miscellaneous

				B.D.V. Sports Cartons (1933–34) (several hundred)		£1.00	—
	D	BW	1	Cricket Fixture Card (Radio Luxembourg) (1936–37)		—	£3.50
				"Private Seal" Wrestling Holds (export)) (No. 15 highest seen)		£20.00	—
				Rugs (miscellaneous designs)		£8.00	—
				Stamp Cards (four colours, several wordings) For other miscellaneous items, see RB13/100		65p	—

JOHN PLAYER & SONS, Nottingham

A. Pre-1919 Issues

Illus. No.	Size	Printing	Number in set		Handbook ref.	Price per card	Complete set
	A	C	25	*Actors and Actresses (1898)	H.337	£16.00	£400.00
	D	BW	50	*Actresses	H.339	£16.00	—
	A	C	? 7	*Advertisement Cards (1893–94)	H.338	From £170.00	—
	J	C	10	Allied Cavalry or Regimental Uniforms:—	H.340		
				Allied Cavalry (1914)		£5.50	£55.00
				Regimental Uniforms		£5.50	£55.00
155	A	C	50	Arms & Armour (Apr. 1909)	H.273	£1.80	£90.00
84	A	C	25	Army Life (Oct. 1910)	H.78	80p	£20.00
	J	C	12	Artillery in Action (1917)		£2.50	£30.00
	A	C	50	Badges & Flags of British Regiments (Feb. 1904):—	H.341		
				A. Brown back, unnumbered		£2.00	£100.00
				B. Brown back, numbered		£2.00	£100.00
143	A	C	50	Badges & Flags of British Regiments:—			
				A. Green back, thick card		£2.00	£100.00
				B. Green back, thin card		£2.00	£100.00
		P	10	*Bookmarks—Authors (Size 148 × 51 mm.)	H.342	£37.00	—
82	A	C	50	British Empire Series (1904):—	H.343		
				A. Grey-white card, matt		80p	£40.00
				B. White card, semi-glossy		90p	£45.00

Illus. No.	Size	Print- ing	Number in set		Handbook ref.	Price per card	Complete set
216		C	25	British Livestock:—	H.344		
	A			Small card (June 1915)		70p	£17.50
	J			Extra-large card, brown back (May 1916) ..		£2.00	£50.00
213	A	C	50	Butterflies & Moths (Dec. 1904)............	H.80	£1.30	£65.00
45		C		Bygone Beauties:—			
	A		25	A. Small card (Jul. 1914)................		70p	£17.50
	J		10	B. Extra-large card (May 1916)		£1.70	£17.00
—		U		*Cabinet Size Pictures, 1898–1900 (220 × 140 mm.):—	Ha.476		
			10	A. Plain back		—	—
			? 5	B. Printed back		—	—
	A	C	20	Castles, Abbeys etc. (? 1894–5):—	H.345		
				A. Without border		£20.00	£400.00
				B. White border......................		£20.00	£400.00
	A	C	50	Celebrated Bridges (Nov. 1903)	H.346	£1.80	£90.00
43	A	C		Celebrated Gateways (Jul. 1909):—	H.347		
			50	A. Thick card		80p	£40.00
			25	B. Thinner card (26–50 only)		£1.00	—
11	A	C	25	Ceremonial and Court Dress (May 1911)....	H.145	70p	£17.50
174		C		Characters from Dickens:—			
	A		25	Small card, 1st series (Mar. 1912)		70p	£17.50
	J		10	Extra large card (Oct. 1912)	H.348	£1.40	£14.00
15	A	C	25	Characters from Dickens, 2nd Series (Jun. 1914)............................		70p	£17.50
256	A	C	25	Characters from Thackeray (Jul. 1913)		70p	£17.50
	A	C	50	Cities of the World:—		—	£175.00
				A. Grey-mauve on white back		£3.50	—
				B. Grey-mauve on toned back		£3.50	—
				C. Bright mauve on white back		£3.50	—
8	A	C	25	Colonial & Indian Army Badges (Jun. 1916).		60p	£15.00
171	A	C	25	*Counties and Their Industries:—	H.349		
				A. Unnumbered (? 1910).................		70p	£17.50
				B. Numbered (Jul. 1914)		70p	£17.50
177	A	C	50	*Countries—Arms and Flags:—			
				A. Thick card (Oct. 1905)................		32p	£16.00
				B. Thin card (Jun. 1912)		32p	£16.00
283	A	C	50	*Country Seats and Arms (Jun. 1906)		45p	£22.50
	A	C		*Country Seats and Arms, 2nd Series (Jan. 1907):—			
			25	A. Nd. 51–75 First Printing..............		£1.00	£25.00
			50	B. Nd. 51–100 Second printing		45p	£22.50
	A	C	50	*Country Seats and Arms, 3rd Series (Jun. 1907)............................		45p	£22.50
170		C		Cries of London:—	H.350		
	A		25	Small cards, 1st Series (Apr. 1913)		90p	£22.50
	J		10	Extra large cards, 1st Series (Oct. 1912).....		£2.00	£20.00
	J		10	Extra large cards, 2nd Series (Apr. 1914) ...		£1.60	£16.00
	A	C	25	Cries of London (2nd Series) (Nov. 1916 and 1922)............................		60p	£15.00
160	A	C	25	Egyptian Kings & Queens, and Classical Deities (Jun. 1911)		60p	£15.00
	J	C	10	Egyptian Sketches (Jun. 1915)	H.351	£3.00	£30.00
	A	C	25	*England's Military Heroes (1898–9):—	H.352		
				A. Wide card........................		£28.00	—
				A1. Wide card plain back..................		£18.00	—
				B. Narrow card		£18.00	—
				B2. Narrow card, plain back...............		£18.00	—
	A	C	25	England's Naval Heroes (1897–8):—	H.353		
				A. Wide card.........................		£28.00	—
				B. Narrow card		£18.00	—
	A	C	25	England's Naval Heroes (1898–9), descrip- tions on back:—	H.353		
				A. Wide card		£28.00	—
				A2. Wide card, plain back		£18.00	—
				B. Narrow card.......................		£18.00	£450.00
				B2. Narrow card, plain back...............		£18.00	—
	A	C	25	Everyday Phrases by Tom Browne (1901):—	H.354		
				A. Thick card		£10.00	£250.00
				B. Thin card		£10.00	£250.00
		C	20	Famous Authors and Poets (1902–3):—			
	A			A. Wide card........................		£16.00	£320.00
				B. Narrow card		£11.00	£220.00
	J	C	10	Famous Paintings (Jun. 1913, reprint 1914)..	H.355	£2.70	£27.00
	A	C	50	Fishes of the World (Feb. 1903).............	H.66	£1.80	£90.00
	A	C		Gallery of Beauty (? 1896):—	H.356		
				A. Wide card:—			
				I. Set of 50......................		£16.00	£800.00
				II. 5 Alternative Pictures		£50.00	—
				B. Narrow Card:—			
				I. Set of 50		£15.00	—
				II. 5 Alternative Pictures		—	—
166	A	C	25	Gems of British Scenery (Sep. 1914).........		50p	£12.50
	A	C	25	Highland Clans (Sep. 1908 reprint 1914).....		£1.80	£45.00
	J	C	10	Historic Ships (Oct. 1910):—			
				A. Thick card		£2.70	£27.00
				B. Thin card		£3.00	£30.00
3	A	C	50	Life on Board a Man of War in 1805 and 1905 (Oct. 1905)	H.38	£1.60	£80.00
	A	C	50	Military Series (1900–01)		£12.00	£600.00

Illus. No.	Size	Print-ing	Number in set		Handbook ref.	Price per card	Complete set
	A	C	25	Miniatures (Dec. 1916, re-issue Jun. 1923)...		28p	£7.00
111	A	C	25	Napoleon (Sep. 1915)	H.364	90p	£22.50
269		C		Nature Series:—			
	A		50	Small card (June 1908)		80p	£40.00
	J		10	Extra large card (Birds) (Oct. 1908)		£12.00	—
	J		10	Extra large card (Animals) (Oct. 1913)		£4.00	£40.00
	A	C	50	Old England's Defenders		£12.00	£600.00
	A	C	25	Players—Past & Present (May 1916, re-issue 1923)........................		40p	£10.00
265	A	C	25	Polar Exploration (Jun. 1911).............		70p	£17.50
277	A	C	25	Polar Exploration, 2nd Series (? 1915).......		70p	£17.50
320	A	C	25	Products of the World:—			
				A. Thick card (May 1909)		44p	£11.00
				B. Thin card (Feb. 1908)...............		50p	£12.50
280	A	C	50	*Regimental Colours and Cap Badges (Oct. 1907)........................		70p	£35.00
52	A	C	50	*Regimental Colours and Cap Badges—Territorial Regiments (May 1910):—			
				A. Blue back......................		70p	£35.00
				B. Brown back.....................		70p	£35.00
	J	C	10	Regimental Uniforms—See "Allied Cavalry".			
232	A	C	50	Regimental Uniforms (1–50):—			
				A. Blue back (Jul. 1912)		90p	£45.00
				B. Brown back (Jul. 1914)		£1.20	£60.00
117	A	C	50	Regimental Uniforms (51–100) (Jul. 1914)...		80p	£40.00
131	A	C	50	Riders of the World:—	H.358		
				A. Thick grey card (Jan. 1905)		80p	£40.00
				B. Thinner white card (Jul. 1914).........		80p	£40.00
	—	P	6	The Royal Family (1902) (101 × 154 mm.)...	H.359	—	£140.00
	—	P	? 22	Rulers and Views (101x154mm.).........	H.363/Ha.363	£45.00	—
278	A	C	25	Shakespearean Series (Jul. 1914, re-issue 1916)........................		50p	£12.50
5	A	C	25	Ships' Figureheads (Oct. 1912):—			
				A. Numerals "sans serif"		80p	£20.00
				B. Numerals with serif		70p	£17.50
	A	BW	? 47	Stereoscopic Series	H.357	£20.00	
281	A	C	25	Those Pearls of Heaven (Jul. 1914).........		50p	£12.50
	A	BW	66	Transvaal Series (1903–4):—	H.360		
				A. Black front......................		£2.60	—
				B. Violet-black front		£2.60	—
	A	C	50	Useful Plants & Fruit (Apr. 1904)...........	H.361	£1.80	£90.00
86	A	C	25	Victoria Cross (Jun. 1914)		80p	£20.00
	A	C		Wild Animals of the World (Sep. 1902):—	H.77		
			50	A. "John Player & Sons Ltd."		£2.20	£110.00
			50	B. "John Player & Sons, Branch, Nottingham"....................		£2.50	—
			50	C. As B, "Branch" omitted...........		—	—
				C1. As B. "Branch" omitted but showing traces of some or all of the letters ...		£3.50	—
			50	C2. As B. New printing with "Branch" omitted....................		£2.20	£110.00
	A1	C	45	Wild Animals of the World, narrow card:—	H.77		
				A. "John Player & Sons Ltd."		£3.50	£160.00
				B. "John Player & Sons, Branch, Nottingham"....................		£3.50	—
				C. As B, "Branch" omitted...........		—	—
				C1. As B. "Branch" omitted but show-ing traces of some or all of the letters.....................		£4.50	—
				C2. As B. New printing with "Branch" omitted		£3.50	£160.00
286	A	C	50	Wonders of the Deep (Aug. 1904)...........	H.365	£1.20	£60.00
121	A	C	25	Wonders of the World, blue back (Oct. 1913)	H.362	40p	£10.00
	J	C	10	Wooden Walls (May 1909):—			
				A. Thick card......................		£3.00	£30.00
				B. Thin card......................		£3.00	£30.00
87	A	C	25	Wrestling and Ju-Jitsu (blue back) (Jan. 1911)	H.467	60p	£15.00

B. Post-1920 Issues. Series with I.T.C. Clause. For export issues see RB21.

		C	1	*Advertisement Card (Sailor):—			
				A. Small size.....................		—	£3.00
				B. Large size.....................		—	£18.00
	A	C	50	Aeroplanes (see RB21/217/6):—			
				A. Home issue (Aug. 1935)—titled "Aeroplanes (Civil)"		20p	£10.00
				B. Irish issue (July 1935)—titled "Aeroplanes".....................		35p	£17.50
	A	C	50	Aircraft of the Royal Air Force (Aug. 1938) (see RB17/7)........................		16p	£8.00
	A	C	50	Animals of the Countryside (Aug. 1939) (see RB17/9):—			
				A. Home issue—adhesive................		13p	£5.50
				B. Irish issue—non-adhesive, green numerals overprinted.................		40p	—
	B	C	25	Aquarium Studies (Sept. 1932).............		80p	£20.00
	B	C	25	Architectural Beauties (Nov. 1927).........		80p	£20.00
176	A	C	50	Army, Corps & Divisional Signs, 1914–1918 (Mar. 1924)...........................		15p	£7.50

Illus. No.	Size	Print- ing	Number in set		Handbook ref.	Price per card	Complete set
	A	C	100	Army, Corps & Divisional Signs, 1914–1918, "2nd Series" (Feb. 1925):—			
				Nos. 51–100		15p	£7.50
				Nos. 101–150		15p	£7.50
	A	U	50	Association Cup Winners (Jan. 1930)		32p	£16.00
		C		Aviary and Cage Birds:—			
	A		50	A. Small size (Aug. 1933):—			
				1. Cards		22p	£11.00
				2. Transfers......................		13p	£5.00
	B		25	B. Large size (Feb. 1935)		70p	£17.50
97	A	C	50	Birds & Their Young (1937) (see RB17/23):—			
				A. Home issue—adhesive.............		13p	£4.50
				B. Irish issue—1. Adhesive		60p	—
				2. Non-adhesive................		60p	—
	A	C	25	Boxing (May 1934)....................		£1.20	£30.00
	A	C	50	Boy Scout & Girl Guide Patrol Signs & Emblems (Jan. 1933):—			
				A. Cards...........................		13p	£6.00
				B. Transfers		13p	£5.00
	B	C	25	British Butterflies (Jan. 1934)		70p	£17.50
	J	C	25	British Live Stock (blue back) (1923)	H.344	90p	£22.50
	B	C	25	British Naval Craft (Feb. 1939)		20p	£5.00
	J	C	20	British Pedigree Stock (Nov. 1925).........		90p	£18.00
	B	C	25	British Regalia (Mar. 1937).................		40p	£10.00
96	A	C	50	Butterflies (Mar. 1932):—			
				A. Cards...........................		35p	£17.50
				B. Transfers		13p	£5.00
	B	C	24	Cats (Mar. 1936).........................		£1.75	£42.00
	B	C	25	Championship Golf Courses (Jan. 1936).....		70p	£17.50
	A	C	50	Characters from Dickens (Nov. 1923)	H.348	40p	£20.00
	B	C	25	Characters from Fiction (Oct. 1933).........		80p	£20.00
	B	C	20	Clocks—Old & New (Aug. 1928)...........		£1.60	£32.00
	A	C	50	Coronation Series Ceremonial Dress (Mar. 1937) (see RB17/53)...................		13p	£6.50
	B	C	25	Country Sports (Sept. 1930)		60p	£15.00
136	A	C	50	Cricketers, 1930 (June 1930)		45p	£22.50
	A	C	50	Cricketers, 1934 (May 1934)		22p	£11.00
	A	C	50	Cricketers, 1938 (June 1938) (see RB17/62) ..		13p	£6.50
316	A	C	50	Cricketers, Caricatures by "Rip" (June 1926)		60p	£30.00
	A	C	50	Curious Beaks (Oct. 1929).................		17p	£8.50
	A	C	50	Cycling (May 1939) (see RB17/67):—			
				A. Home issue—adhesive.............		13p	£6.00
				B. Irish issue—1. Adhesive		60p	—
				2 Non-adhesive		60p	—
		C		Dandies:—			
	A		50	A. Small size (July 1932).................		13p	£6.50
	B		25	B. Large size (May 1932)		30p	£7.50
	A	C	50	Derby and Grand National Winners (Apr. 1933):—			
				A. Cards...........................		36p	£18.00
				B. Transfers		13p	£5.00
		C		Dogs (1924–5)—Scenic backgrounds (see RB17/71):—			
	A		50	A. Small size......................		18p	£9.00
	J		12	B. Extra-large size		70p	£8.50
40		C		Dogs (1926–29)—Heads (see RB17/72):—			
	A		50	A. Small size—Home issue (Apr. 1929)....		26p	£13.00
	A		25	B. Small size—Irish issue, "A Series of 25" (Apr. 1927)		80p	£20.00
	A		25	C. Small size—Irish issue, "2nd Series of 25" (Dec. 1929)		80p	£20.00
	B		20	D. Large size—Home issue, "A Series of 20" (Dec. 1926)		£1.00	£20.00
	B		20	E. Large size—Home issue, "2nd Series of 20" (May 1928)		90p	£18.00
		C		Dogs (1931–33)—Full length:—			
	A		50	A. Small size (Sept. 1931):—			
				1. Cards		15p	£7.50
				2. Transfers......................		13p	£5.00
	B		25	B. Large size (May 1933)		70p	£17.50
	A	C	50	Dogs' Heads (silver-grey backgrounds) (Aug. 1940)................................		80p	—
	A	C	50	Drum Banners & Cap Badges (Sept. 1924):—			
				A. Base panel joining vertical framelines...		36p	£18.00
				B. Fractional space between the above		32p	£16.00
	B	BW	25	Fables of Aesop (Mar. 1927)................		£1.00	£25.00
	B	C	25	Famous Beauties (Sept. 1937) (see RB17/86).		26p	£6.50
266	A	C	50	Famous Irish-Bred Horses (Nov. 1936)......		80p	£40.00
	A	C	50	Famous Irish Greyhounds (Mar. 1935).......		90p	£45.00
	A	C	50	Film Stars—"Series of 50" (Mar. 1934)......		36p	£18.00
	A	C	50	Film Stars—"Second Series ...":—			
				A. Home issue—Album "price one penny" (Dec. 1934)		22p	£11.00
				B. Irish issue—Album offer without price (Nov. 1935)......................		60p	£30.00
30	A	C	50	Film Stars (see RB17/92):—			
				A. Home issue—titled "Film Stars—Third Series..." (Nov. 1938)		15p	£7.50
				B. Irish issue—titled "Screen Celebrities" (Jan. 1939)........................		90p	—

Illus. No.	Size	Printing	Number in set		Handbook ref.	Price per card	Complete set
	B	BW	25	Film Stars—Large size (Nov. 1934):—			
				A. Home issue—with album offer		90p	£22.50
				B. Irish issue—without album offer		£1.20	—
268	A	C	50	Fire-Fighting Appliances (Dec. 1930)		40p	£20.00
258	A	C	50	Flags of the League of Nations (Mar. 1928)..		18p	£9.00
	A	C	50	Football Caricatures by "Mac" (Sep. 1927)..		17p	£8.50
144	A	C	50	Football Caricatures by "Rip" (Aug. 1926) ..		17p	£8.50
241	A	C	50	Footballers, 1928 (Oct. 1928)		28p	£14.00
233	A	C	25	Footballers, 1928–9—"2nd Series" (Feb. 1929)...................		44p	£11.00
		C		Fresh-Water Fishes:—			
	A		50	A. Small size, Home issue—			
				1. Pink card (Nov. 1933)..............		25p	£12.50
				2. White card (Feb. 1934).............		40p	£20.00
	B		25	B. Large size, Home issue—adhesive (June 1935)................		70p	£17.50
	B		25	C. Large size, Irish issue—non-adhesive...		£1.50	—
346	A	C	25	From Plantation to Smoker (Mar. 1926).....		26p	£6.50
		C		Game Birds and Wild Fowl (see RB21/217/105):—			
	A		50	A. Small size (June 1927)		32p	£16.00
	B		25	B. Large size (Nov. 1928)...............		£1.40	£35.00
		C		Gilbert and Sullivan—"A Series of ...":—			
1	A		50	A. Small size (Dec. 1925)		30p	£15.00
	J		25	B. Extra-large size (Apr. 1926)...........		£1.00	£25.00
		C		Gilbert and Sullivan—"2nd Series of ...":—			
	A		50	A. Small size (Dec. 1927)		22p	£11.00
	B		25	B. Large size (Jan. 1928)................		£1.00	£25.00
	B	C	25	Golf (July 1939) (see RB17/109)............		80p	£20.00
	A	C	25	Hidden Beauties (July 1929)		16p	£4.00
	A	C	50	Hints on Association Football (Sep. 1934) (see RB21/217/112)		25p	£12.50
		C		History of Naval Dress:—			
	A		50	A. Small size (Sep. 1930).................		32p	£16.00
	B		25	B. Large size (July 1929)................		90p	£22.50
	A	C	50	International Air Liners (see RB17/116):—			
				A. Home issue—Album "price one penny" (Nov. 1936)......................		17p	£8.50
				B. Irish issue—Album offer without price (July 1937)......................		45p	£22.50
	A	C	25	Irish Place Names—"A Series of 25" (Aug. 1927).............................		90p	£22.50
	A	C	25	Irish Place Names—"2nd Series of 25" (Apr. 1929).............................		90p	£22.50
162		C	50	Kings & Queens of England:—			
	A			A. Small size (Apr. 1935)		35p	£17.50
	B			B. Large size (Sep. 1935)...............		80p	£40.00
	A	C	25	Live Stock (Aug. 1925)		£1.20	£30.00
309	A	C	50	Military Head-Dress (Mar. 1931)		40p	£20.00
	A	C	50	Military Uniforms of the British Empire Overseas (Feb. 1938) (see RB17/126)......		17p	£8.50
	A	C	50	Modern Naval Craft (see RB17/129):—			
				A. Home issue—adhesive (Feb. 1939)		13p	£4.50
				B. Irish issue—non-adhesive (Aug. 1939)..		40p	—
	A	C	50	Motor Cars—"A Series of 50" (see RB17/130):—			
				A. Home issue—Album "price one penny" (Mar. 1936)......................		45p	£22.50
				B. Irish issue—Album offer without price (July 1936)......................		80p	£40.00
	A	C	50	Motor Cars—"Second Series ..." (May 1937) (see RB17/131)...................		32p	£16.00
	B	U	20	Mount Everest (June 1925)		£1.40	£28.00
	A	C	50	National Flags and Arms (see RB17/134):—			
				A. Home issue—Album "price one penny" (Sep. 1936).......................		13p	£6.00
				B. Irish issue—Album offer without price (Mar. 1937)......................		40p	£20.00
	B	C	25	The Nation's Shrines (Oct. 1929) (see RB17/135)......................		90p	£22.50
		C		Natural History:—			
	A		50	A. Small size (June 1924)		15p	£7.50
	J		12	B. Extra-large size—"A Series of 12" (Nov. 1923)..........................		90p	£11.00
	J		12	C. Extra-large size—"2nd Series of 12" (Sep. 1924)......................		90p	£11.00
139	B	C	24	A Nature Calendar (Apr. 1930)		£1.10	£27.00
	B	C	25	"Old Hunting Prints" (Feb. 1938) (see RB17/140)......................		80p	£20.00
48	B	C	25	Old Naval Prints (Oct. 1936) (see RB17/141).		90p	£22.50
	J	BW	25	Old Sporting Prints (Dec. 1924)............		£1.00	£25.00
	B	C	25	Picturesque Bridges (Feb. 1929)............		90p	£22.50
371	B	C	25	Picturesque Cottages (Dec. 1929)		90p	£22.50
369	B	C	25	Picturesque London (Sep. 1931)		£1.00	£25.00
	B	C	25	Portals of the Past (Dec. 1930)		80p	£20.00
108	A	C	50	Poultry (Dec. 1931):—			
				A. Cards.....................		32p	£16.00
				B. Transfers		13p	£5.00
	A	C	50	Products of the World—Scenes only (June 1928) (see RB21/200/294)		15p	£7.50

Illus. No.	Size	Printing	Number in set		Handbook ref.	Price per card	Complete set
	A	C	25	Racehorses (Dec. 1926)...............		£1.60	£40.00
	A	U	40	Racing Caricatures (Aug. 1925)...........		32p	£13.00
	B	C	25	Racing Yachts (July 1938) (see RB17/159)...		40p	£10.00
	A	C	50	R.A.F. Badges (Nov. 1937) (see RB17/160):—			
				A. Without motto......................		15p	£7.50
				B. With motto........................		17p	£8.50
267	A	C	50	Regimental Standards and Cap Badges (Mar. 1930)................................		40p	£20.00
	—	C	1	The Royal Family (Mar. 1937) (85 × 66 mm.)		—	£1.00
				Screen Celebrities—see Film Stars			
	A	C	50	Sea Fishes (see RB17/172):—			
				A. Home issue—Album "price one penny" (Nov. 1935).......................		13p	£6.50
				B. Irish issue—Album offer without price (Dec. 1937)		60p	—
	A	C	50	A Sectional Map of Ireland		£1.20	£60.00
	B	C	20	Ship-Models (Sep. 1926).................		£1.40	£28.00
	B	C	25	Ships' Figure-Heads (Dec. 1931)...........		90p	£22.50
184	A	C	50	Speedway Riders (Aug. 1937).............		40p	£20.00
	A	C	50	Straight Line Caricatures (Dec. 1926)		25p	£12.50
	A	C	25	Struggle for Existence (Feb. 1923):—			
				A. With comma in I.T.C. Clause, back chocolate-brown		24p	£6.00
				B. Without comma, back reddish-brown ..		24p	£6.00
	A	C	50	Tennis (July 1936).....................		13p	£6.00
	B	C	25	Treasures of Britain (Apr. 1931)		50p	£12.50
	A	C	25	Treasures of Ireland (May 1930)		£1.00	£25.00
	B	C	25	Types of Horses (Feb. 1939) (see RB17/190) .		70p	£17.50
	A	C	50	Uniforms of the Territorial Army (Oct. 1939)		16p	£8.00
	A	C	90	War Decorations & Medals (Mar. 1927).....		40p	£36.00
		C		Wild Animals (see RB17/196):—			
	A		50	A. Small size—"Wild Animals' Heads" (Jan.–June 1931)		15p	£7.50
	A		25	B. Small transfers, number in series not stated (1931)		70p	—
	A		50	C. Small transfers—"A Series of 50" (1931)		13p	£5.00
	B		25	D. Large size—"Wild Animals—A Series of ..." (July 1927)..................		£1.00	£25.00
	B		25	E. Large size—"Wild Animals—2nd Series ..." (Dec. 1932).....................		80p	£20.00
		C		Wild Birds:—			
	A		50	A. Small size (Oct. 1932):—			
				1. Cards		15p	£7.50
				2. Transfers........................		13p	£5.00
	B		25	B. Large size (June 1934)		80p	£20.00
	B	C	25	Wild Fowl (June 1937)		80p	£20.00
	A	C	25	Wonders of the World (grey back) (Aug. 1926)................................	H.362	60p	£15.00
	A	C	25	Wrestling & Ju-Jitsu (grey back) (May 1925).	H.467	70p	£17.50
	A	C	26	Your Initials (transfers) (July–Dec. 1932)		20p	£5.00
366	B	C	25	Zoo Babies (Oct. 1938) (see RB17/205)		24p	£6.00

C. Post-1940 Issues

	—	BW	9	Basket Ball Fixtures (1972) (114×71 mm.)...		80p	—
	—	C	32	Britain's Endangered Wildlife (90×50 mm.) .			
				A. Grandee Issue (1984)..............		—	—
				B. Doncella Issue (1984)..............		—	—
91	—	C	32	British Birds (1980) (89×50 mm.)..........		20p	£6.00
	—	C	32	British Butterflies (90×50 mm.):—			
				A. Grandee Issue (1983)..............		20p	£6.00
				B. Doncella Issue (1984)..............		—	—
351	—	C	30	British Mammals (90×50 mm.):—			
				A. Grandee Issue (1982)..............		20p	£6.00
				B. Doncella Issue (1983)..............		20p	£6.00
92	—	C	32	Country Houses and Castles (90×50 mm.) .. (1981).............................		20p	£6.00
	—	U	116	Corsair Game (63×38 mm.) (Player/Wills Joint issue).........................		50p	—
	—	C	32	Exploration of Space (75×56 mm.) (1983)...		20p	£6.00
	—	C	28	Famous MG Marques (90×50 mm.) (1981)		10p	£3.00
	—	C	24	The Golden Age of Flying (1977) (89×50 mm.)................................		10p	£2.50
	—	C	1	The Golden Age of Flying Completion Offer		—	40p
	—	C	24	The Golden Age of Motoring (1975) (89×50 mm.):—			
				A. With set completion offer...........		70p	—
				B. Without set completion offer.........		08p	£2.00
	—	C	24	The Golden Age of Sail (1978) (89×50 mm.)		10p	£2.50
	—	C	1	The Golden Age of Sail Completion Offer		—	40p
	—	C	24	The Golden Age of Steam (1976) (89×50 mm.)		08p	£2.00
	—	C	1	The Golden Age of Steam Completion Offer		—	40p
	—	U	7	Grandee Limericks (1977) (86×50 mm.)		80p	—
	—	C	24	History of the VC (1980) (89×50 mm.)		24p	£6.00
	—	BW	5	Jubilee Issue 1960 (70×55 mm.)...........		60p	£3.00
	—	C	30	The Living Ocean (1985) (90×50 mm.)		—	—
	—	C	32	Myths and Legends (72×57 mm.) (1982)....		20p	£6.00
	—	C	24	Napoleonic Uniforms (1979) (89×50 mm.) ..		10p	£2.50
	—	C	1	Napoleonic Uniforms Completion Offer ...		—	40p
	—	C	8	Panama Puzzles (89×50 mm.).............		£1.00	—
	—	BW	6	Play Ladbroke Spot-Ball (1975) (90×50 mm.)		£1.00	—

Illus. No.	Size	Print-ing	Number in set		Handbook ref.	Price per card	Complete set
—	U		4	Tom Thumb Record Breakers (82×65 mm.) (1976).............................		£1.00	—
—	C		25	Top Dogs (1979) (89×57 mm.).............		24p	£6.00
—	C		32	Wonders of the Ancient World (72×57 mm.) (1984).................................		—	—
—	C		30	Wonders of the Modern World (72×57 mm.) (1985).................................		—	—
—	C		6	World of Gardening (1976) (90×50 mm.) ...		£1.00	—

D. Unissued Series

	A	C	25	Birds & Their Young, 1st series		13p	£1.50
	A	C	25	Birds & Their Young, 2nd series		13p	£1.50
	A	C	50	Civil Aircraft (Prepared but not issued)......		—	—
	A	C	25	Cries of London, "2nd Series ..." (black back)...............................		£4.50	—
	A	C	50	Decorations & Medals		£1.30	£65.00
	A	C	50	Dogs' Heads by Biegel.....................		13p	£4.50
	B	C	25	Dogs—Pairs and Groups...................		28p	£7.00
	A	C	25	Napoleon (black back)	H.364	—	—
	A	C	50	Products of the World—Scenes only (black back).................................		—	—
	A	C	50	Shipping..................................		90p	£45.00
	A	C	50	Wonders of the Deep (black back)	H.365	—	—
	A	C	25	Wonders of the World (black back)		—	—

E. Miscellaneous

	A1	U	1	Advertisement Insert Grosvenor Cigarettes (1970).................................		—	£0.90
	A	C	1	Card Scheme—Joker Card (?1930's)		—	£3.50
	—	C	?	Football Fixture Folders (1946–61)		£4.00	—
	—	C	8	Snap Cards (93 × 65 mm.) (1930's)		£6.50	—

F. Reprint Series by "Nostalgia"

	A	C	50	Military Series 1900 (1983)		—	£6.00

JAS. PLAYFAIR & CO., London

Pre-1919 Issue

	A	C	25	How to Keep Fit—Sandow Exercises	H.136	£20.00	—

THE PREMIER TOBACCO MANUFACTURERS LTD., London

Post-1920 Issues

	D	U	48	Eminent Stage & Screen Personalities (1936).	Ha.569	£1.20	—
	—	BW		Stage & Screen Personalities (1937) (57 × 35 mm.):—			
			100	A. Back in grey		80p	—
			50	B. Back in brown (Nos. 51–100)		80p	—

PRITCHARD & BURTON LTD., London

Pre-1919 Issues

	A2	C	50	*Actors and Actresses—"FROGA B and C":—	H.20/Ha.20		
				A. Blue back...........................		£13.00	—
				B. Grey-black back		£18.00	—
	A	C	15	*Beauties—"PAC"..........................	H.2	£30.00	—
	D	BW	20	*Boer War Cartoons (1900).................	H.42/Ha.42	£50.00	—
	A1	C		*Flags and Flags with Soldiers:—	H.41		
				A. Flagstaff Draped:			
			30	1st printing		£8.00	£240.00
			15	2nd printing.........................		£12.00	£180.00
			15	B. Flagstaff not Draped (Flags only)		£10.00	—
	D	U	25	*Holiday Resorts and Views.................	H.366	£8.00	—
	A	C	40	*Home and Colonial Regiments:—	H.69		
				20. Caption in blue		£35.00	—
				20. Caption in brown		£35.00	—
	D	U	25	*Royalty Series (1902)...................	H.367	£11.00	—
	A2	C	25	*Star Girls................................	H.30	£90.00	—
	D	U	25	*South African Series (1901)................	H.368	£8.00	—

G. PRUDHOE, Darlington

Pre-1919 Issues

	C	C	30	*Army Pictures, Cartoons, etc................	Ha.12	—	—

JAMES QUINTON LTD., London

Pre-1919 Issue

	A	C	26	*Actresses—"FROGA A"....................	H.20	—	—

RAY & CO. LTD., London

Pre-1919 Issues

	A	BW	25	War Series—1–25—Battleships		£9.00	—
	A	C	75	War Series—26–100—British & Foreign Uniforms.................................		£7.50	—
	A	C	25	War Series—101–125—British & Dominion Uniforms.................................		£14.00	—

RAYMOND REVUEBAR, London

Illus. No.	Size	Print-ing	Number in set		Handbook ref.	Price per card	Complete set
Post-1940 Issue		P	25	Revuebar Striptease Artists (1960) (72 × 46 mm.)		£5.00	—

RECORD CIGARETTE CO., London

Post 1920 Issue		U	? 25	The "Talkie" Cigarette Card—Variety Series of 25 (gramophone record on reverse) (70 mm. square)		£24.00	—

J. REDFORD & CO., London

Pre-1919 Issues							
	A	BW	20	*Actresses—"BLARM"	H.23	£45.00	—
	A2	C	25	*Armies of the World	H.43	£45.00	—
	A2	C	25	*Beauties—"GRACC"	H.59	£80.00	—
	A2	C	30	*Colonial Troops	H.40	£40.00	—
	D2	C	40	*Naval and Military Phrases	H.14	£26.00	—
	D	C	? 23	*Nautical Expressions	H.174	£80.00	—
	A	C	25	Picture Series	H.369	£24.00	—
	A	C	25	Sports & Pastimes Series 1	H.225	—	—
	D1	BW	50	Stage Artistes of the Day	H.370	£5.00	£250.00

RELIANCE TOBACCO MFG. CO. LTD.

Post-1920 Issues							
	A2	C	24	British Birds	Ha.604	£2.20	£55.00
	A2	C	35	*Famous Stars*	Ha.572	£2.20	£75.00

RICHARDS & WARD

Pre-1919 Issue							
	A1	P	? 2	*Beauties "Topsy Cigarettes"	H.371	£125.00	—

THE RICHMOND CAVENDISH CO. LTD., London

Pre-1919 Issues							
	A2	C	26	*Actresses—"FROGA A"	H.20	£16.00	—
	D2	BW	28	*Actresses—"PILPI I"	H.195	£8.00	—
	D	P	50	*Actresses—"PILPI II"	H.196	£6.00	—
	A	U		*Actresses Photogravure, "Smoke Pioneer Cigarettes" back:—	H.372/Ha.372		
			50	I. Reading bottom to top		£4.50	£225.00
			?164	IIA. Reading top to bottom. Different Subjects		£4.50	—
			? 13	B. Plain back		—	—
	A	C	14	*Beauties "AMBS" (1899–1900):	H.373		
				A. Verses "The Absent-minded Beggar" back (4 verses and 4 choruses)		£26.00	—
				B. Verses "Soldiers of the Queen" back (3 verses and 1 chorus)		£26.00	—
	A	C	52	*Beauties—"ROBRI" playing card inset	H.374	£26.00	—
	—	C	40	*Medals (34 × 72 mm.)	H.200	£9.00	£360.00
	A2	C	20	Music Hall Artistes	H.202	£16.00	£320.00
	A	C	12	*Pretty Girl Series—"RASH":—	H.8		
				i. 1–6 Head and Shoulders		£22.00	£130.00
				ii. 7–12 Full length		£22.00	£130.00
	A	C	20	*Yachts:—	H.204		
				A. Gold on black back		£32.00	—
				B. Black on white back		£32.00	—

R. ROBERTS & SONS, London

Pre-1919 Issues							
	A2	C	26	*Actresses—"FROGA A"	H.20	£45.00	—
	A	C	25	*Armies of the World:—	H.43		
				A. "Fine Old Virginia" back		£27.00	—
				B. Plain back		£22.00	—
	A2	C	50	*Beauties—"CHOAB":—	H.21		
				1–25 without borders to back		£65.00	—
				26–50 with borders to back		£85.00	—
	A2	C	50	*Colonial Troops:—	H.40		
				1–30 "Fine Old Virginia"		£15.00	—
				31–50 "Bobs Cigarettes"		£25.00	—
	A	BW	28	*Dominoes		£80.00	—
	K1	C	52	*Miniature Playing Cards	H.334/Ha.334	—	—
	D2	C	? 23	*Nautical Expressions:—	H.174		
				A. "Navy Cut Cigarettes" on front		£45.00	—
				B. Firm's name only on front		£50.00	—
	A2	C	70	Stories without words—10 sets of 7 cards:— per card and per set of 7		£25.00	—
	A2	C	25	*Types of British and Colonial Troops	H.76/Ha.76	£35.00	—

ROBINSON & BARNSDALE LTD., London

Illus. No.	Size	Print-ing	Number in set		Handbook ref.	Price per card	Complete set
Pre-1919 Issues							
—		C	1	*Advertisement Card—Soldier, "Colin Campbell Cigars" (29 × 75 mm.).........		—	£65.00
—		BW	? 19	*Actresses, "Colin Campbell Cigars":—	H.375		
				A. Size—43 × 70 mm.....................		£60.00	—
				B. Officially cut narrow—32 × 70 mm......		£50.00	—
A	P		? 14	*Actresses, "Cupola" Cigarettes	H.376	£95.00	—
A1	P		? 13	*Beauties—collotype:—	H.377		
				A. "Our Golden Beauties" back in black ..		—	—
				B. "Nana" back in red on white..........		—	—
				C. "Nana" back in vermillion on cream ...		—	—
A	C		? 1	*Beauties—"Blush of Day"...................	H.378	—	—
—	C		? 4	*Beauties—"Highest Honors" (44 × 73 plus— i.e. card probably cut), "Virginia Crown" label on back	H.379/Ha.379	—	—

E. ROBINSON & SONS LTD., Stockport

Illus. No.	Size	Print-ing	Number in set		Handbook ref.	Price per card	Complete set
A. Pre-1919 Issues							
A1	C		10	*Beauties—"ROBRI".......................	H.374	£40.00	—
A	BW		? 4	Derbyshire and the Peak...................	H.380	—	—
A2	C		25	Egyptian Studies..........................		£12.00	£300.00
A	C		? 6	Medals and Decorations of Great Britain....	Ha.484	—	—
A2	C		40	Nature Studies...........................		£10.00	£400.00
A2	C		25	Regimental Mascots (1916).................		£35.00	—
A2	C		25	Wild Flowers		£9.00	£225.00
B. Post-1920 Issue							
A	C		25	King Lud Problems		£11.00	—

ROTHMAN'S LTD., London

Illus. No.	Size	Print-ing	Number in set		Handbook ref.	Price per card	Complete set
A. Post-1920 Issues							
		C		Beauties of the Cinema (1939):—	Ha.605		
	D1		40	A. Small size...........................		35p	£14.00
	—		24	B. Circular cards, 64 mm. diam.:—			
				1. Varnished		70p	£17.50
				2. Unvarnished		60p	£15.00
154	A2	P	24	Cinema Stars—Small size.................		40p	£10.00
	B	P	25	Cinema Stars—Large size		14p	£3.50
	C	U	36	Landmarks in Empire History		30p	£11.00
	D1	U	50	Modern Inventions (1935).................		35p	£17.50
	B2	P	54	New Zealand		50p	£27.00
331	D1	U	24	Prominent Screen Favourites (1934).........	Ha.568	28p	£7.00
	A2	BW	50	"Punch Jokes"..........................		13p	£6.00
B. Post-1940 Issues							
—		C	30	Country Living (Consulate) (112 × 102 mm.) (1973).................................		—	£10.00
A1	C		5	Rare Banknotes (1970)		90p	£4.50
C. Miscellaneous							
—		C	6	Diamond Jubilee Folders (1950) (127 × 95 mm.).................................		—	—
		?		Metal Charms		£1.20	—

WM. RUDDELL LTD., Dublin and Liverpool

Illus. No.	Size	Print-ing	Number in set		Handbook ref.	Price per card	Complete set
Post-1920 Issues							
	D	C	25	Grand Opera Series (1924).................		£2.20	£55.00
	A2	C	25	Rod & Gun (1924)		£2.20	£55.00
	D	C	50	Songs that will Live for Ever...............		£1.60	£80.00

I. RUTTER & CO., Mitcham

Illus. No.	Size	Print-ing	Number in set		Handbook ref.	Price per card	Complete set
Pre-1919 Issues							
	D	BW	15	*Actresses—"RUTAN" :—	H.381		
				A. Rubber-stamped on plain back.........		£22.00	—
				B. Red printed back.....................		£20.00	—
				C. Plain back		£20.00	—
	A	BW	1	Advertisement Card "Tobacco Bloom"	Ha.485	—	—
	A	BW	? 7	*Boer War Celebrities	H.382/Ha.382	£18.00	—
	D1	C	54	*Comic Phrases...........................	H.223	£8.00	£430.00
	A	BW	20	Cricketers Series	H.29	£50.00	—
	C	C		*Flags and Flags with Soldiers:—	H.41		
			15	A. Flagstaff Draped, 2nd printing.........		£13.00	—
			15	B. Flagstaff not Draped (Flags only)			
				(a) white back.....................		£13.00	—
				(b) cream back		£13.00	—
19	C	C	24	*Girls, Flags & Arms of Countries:—	H.383		
				A. Blue back...........................		£20.00	—
				B. Plain back			
	A	C	? 20	Proverbs...............................	H.384/Ha.384	£20.00	—
	A	C	25	*Shadowgraphs..........................	H.44	£18.00	—

S.D.V. TOBACCO CO. LTD., Liverpool

Illus. No.	Size	Print-ing	Number in set		Handbook ref.	Price per card	Complete set
Pre-1919 Issues							
	A	BW	16	British Royal Family	H.28	£90.00	—

ST. DUNSTAN'S, London

Post-1920 Issue							
	—	C	6	Famous Posters (folders) (65 × 41 mm.)	Ha.606	£11.00	—

ST. PETERSBURG CIGARETTE CO. LTD., Portsmouth

Pre-1919 Issues							
	A	BW	? 4	Footballers	H.410/Ha.410	—	—

SALMON & GLUCKSTEIN LTD., London

A. Pre-1919 Issues							
		C	1	*Advertisement Card ("Snake Charmer" Cigarettes) (73 × 107 mm.)		—	£200.00
	C	C	15	*Billiard Terms:—			
				A. Small numerals		£22.00	—
				B. Larger numerals		£22.00	—
	A	C	12	British Queens (? 1897)	Ha.480	£20.00	£240.00
	—	C	30	*Castles, Abbeys & Houses (76 × 73 mm.):—			
				A. Brown back		£13.00	—
				B. Red back		£16.00	—
	C	C	32	*Characters from Dickens	H.385	£14.00	£450.00
	A	C	25	Coronation Series (1911)		£6.00	£150.00
	—	U	25	*Famous Pictures—Brown photogravure (57 × 76 mm.)	H.386	£4.00	£100.00
	—	U	25	*Famous Pictures—Green photogravure (58 × 76 mm.)	H.387	£4.00	£100.00
	A2	C	6	Her Most Gracious Majesty Queen Victoria (1897):—	H.388		
				A. Thin card		£17.00	£100.00
				B. Thick card		£17.00	£100.00
	A	C	50	The Great White City		£4.50	£225.00
	C	C	40	Heroes of the Transvaal War (1901–2)	H.389	£8.00	£320.00
	C	C	30	*Music Hall Celebrities		£15.00	£450.00
		C	? 20	*Occupations, narrow cards	H.390/Ha.390	£200.00	—
	C	C	20	"Owners & Jockeys' Series	H.392	£20.00	—
	—	C	48	*The Post in Various Countries (41 × 66 mm.)	H.391	£18.00	—
	A2	C	6	*Pretty Girl Series—"RASH" ("Raspberry Buds" Cigarettes)	H.8	£35.00	—
	—	C	22	Shakespearian Series:—	H.393		
				A. Large format, frame line back (38 × 69 mm.)		£12.00	£265.00
				B. Re-drawn, small format, no frame line to back (37 × 66 mm.)		£12.00	—
	A	C	25	*Star Girls:—	H.30		
				A. Red back		£65.00	—
				B. Brown back, different setting		£65.00	—
	A	C	25	Traditions of the Army & Navy (? 1917):—			
				A. Large numerals		£6.00	£150.00
				B. Smaller numerals, back redrawn		£6.00	£150.00
B. Post-1920 Issues							
	D2	C	25	Magical Series (1923)		£1.60	£40.00
214	A2	C	25	Wireless Explained (1923)		£1.60	£40.00
C. Silks							
	—	C	50	*Pottery Types (paper-backed) (83 × 55 mm.) (see RB21/311):—			
				1. Numbered on front and back		£1.80	£90.00
				2. Numbered on back only		£1.80	£90.00

W. SANDORIDES & CO. LTD., London

Post-1920 Issues							
		U	25	Aquarium Studies from the London Zoo— "Lucana" (1925):—	Ha.607		
	C2			A. Small size:—			
				1. Small lettering on back		£1.40	£35.00
				2. Larger lettering on back		£1.40	£35.00
	B1			B. Large size		£1.40	£35.00
		C	25	Cinema Celebrities (1924):—	Ha.530		
	C2			A. Small size		£1.20	£30.00
	—			B. Extra-large size, (109 × 67 mm.)		£1.40	£35.00
		C	25	Cinema Stars (export):—	Ha.530		
	C2			A. Small size, with firm's name at base of back		—	—
	C2			B. Small size, "Issued with Lucana Cigarettes…"		£3.00	—
	C2			C. Small size, "Issued with Big Gun Cigarettes…"		—	—

Illus. No.	Size	Print-ing	Number in set		Handbook ref.	Price per card	Complete set
—				D. Extra-large size, (109 × 67 mm.) "Issued with Big Gun Cigarettes …"...........		£1.00	—
		U	50	Famous Racecourses (1926) — "Lucana":—	Ha.608		
	C2			A. Small size............................		£1.00	£50.00
	B1			B. Large size.............................		£1.20	£60.00
225	C2	U	50	Famous Racehorses (1923):—	Ha.609		
				1A. Back in light brown..............		90p	£45.00
				1B. Back in dark brown..............		90p	£45.00
				2. As 1A, with blue label added, inscribed "Issued with Sandorides Big Gun Cigarettes …"..........		—	—
	A	C	25	Sports & Pastimes—Series I—"Big Gun Cigarettes"............................	H.225	£3	—

NICHOLAS SARONY & CO., London

A. Pre-1919 Issue							
—		U	? 1	Boer War Scenes (67 × 45 mm.)	H.394	—	—
B. Post-1920 Issues		C	50	Around the Mediterranean (June 1926):—	Ha.610		
	C2			A. Small size...........................		32p	£16.00
	B1			B. Large size............................		40p	£20.00
		U	25	Celebrities and Their Autographs, Nd. 1–25 (1923):—			
	C1			A. Small size...........................		30p	£7.50
	B1			B. Large size............................		30p	£7.50
		U	25	Celebrities and Their Autographs, Nd. 26–50 (1924):—			
	C1			A. Small size:—			
				1. Small numerals		30p	£7.50
				2. Large numerals		30p	£7.50
	B1			B. Large size:—			
				1. Small numerals		30p	£7.50
				2. Large numerals		30p	£7.50
		U	25	Celebrities and Their Autographs, Nd. 51–75 (1924):—			
	C1			A. Small size...........................		30p	£7.50
	B1			B. Large size............................		30p	£7.50
		U	25	Celebrities and Their Autographs, Nd. 76–100 (1925):—			
	C1			A. Small size...........................		30p	£7.50
	B1			B. Large size............................		30p	£7.50
	A2	U	50	Cinema Stars—Set 7 (June 1933)............	Ha.515–7	25p	£12.50
—		U		Cinema Stars—Postcard size (137 × 85 mm.):—			
			38	"of a Series of 38 Cinema Stars" (June 1929)		£3.50	—
			42	"of a second Series of 42 Cinema Stars"		£1.00	£42.00
			50	"of a third Series of 50 Cinema Stars"......		£1.00	£50.00
			42	"of a fourth Series of 42 Cinema Stars"		£1.00	£42.00
			25	"of a fifth Series of 25 Cinema Stars".......		£1.00	£25.00
299	D	U	25	Cinema Studies (Sep. 1929)		22p	£5.50
		C	25	A Day on the Airway (Feb. 1928):—			
	C2			A. Small size..., ...		28p	£7.00
	B2			B. Large size...........................		28p	£7.00
	A2	P	54	Life at Whipsnade Zoo (Dec. 1934)	Ha.556	25p	£13.50
		BW	25	Links with the Past—First 25 subjects, Nd. 1–25 (1925):—			
	C1			A. Small size...........................		34p	£8.50
	B			B. Large size............................		30p	£7.50
		BW	25	Links with the Past—Second 25 subjects (1926):—			
	C			A. Home issue, Nd. 26–50:—			
				1. Small size.........................		26p	£6.50
	B			2. Large size, descriptive back........		22p	£5.50
	B			3. Large size, advertisement back		£1.50	—
				B. Sydney issue, Nd. 1–25:—			
	C			1. Small size.........................		40p	£10.00
	B			2. Large size		32p	£8.00
	C			C. Christchurch issue, Nd. 1–25:—			
				1. Small size.........................		40p	£10.00
				2. Large size		20p	£5.00
115		BW	25	Museum Series (1927):—			
				A. Home issue:—			
	C2			1 Small size.......................		14p	£3.50
	B			2. Large size, descriptive back........		13p	£3.00
	B			3. Large size, advertisement back		28p	£7.00
	B			B. Sydney issue, large size		24p	£6.00
				C. Christchurch issue:—			
	C2			1. Small size.......................		20p	£5.00
	B			2. Large size		20p	£5.00
		P	36	National Types of Beauty (Apr. 1928):—	Ha.558		
	A2			A. Small size...........................		20p	£7.00
—				B. Medium size (76 × 51 mm.)		20p	£7.00
		C	15	Origin of Games (1923):—			
	A			A. Small size...........................		£1.35	£20.00
	B2			B. Large size..........................		£1.35	£20.00

NICHOLAS SARONY & CO. *(continued)*

Illus. No.	Size	Print-ing	Number in set		Handbook ref.	Price per card	Complete set
113		C	50	'Saronicks' (June 1929):—	Ha.557		
	D2			A. Small size..........................		13p	£3.75
	—			B. Medium size (76 × 51 mm.)		13p	£3.75
249		C	50	Ships of All Ages (Dec. 1929):—			
	D			A. Small size.........................		13p	£5.00
	—			B. Medium size (76 × 52 mm.)		13p	£6.00
	D	C	25	Tennis Strokes (1923)		90p	£22.50

SCOTTISH CO-OPERATIVE WHOLESALE SOCIETY LTD., Glasgow ("S.C.W.S.")

Post-1920 Issues

Illus. No.	Size	Print-ing	Number in set		Handbook ref.	Price per card	Complete set
	A2	C	25	Burns (1924):—	Ha.611		
				A. Printed back:—			
				1. White card		£1.00	—
				2. Cream card......................		34p	£8.50
				*B. Plain back		£1.00	—
	C	C	20	Dogs (1925)...............................	H.211	£3.00	£60.00
79	A2	C	25	Dwellings of All Nations (1924):—	Ha.612		
				A. Printed back:—			
				1. White card		£1.20	—
				2. Cream card......................		£1.00	£25.00
				*B. Plain back		—	—
	B	C	25	Famous Pictures (1924).....................		£2.40	£60.00
	H2	C	25	Famous Pictures—Glasgow Gallery:—			
				A. Non-adhesive back (1927)		90p	£22.50
				B. Adhesive back		70p	£17.50
	H2	C	25	Famous Pictures—London Galleries:—			
				A. Non-adhesive back (1927)		90p	£22.50
				B. Adhesive back		70p	£17.50
222	A2	C	50	Feathered Favourites:—			
				A. Grey borders (1926)		70p	£35.00
				B. White borders:—			
				1. Non adhesive back (1926)		80p	£40.00
				2. Adhesive back		70p	£35.00
	A	C	25	Racial Types (1925)		£3.00	£75.00
	A2	C	50	Triumphs of Engineering (1926):—			
				A. Brown border........................		£1.40	£70.00
				B. White border........................		£1.60	—
	A2	C	50	Wireless (1924)............................		£1.50	£75.00

SELBY'S TOBACCO STORES, Cirencester

Post-1920 Issue

	Size	Print-ing	Number in set			Price per card	Complete set
	—	U	? 12	"Manikin" Cards (79 × 51 mm.)		—	—

SHARPE & SNOWDEN, London

Pre-1919 Issue

	Size	Print-ing	Number in set		Handbook ref.	Price per card	Complete set
	A	U	? 8	*Views of London..........................	H.395	—	—

W. J. SHEPHERD, London

Pre-1919 Issue

	Size	Print-ing	Number in set		Handbook ref.	Price per card	Complete set
	A	U	25	*Beauties—"FECKSA".....................	H.58	£60.00	—

SHORT'S, London

Post-1920 Issue

	Size	Print-ing	Number in set		Handbook ref.	Price per card	Complete set
	—	BW		*Short's House Views:—	Ha.562		
			? 13	1. Numbered (75 × 60 mm.)		—	—
			? 5	2. Unnumbered (77 × 69 mm.)............		—	—

JOHN SINCLAIR LTD., Newcastle-on-Tyne

A. Pre-1919 Issues

	Size	Print-ing	Number in set		Handbook ref.	Price per card	Complete set
	D2	U	? 57	*Actresses (42 × 63 mm.).....................	H.396	£32.00	—
	D	P	50	Football Favourites, Nd. 51–100 (? 1910)....		£22.00	—
	A	BW	4	*North Country Celebrities..................	H.397	£25.00	£100.00
	D	P	? 80	Northern Gems		£40.00	—
	A	C	50	Picture Puzzles & Riddles..................		£10.00	£500.00
	A	C	50	Trick Series..............................		£12.00	£600.00
	D2	C	50	World's Coinage	H.398	£9.00	£450.00

B. Post-1920 Issues

	Size	Print-ing	Number in set		Handbook ref.	Price per card	Complete set
	—	P		*Birds (1924):—	Ha.613		
	C		? 13	A. Small size, back "Specimen Cigarette Card"		£2.50	
	C		48	B. Small size, descriptive back:—			
				1. White front.......................		£1.20	£60.00
				2. Pinkish front		£1.20	£60.00
	—		50	C. Large size (78 × 58 mm.)		£2.00	£100.00
	A	C	50	British Sea Dogs (1926)...................		£1.60	£80.00

JOHN SINCLAIR LTD. *(continued)*

Illus. No.	Size	Printing	Number in set		Handbook ref.	Price per card	Complete set
		P		Champion Dogs—"A Series of . . ." (1938):—			
	A2		54	A. Small size....................		13p	£4.50
	B2		52	B. Large size....................		13p	£5.50
		P		Champion Dogs—"2nd Series . . ." (1939):—			
	A2		54	A. Small size....................		70p	£35.00
	B2		52	B. Large size....................		70p	£35.00
28	A2	P	50	English & Scottish Football Stars (1935)		15p	£7.50
	A	P	54	Film Stars—"A Series of 54 Real Photos" (1934)...................		35p	£18.00
328	A	P	54	Film Stars—"A Series of Real Photos", Nd. 1–54 (1937)...................		30p	£16.00
	A	P	54	Film Stars—"A Series of Real Photos", Nd. 55–108 (1937)...................		14p	£7.50
		P		*Flowers and Plants (1924):—	Ha.614		
	C		? 11	A. Small size, back "Specimen Cigarette Card"...................		£2.50	—
	C		96	B. Small size, descriptive back:—			
				1. White front...................		£1.20	£115.00
				2. Pinkish front...................		£1.20	£115.00
	—		? 96	C. Large size, 78 × 58 mm..........		£2.00	—
	A	P	54	Radio Favourites (1935)...................		50p	£27.00
	K2	C	53	Rubicon Cards (miniature playing cards)....		£3.00	—
	A	BW	50	Well-Known Footballers—North Eastern Counties (1938)...................		13p	£6.00
	A	BW	50	Well-Known Footballers—Scottish (1938) ..		13p	£4.75

C. Silks

	—	C		*Flags—Set 11 (unbacked and anonymous):—	Ha.501–11		
			50	"Fourth Series" (49 × 70 mm.).............		£4.00	—
			50	"Fifth Series" (49 × 70 mm.)		£4.00	—
			50	"Sixth Series":			
				1. Nos. 1–25 (49 × 70 mm.).............		£5.00	—
				2. Nos. 26–50 (68 × 80 mm.)		£5.00	—
			? 9	"Seventh Series" (115 × 145 mm.)		—	—
	—	C	? 1	The Allies (140 × 100 mm.) (Numbered 37) ..		—	£5.00
	—	C	50	*Regimental Badges I (includes two Regimental Colours and a Union Jack) (paper-backed) (70 × 52 mm.)...................	Ha.502–1	£2.00	—
	—	C	? 24	*Regimental Colours II (unbacked and anonymous):—	Ha.502–7		
				1. Nos. 38–49 (No. 49 not seen) (76 × 70 mm.)...................		£7.50	—
				2. Nos. 50–61 (65 × 51 mm.)		£7.50	—

ROBERT SINCLAIR TOBACCO CO. LTD., Newcastle-on-Tyne ——

A. Pre-1919 Issues

	A2	U	28	Dominoes		—	—
	A	BW	? 3	*Footballers...................	H.399	£90.00	—
	D	C	12	*Policemen of the World (? 1899)	H.164	£75.00	—

B. Post-1920 Issues

230	C2	C		Billiards by Willie Smith (1928):—			
			10	1. First Set of 10...................		£1.80	£18.00
			15	2. Second Set of 15...................		£1.80	£27.00
			3	3. Third Set of 25 (Nos. 26–28 only issued)		£4.00	£12.00
		C	12	The "Smiler" Series (1924):—			
	A			A. Small size (inscribed ". . . 24 cards", 12 only issued)		£2.20	£26.00
	H			B. Large size...................		£3.50	—

C. Silks *Unbacked silks, inscribed with initials "R.S." in circle.*

	—	C	4	*Battleships and Crests (73 × 102 mm.).......	Ha.499–1	£20.00	—
	—	C	? 7	*Flags (70 × 51 mm.)	Ha.499–2	—	—
	—	C	? 4	*Great War Area—Cathedrals and Churches (140 × 102 mm.)...................	Ha.499–3	£15.00	—
	—	C	? 9	*Great War Heroes (70 × 51 mm.).............	Ha.499–4	£15.00	—
	—	C	1	*Red Cross Nurse (73 × 102 mm.)...........	Ha.499–5	—	£50.00
	—	C	? 4	*Regimental Badges (70 × 51 mm.)...........	Ha.499–6	£15.00	—

J. SINFIELD, Scarborough ———————————————

Pre-1919 Issue

	A	U	? 24	*Beauties—"HUMPS"...................	H.222	£100.00	—

SINGLETON & COLE LTD., Shrewsbury ———————

A. Pre-1919 Issues

	A	C	50	*Atlantic Liners (1910)		£11.00	£550.00
	D1	BW	50	*Celebrities—Boer War Period:—	H.400		
				25. Actresses		£8.00	£200.00
				25. Boer War Celebrities		£8.00	£200.00
	A	BW	35	Famous Officers—Hero Series:—			
				A1. "Famous Officers" on back toned card (1915)...................		£8.00	£280.00
				A2. "Famous Officers" thin white card.		£25.00	—
				B. "Hero Series" on back		£100.00	—
	D1	BW	50	*Footballers, Nd. on front...................		£24.00	—

SINGLETON & COLE LTD. *(continued)*

Illus. No.	Size	Print- ing	Number in set		Handbook ref.	Price per card	Complete set
	C	C	40	*Kings and Queens (1902)	H.157	£9.00	£360.00
	A	C	25	Maxims of Success:—	H.401		
				A. Orange border		£9.00	—
				B. Lemon yellow border..................		£13.00	—
	A	BW	? 14	Orient Royal Mail Line:—	H.402		
				A. "Orient-Pacific Line," Manager's back .		£20.00	—
				B. "Orient Royal Mail Line," Singleton & Cole back............................		£20.00	—
				C. "Orient Line", Manager's back		£20.00	—
	A	C	25	Wallace Jones—Keep Fit System		£8.00	£200.00

B. Post-1920 Issues

Illus. No.	Size	Print- ing	Number in set		Handbook ref.	Price per card	Complete set
	A	C	25	Bonzo Series (1928) (see RB21/217/25)		£2.00	£50.00
	A2	BW	35	Famous Boxers (1930):—			
				A. Numbered..........................		£2.50	—
				B. Unnumbered........................		—	—
	A2	BW	25	Famous Film Stars (1930)		£2.00	—
	—	U	? 12	"Manikin" Cards (79 × 51 mm.)		—	—

C. Silks

Illus. No.	Size	Print- ing	Number in set		Handbook ref.	Price per card	Complete set
	—	C	110	Crests & Badges of the British Army (paper-backed) (66 × 40 mm.)...................	Ha.502–2	£4.00	—

F. & J. SMITH, Glasgow ——————————————————————

(Refer to F. & J. Smith reference book for further information)

A. Pre-1919 Issues

Illus. No.	Size	Print- ing	Number in set		Handbook ref.	Price per card	Complete set
	A	C	25	*Advertisement Cards.......................	H.403	£100.00	—
	A	C	50	Battlefields of Great Britain (Dec. 1913).....	Ha.475	£5.00	£250.00
	A1	BW	25	*Boer War Series (1900) "Studio" Cigarettes back		£26.00	—
	A	C	50	*Boer War Series (1900–01).................		£18.00	—
	D	BW		*Champions of Sport (1902–3):—	H.404/Ha.404		
			50	Red back. Numbered		£16.00	—
			50	Blue back. Unnumbered.................		£20.00	—
	A	U	50	Cricketers (May 1912)...................		£6.00	£300.00
	A	U	20	Cricketers, 2nd Series, Nd. 51–70 (Aug. 1912)		£15.00	£300.00
	A	U	50	Derby Winners (Jul. 1913).................		£4.00	£200.00
	A	C	50	Famous Explorers (Oct. 1911)		£4.00	£200.00
	D	U	120	*Footballers, "Cup Tie Cigarettes," brown back (1902–3).........................		£11.00	—
	A	U	50	*Footballers, "Cup Tie Cigarettes," blue back "10 for 2½d" (1910–11) Nd. 1–52 (Nos. 1 and 13 not issued):—		—	£175.00
				A. Black portrait......................		£3.50	—
				B. Brown portrait.....................		£3.50	—
	A	U	50	*Footballers, "Cup Tie Cigarettes," blue back, "In packets of 10" (1910–11). Nd. 55–104 (Nos. 53 and 54 not issued):—		—	£175.00
				A. Black portrait......................		£3.50	—
				B. Brown portrait.....................		£3.50	—
	A	U	150	*Footballers, var. advertisements, yellow frame line (Nov. 1914):—		—	£450.00
				A. Pale blue back......................		£3.00	—
				B. Deep blue back		£3.00	—
	A	C	50	Football Club Records, 1913 to 1917 (?1918)		£4.00	£200.00
	A	C	50	Fowls, Pigeons & Dogs (May 1908)	H.64	£4.00	£200.00
	A	C		*Medals:—	H.71/Ha.71		
			20	A. Unnumbered—thick card (Apr. 1902)..		£6.00	£120.00
			50	B. Numbered. "F. & J. Smith" thick card (1902)		£4.00	£200.00
			50	C. Numbered. "The Imperial Tobacco Co." very thin card (1903)		£16.00	—
			50	D. Numbered. "The Imperial Tobacco Company" thin card (Feb. 1906).......		£4.00	£200.00
	A	C	50	Naval Dress & Badges:—	H.172/Ha.172		
				A. Descriptive back (Oct. 1911)		£4.00	£200.00
				B. Non-descriptive back (Nov. 1914)......		£4.00	£200.00
	A	C	50	*Phil May Sketches, blue-grey back (May 1908).................................	H.72/Ha.72	£4.00	£200.00
	A	C	40	Races of Mankind:—	Ha.483		
				A. Series title on front		£32.00	—
				*B. Without series title		£40.00	—
	A	C	25	Shadowgraphs (Apr. 1915)	H.466/Ha.466	£4.00	£100.00
	A	C	50	*A Tour Round the World:—			
				A. Script Advertisement back (Jan. 1904)..		£14.00	£700.00
				B. Post-card format back (Sep. 1905)......		£30.00	—
	A	C	50	A Tour Round the World (titled series, different from previous item) (Jan. 1906) ..	H.75/Ha.75	£4.00	£200.00
	A	BW	25	War Incidents (Nov. 1914):—	H.405		
				A. White back		£4.00	£100.00
				B. Toned back		£3.40	£80.00
	A	BW	25	War Incidents, 2nd Series (Feb. 1915):—	H.405		
				A. White back		£4.00	£100.00
				B. Toned back		£3.40	£80.00

B. Post-1920 Issues

Illus. No.	Size	Print- ing	Number in set		Handbook ref.	Price per card	Complete set
	A	C	25	"Cinema Stars"...........................	Ha.615	£2.40	£60.00
	A	C	50	Football Club Records, 1921–2 (Oct. 1922)..		£4.00	£200.00
	A	C	25	Holiday Resorts (July 1925)		£2.60	£65.00

F. & J. SMITH *(continued)*

Illus. No.	Size	Print-ing	Number in set		Handbook ref.	Price per card	Complete set
	A	C	50	Nations of the World (Oct. 1923)	H.454	£1.80	£90.00
	A	C	50	Phil May Sketches (brown back) (Sep. 1924).	Ha.72	£2.00	£100.00
	A	C	25	Prominent Rugby Players (Nov. 1924)		£2.60	£65.00

SNELL & CO., Plymouth and Devonport

Pre-1919 Issue

	A	BW	25	*Boer War Celebrities—"STEW"	H.105	£90.00	—

SOCIETE JOB, London (and Paris)

A. Pre-1919 Issues

	D	BW	25	*Dogs (? 1911)	H.406	£5.00	£125.00
	D	BW	25	*Liners (1912).	H.407	£15.00	—
	D	BW	25	*Racehorses—1908–9 Winners (1909)........	H.408	£6.00	£150.00

B. Post-1920 Issues

	A	C	25	British Lighthouses		£2.00	£50.00
	—	U	48	*Cinema Stars (58 × 45 mm.)—"Cigarettes Job" on front	Ha.616	—	£24.00
			46/48	Ditto...............................		20p	£10.00
	A2	C	25	Orders of Chivalry (1924).		£1.40	£35.00
	A2	C	25	Orders of Chivalry (Second Series) (1927) ...		£1.40	£35.00
	A2	C	3	Orders of Chivalry (unnumbered) (1927)		£2.50	£7.50

LEON SOROKO, London

Post-1920 Issue

	—	U	6	Jubilee Series (1935):—			
				A. Small size (75 × 41 mm.)		—	—
				B. Large size (83 × 73 mm.)		—	—

SOUTH WALES TOB. MFG. CO. LTD., Newport and London

Pre-1919 Issues

	A	U	25	*Views of London.........................	H.409	£8.00	£200.00
	A	BW	? 91	Game of Numbers		£50.00	—

SOUTH WALES TOBACCO CO. (1913) LTD., Newport

Pre-1919 Issue

	D	C	30	*Army Pictures, Cartoons, etc................	H.12	£75.00	—

S. E. SOUTHGATE & CO., London

Pre-1919 Issue

	A1	C	25	*Types of British and Colonial Troops	H.76	—	—

G. STANDLEY, Newbury

Post-1920 Issue

	—	U	? 12	"Manikin" Cards (79 × 51 mm.)	Ha.481	—	—

A. & A. E. STAPLETON, Hastings

Post-1920 Issue

	—	U	? 12	*"Manikin" Cards (79 × 51 mm.)	Ha.481	—	—

H. STEVENS & CO., Salisbury

Post-1920 Issues

	A1	C	20	*Dogs (1923)...............................	H.211	£2.25	£45.00
	A1	U	25	*Zoo Series (1926).........................	Ha.588	£1.80	£45.00

A. STEVENSON, Middleton

Pre-1919 Issue

	A	U	50	War Portraits.............................	H.86	—	—

ALBERT STOCKWELL, Porthcawl

Pre-1919 Issue

	D	C	30	*Army Pictures, Cartoons, etc...............	H.12	—	—

STRATHMORE TOBACCO CO. LTD., London

Post-1920 Issue

186	—	U	25	British Aircraft (76 × 50 mm.)..............		24p	£6.00

TADDY & CO., London

Illus. No.	Size	Print-ing	Number in set		Handbook ref.	Price per card	Complete set
Pre-1919 issues							
—	U		? 71	*Actresses—collotype (40 × 70 mm.)	H.411/Ha.411	£45.00	—
A	C		25	*Actresses—with flowers		£60.00	—
A	BW		38	Admirals & Generals—			
				The War A.	H.412	£8.00	—
				Scarce Cards B.		£25.00	—
A	BW		38	Admirals & Generals—The War (South Africar. printing).......................		£25.00	—
A1	BW		1	*Advertisement Card, "Imperial Tobacco"...		—	—
A	C		25	Autographs............................	H.413	£8.00	£200.00
A	C		20	Boer Leaders:—			
				A. White back		£9.00	£180.00
				B. Cream back.....................		£9.00	
A	C		50	British Medals & Decorations—Series 2.....		£6.00	£300.00
A	C		50	British Medals & Ribbons		£6.00	£300.00
A	C		20	*Clowns and Circus Artistes	H.414	£250.00	
C2	C		30	Coronation Series (38 × 66 mm.):—			
				A. Grained card......................		£11.00	£330.00
				B. Smooth card......................		£11.00	£330.00
A	BW		238	County Cricketers.......................	H.415	£16.00	—
A	C		50	Dogs	Ha.487	£9.00	£450.00
C	U		5	*English Royalty—collotype	H.416	£170.00	—
A	C		25	Famous Actors—Famous Actresses........		£9.00	£225.00
A	BW		50	Famous Horses & Cattle		£25.00	—
A2	C		25	Famous Jockeys:—	H.417		
				A. Without frame line—blue title		£12.00	£300.00
				B. With frame line—brown title..........		£8.00	£200.00
A	BW		? 32	Footballers (export issue)....................	H.418	£28.00	—
A	C		25	"Heraldry" Series		£8.00	£200.00
A	C		25	Honours & Ribbons......................		£11.00	£275.00
C	C		10	Klondyke Series		£26.00	£260.00
C	BW		60	Leading Members of the Legislative Assembly (export issue)......................		—	—
A	C		25	*Natives of the World	H.419	£32.00	£800.00
A	C		25	Orders of Chivalry	H.301	£8.00	£200.00
A	C		25	Orders of Chivalry, Second Series	H.301	£16.00	£400.00
A	BW		?996	Prominent Footballers—Grapnel and/or Imperial back:—	H.420		
				A. 595 Without "Myrtle Grove" footnote (1907)............................		£3.50	—
				B. 401 With "Myrtle Grove" footnote (1908-9)		£3.50	—
A	BW		?311	Prominent Footballers—London Mixture back (1913-14).........................	H.420/Ha.420	£13.00	—
—	C		20	*Royalty, Actresses, Soldiers (39 × 72 mm.)...	H.421	£130.00	—
A	C		25	"Royalty" Series		£7.00	£175.00
A	C		25	*Russo-Japanese War (1904) (1–25)........		£7.00	£175.00
A	C		25	*Russo-Japanese War (1904) (26–50)........		£12.00	£300.00
A	BW		16	South African Cricket Team, 1907	H.422	£30.00	—
A	BW		26	South African Football Team, 1906-7.......	H.423	£13.00	—
A	C		25	Sports & Pastimes—Series 1	H.225	£8.00	£200.00
A	C		25	Territorial Regiments—Series I (1908)		£12.00	£300.00
A	C		25	Thames Series		£22.00	£550.00
C	C		20	Victoria Cross Heroes (1–20)		£24.00	—
C	C		20	Victoria Cross Heroes (21–40)		£24.00	—
A	C		20	V.C. Heroes—Boer War (41–60):—			
				A. White back		£10.00	—
				B. Toned back		£9.00	£180.00
A	C		20	V.C. Heroes—Boer War (61–80):—			
				A. White back		£10.00	—
				B. Toned back		£9.00	£180.00
A	C		20	V.C. Heroes—Boer War (81–100):—			
				A. White back		£11.00	—
				B. Toned back		£11.00	£220.00
A	C		25	Victoria Cross Heroes (101–125)............		£50.00	—
A2	BW		2	*Wrestlers	H.424	£130.00	—

TADDY & CO., London and Grimsby

Illus. No.	Size	Print-ing	Number in set		Handbook ref.	Price per card	Complete set
Post-1940 Issues							
—	C		8	Advertisement Cards, three sizes (1980)		30p	£2.50
A	C		26	Motor Cars, including checklist (1980):—			
				A. "Clown Cigarettes" back		13p	£3.25
				B. "Myrtle Grove Cigarettes" back		13p	£3.25
A	C		26	Railway Locomotives including checklist (1980):—			
				A. "Clown Cigarettes back		13p	£3.25
				B. "Myrtle Grove Cigarettes" back		13p	£3.25

TAYLOR WOOD, Newcastle

Illus. No.	Size	Print-ing	Number in set		Handbook ref.	Price per card	Complete set
Pre-1919 Issue							
C	C		18	Motor Cycle Series........................	Ha.469	—	—

W. & M. TAYLOR, Dublin

TEOFANI & CO. LTD., London

TETLEY & SONS LTD., Leeds

THEMANS & CO., Manchester

Illus. No.	Size	Print-ing		Number in set	Handbook ref.	Price per card	Complete set
A. Pre-1919 Issues							
	A	C	? 1	*Advertisement card with Riddles............	H.426	—	—
	A1	C	? 1	Allied Flags ("United Strength" in centre)...	Ha.486	—	—
	A	—	55	Dominoes (sunspot broad issue)		—	—
	C	C	18	Motor Cycle Series........................	Ha.469	£20.00	—
	A	U	50	*War Portraits	H.86	£27.00	—
	—		13	War Posters (63 × 41 mm.).................			
B. Silks							
				Anonymous silks with blue border, plain board backing. Reported also to have been issued with firm's name rubber stamped on backing.			
	—	C		*Miscellaneous Subjects:—	Ha.500		
			? 8	Series B1—Flags (50 × 66 mm.)		—	—
			? 12	Series B3—Regimental Badges (50 × 66 mm.)		£4.00	—
			? 2	Series C1—Flags (65 × 55 mm.)		—	—
			? 1	Series C2—Flags (70 × 65 mm.)		—	—
			? 4	Series C3—Regimental Badges (64 × 77 mm.)		£4.00	—
			? 2	Series C4—Crests of Warships (64 × 77 mm.)		—	—
			? 1	Series D1—Royal Standard (138 × 89 mm.) .		—	—
			? 1	Series D2—Shield of Flags (138 × 89 mm.) ..		—	—
			? 1	Series D3—Regimental Badge (138 × 89 mm.)		—	—

THOMSON & PORTEOUS, Edinburgh

Pre-1919 Issues							
	D2	C	50	Arms of British Towns		£4.00	£200.00
	A	BW	25	*Boer War Celebrities—"STEW"...........	H.105	£30.00	—
	A	C	20	European War Series......................	H.129	£7.00	£140.00
	A	C	25	*Shadowgraphs...........................	H.44	£24.00	—
	A	C	41	V.C. Heroes:—	H.427		
				Ai. Name on back—Luntin Cigarettes....		—	£225.00
				Aii. As above, but No. 6 Type B..........		£4.50	£185.00
				B. Without Maker's Name..............		£4.50	£185.00

TOBACCO SUPPLY SYNDICATE, London (T.S.S.)

Pre-1919 Issue							
	D	C	? 23	*Nautical Expressions......................	H.174	£70.00	—

TURKISH MONOPOLY CIGARETTE CO. LTD.

Pre-1919 Issue							
	—	C	? 7	*Scenes from the Boer War (113 × 68 mm., folded in three)	Ha.478	£55.00	—

UNITED KINGDOM TOBACCO CO., London

Post-1920 Issues							
	A	C	50	Aircraft—"The Greys Cigarettes" (Feb. 1938)...................................	Ha.598	50p	£25.00
	—	U	48	Beautiful Britain—"The Greys Cigarettes" (postcard size, 140 × 90 mm.) (Jan. 1929)..		90p	£45.00
	—	U	48	Beautiful Britain—"The Greys Cigarettes" (postcard size, 140 × 90 mm.) Second Series (Oct. 1929)		80p	£40.00
	A2	C	25	British Orders of Chivalry & Valour (Nov. 1936)—"The Greys Cigarettes"..........	Ha.599	22p	£5.50
	A	U	24	Chinese Scenes (Mar. 1933).................		13p	£2.25
234	A2	U	32	Cinema Stars—Set 4 (1933).................	Ha.515–4	30p	£10.00
244	A2	U	50	Cinema Stars—Set 7 (1934):—	Ha.515–7		
				A. Anonymous back		40p	£20.00
				B. Back with firm's name		32p	£16.00
	A2	C	36	Officers Full Dress (Mar. 1936)		44p	£16.00
	A2	C	36	Soldiers of the King—"The Greys Cigarettes" (Aug. 1937)	Ha.603	40p	£15.00

UNITED SERVICES MANUFACTURING CO. LTD., London

A. Post-1920 Issues							
196	A1	C	50	Ancient Warriors (1938)....................		60p	£30.00
290	A1	BW	50	Bathing Belles (1939)......................	Ha.592	14p	£7.00
	D	U	100	Interesting Personalities (1935)		£1.10	—
	D	U	50	Popular Footballers (1936)		£1.50	—
	D	U	50	Popular Screen Stars (1937)................		£1.20	—
B. Post-1940 Issue							
	A	C	25	Ancient Warriors (1954)...................		£1.20	—

UNITED TOBACCONISTS' ASSOCIATION, LTD.

Illus. No.	Size	Printing	Number in set		Handbook ref.	Price per card	Complete set
Pre-1919 Issue							
	A	C	? 9	*Actresses—"MUTA"	H.265/Ha.265	£80.00	—

WALKER'S TOBACCO CO. LTD., Liverpool

Illus. No.	Size	Printing	Number in set		Handbook ref.	Price per card	Complete set
Post-1920 Issues							
	C	P	60	*British Beauty Spots	Ha.553	—	—
	D2		28	*Dominoes:—			
		U		A. "W.T.C." Monogram back	Ha.535-2	£1.50	—
		BW		B. Text back		£40.00	—
31	A2	P	32	Film Stars—"Tatley's Cigarettes" (1936)	Ha.623	—	£25.00
			31	Different (minus Lombard)		26p	£8.00
	A2	P	48	*Film Stars—Walker's name at base (1937)	Ha.623	£1.30	—

WALTERS TOBACCO CO. LTD., London

Illus. No.	Size	Printing	Number in set		Handbook ref.	Price per card	Complete set
Post-1920 Issue							
	B	U	6	Angling Information (wording only)	Ha.624	35p	£2.00

E. T. WATERMAN, Coventry

Illus. No.	Size	Printing	Number in set		Handbook ref.	Price per card	Complete set
Pre-1919 Issue							
	D	C	30	*Army Pictures, Cartoons, etc.	H.12	—	—

WEBB & RASSELL, Reigate

Illus. No.	Size	Printing	Number in set		Handbook ref.	Price per card	Complete set
Pre-1919 Issue							
	A	U	50	War Portraits	H.86	£18.00	—

H. C. WEBSTER ("Q. V. Cigars")

Illus. No.	Size	Printing	Number in set		Handbook ref.	Price per card	Complete set
Pre-1919 Issue							
	—	BW	?	*Barnum and Bailey's Circus (60 × 42 mm.)	H.428	£95.00	—

HENRY WELFARE & CO., London

Illus. No.	Size	Printing	Number in set		Handbook ref.	Price per card	Complete set
Pre-1919 Issue							
	D	P	? 22	Prominent Politicians (? 1911)	H.429	£55.00	—

WESTMINSTER TOBACCO CO. LTD., London

Post-1920 Issues

Inscribed "Issued by the Successors in the United Kingdom to the Westminster Tobacco Co., Ltd. ..." For other issues see Section II Foreign Cards.

Illus. No.	Size	Printing	Number in set		Price per card	Complete set
	A2	P	36	Australia—"First Series" (1932)	13p	£3.00
	A2	P	48	British Royal and Ancient Buildings (1925) (see RB21/200/159–I):—		
				A. Unnumbered, without descriptive text	40p	£20.00
				B. Numbered, with descriptive text	32p	£16.00
124	A2	P	48	British Royal and Ancient Buildings—"A Second Series ..." (1926).	30p	£15.00
	A2	P	36	Canada — "First Series" (1927) (see RB21/292–1)	33p	£12.00
	A2	P	36	Canada—"Second Series" (1928) (see RB21/292–2)	33p	£12.00
	A2	P	48	Indian Empire—"First Series" (1926) (see RB21/293/1)	25p	£12.50
	A2	P	48	Indian Empire—"Second Series" (1927) (see RB21/293–2)	25p	£12.50
	A2	P	36	New Zealand—"First Series" (1929) (see RB21/294–1)	30p	£11.00
	A2	P	36	New Zealand—"Second Series" (1930) (see RB21/294–2)	13p	£4.00
	A2	P	36	South Africa—"First Series" (1930) (see RB21/295–1)	30p	£11.00
	A2	P	36	South Africa—"Second Series" (1931) (see RB21/295–2)	25p	£9.00
Not Issued						
	A2	P	36	*Australia, Second Series, plain back*	13p	£2.25

WHALE & CO.

Illus. No.	Size	Printing	Number in set		Handbook ref.	Price per card	Complete set
Pre-1919 Issue							
	A	C	? 2	Conundrums	H.232	£150.00	—

M. WHITE & CO., London

WHITFORD & SONS, Evesham

Post-1920 Issue							
C2		C	20	*Inventors Series	H.213	£6.00	—

WHOLESALE TOBACCO SUPPLY CO., London ("Hawser" Cigarettes)

Pre-1919 Issues							
A		C	25	Armies of the World	H.43	£50.00	—
A		C	40	Army Pictures	H.69/Ha.69	£50.00	—

P. WHYTE, England

Pre-1919 Issue							
D		C	30	*Army Pictures, Cartoons, etc.	H.12	—	—

W. WILLIAMS & CO., Chester

A. Pre-1919 Issues							
A		BW	25	*Boer War Celebrities—"STEW"	H.105	£30.00	—
A		C	50	Interesting Buildings	H.70	£5.50	£275.00
A		BW	12	Views of Chester	H.430	£10.00	£120.00
A		BW	12	Views of Chester—As It Was:—	H.430		
				A. Toned card		£11.00	£135.00
				B. Bleuté card		£12.00	—
B. Post-1920 Issues							
A		U	30	Aristocrats of the Turf	Ha.554	£2.20	£65.00
A		U	36	Aristocrats of the Turf 2nd Series		£8.00	—
A		C	25	Boxing	H.311	£2.40	£60.00

W. D. & H. O. WILLS, Bristol

A. Period to 1902—including series issued abroad.							
A		U	? 45	*Actresses—collotype:—	H.431		
				A. "Wills' Cigarettes"—"4 brands" back		£50.00	—
				B. "Wills' Cigarettes"—"no brands" back		£50.00	—
				C. "Wills' Cigarettes"—plain back		—	—
				D. "Wills' Cigarettes"—"4 brands" back		—	—
				E. "Wills' Cigarettes"—"no brands" back		£60.00	—
				F. "Wills' Cigarettes"—plain back		—	—
A		C	? 1	*Actresses, brown type-set back	H.432	—	—
A		C	52	*Actresses, brown scroll back, with P.C. inset		£10.00	£520.00
A		C	52	*Actresses, grey scroll back:—	H.433		
				A. Without P.C. inset		£10.00	£520.00
				B. With P.C. inset		£10.00	£520.00
A		U		*Actresses and Beauties—collotype, "Three Castles" and "Firefly" front:—	H.434		
		? 30		Actresses		£70.00	—
		? 16		Beauties		£70.00	—
A		C		*Advertisement Cards:—	H.435		
		?		1888 issue		—	—
		? 1		1889–90 issues		—	—
		? 11		1890–93 issues		—	—
		? 3		1893 issue (various backs)		£140.00	—
		? 6		1893–94 issue		£140.00	—
A		C	50	*Animals and Birds in Fancy Costumes	H.436/Ha.436	£32.00	£1600.00
A		U	? 10	*Beauties—collotype:—	H.437		
				A. "W. D. & H. O. Wills' Cigarettes"		£90.00	—
				B. "Firefly" Cigarettes		—	—
A1		C	? 1	*Beauties ("Girl Studies"), type-set back	H.438	—	—
A		C		*Beauties, brown backs:—	H.439/Ha.439		
		52		A. With P.C. inset—scroll back		£10.00	£520.00
		10		B. As A, 10 additional pictures		£35.00	—
		? 11		C. "Wills' Cigarettes" front, scroll back		£90.00	—
		? 14		D. "Wills' Cigarettes" front, type-set back		£100.00	—
K		C	52	*Beauties, miniature cards, P.C. inset, grey scroll back		£13.00	£675.00
A		C	50	Builders of the Empire (1898):—			
				A. White card		£3.50	£175.00
				B. Cream card		£3.50	£175.00
A		C	60	Coronation Series (1902):—			
				A. "Wide arrow" type back		£3.00	£180.00
				B. "Narrow arrow" type back		£3.00	£180.00
A		C	50	*Cricketers (1896)	H.440	£36.00	—
A		C		Cricketer Series, 1901:—			
		50		A. With Vignette		£11.00	£550.00
		25		B. Without Vignette		£11.00	£275.00

Illus. No.	Size	Print-ing	Number in set		Handbook ref.	Price per card	Complete set
	A	C		*Double Meaning (1898):—			
			50	A. Without P.C. inset....................		£4.50	£225.00
			52	B. With P.C. inset.......................		£4.50	£235.00
	A	C	50	Japanese Series	H.441/Ha.441	£30.00	—
		C		*Kings and Queens:—	H.442		
	A1		50	A. Short card (1897):			
				(a) Grey back, thin card		£2.40	£120.00
				(b) Grey back, thick card		£2.60	£130.00
				(c) Brown back		£8.00	—
	A			B. Standard size card (1902):			
			51	(a) Blue-grey back with 5 substitute titles		£3.00	£155.00
			50	(b) Grey back, different design, thinner card.............................		£6.00	£300.00
	A	C		*Locomotive Engines and Rolling Stock:—	H.443		
			50	A. Without I.T.C. Clause (1901–2)........		£3.60	£180.00
			7	B. As A, 7 additional cards		£12.00	—
				C. With I.T.C. Clause—See B Period.			
142	A	C	50	*Medals:—	H.71		
				A. White card........................		£1.70	£85.00
				B. Toned card		£2.00	£100.00
	A	C	25	*National Costumes.....................		£140.00	—
	A	C	20	Our Gallant Grenadiers:—	H.163		
				A. Deep grey on toned card..............		£16.00	—
				B. Blue-grey on bluish card		£16.00	—
	A	C	50	Seaside Resorts (1899)....................		£6.00	£300.00
	A	C		*Ships:—	H.444		
			25	A. Without "Wills" on front (1895):			
				(a) "Three Castles" back		£18.00	£450.00
				(b) Grey scroll back		£18.00	£450.00
			50	B. With "Wills" on front, dark grey back (1896)		£11.00	—
			100	C. Green scroll back on brown card (1898–1902):		—	£1450.00
				i. 1898–25 subjects as A		£14.00	—
				ii 1898–50 subjects as B		£14.00	—
				iii. 1902–25 additional subjects		£16.00	—
	A	C		*Soldiers of the World (1895–7):—	H.445		
				A. Without P.C. Inset:			
			100	(a) With "Ld." back, thick card........		£6.00	£600.00
			100	(b) With "Ld." back, thin card........		£6.50	—
			100	(c) Without "Ld." back, thin card......		£6.00	£600.00
			1	Additional card (as c) "England, Drummer Boy"		—	£80.00
			52	B. With P.C. inset.......................		£18.00	£940.00
	A	C	50	*Soldiers and Sailors:—	H.446		
				A. Grey back		£32.00	—
				B. Blue back		£32.00	—
	A	C	50	Sports of All Nations (1900)		£4.00	£200.00
321	A	BW		Transvaal Series:—	H.360		
			50	A. With black border (1899).............		£6.50	—
			66	Bi. Without black border (1900–01)		£1.40	£90.00
			258	Bii. Intermediate cards—additions and alternatives (1900–01)...............		£1.40	—
			66	C. Final 66 subjects, as issued with "Capstan" back (*see B Period*) (1902) .			
	A	C		"Vanity Fair" Series (1902):—	H.447		
			50	1st Series		£2.20	£110.00
			50	2nd Series		£2.00	£100.00
			50	Unnumbered —43 subjects as in 1st and 2nd, 7 new subjects.....................		£2.00	£100.00
	A	C		Wild Animals of the World:—	H.77		
			50	A. Green scroll back		£3.00	£150.00
			52	B. Grey back, P.C. inset		£6.00	£310.00

B. Period to 1902–1919—Home Issues i.e. series bearing Imperial Tobacco Co. ("I.T.C.") Clause.

Illus. No.	Size	Print-ing	Number in set		Handbook ref.	Price per card	Complete set
6	A	C	50	Allied Army Leaders (Mar. 1917):—			
				A. Without comma in I.T.C. Clause.......		90p	—
				B. With comma (or stop) in I.T.C. Clause .		90p	£45.00
	A	C	50	Alpine Flowers (Oct. 1913)		34p	£17.00
18	A	C	50	Arms of the Bishopric (Aug. 1907)		50p	£25.00
17	A	C	50	Arms of the British Empire (Oct. 1910)......		50p	£25.00
275	A	C	50	Arms of Companies (Jul. 1913)		50p	£25.00
134	A	C	50	Arms of Foreign Cities (Jul. 1912):—			
				A. White card.........................		50p	£25.00
				B. Cream card		70p	—
				C. As A, with "Mark"...................		80p	—
274	A	C	50	Aviation (Jan. 1910)......................		£1.00	£50.00
324	A	C	50	Billiards (May 1909)......................		60p	£30.00
262	A	C	50	*Borough Arms (1–50)—from June 1904:—	H.448		
				A. Scroll back, unnumbered		60p	£30.00
				B. Scroll back, numbered on front		£5.00	—
				C. Descriptive back, numbered on back ...		80p	£40.00
				D. 2nd Edition—1–50		40p	£20.00
27	A	C	50	*Borough Arms (51–100):—			
				A. 2nd Series		40p	£20.00
				B. 2nd Edition, 51–100		40p	£20.00

Illus. No.	Size	Print- ing	Number in set		Handbook ref.	Price per card	Complete set
55	A	C	50	*Borough Arms (101–150):—			
				A. 3rd Series, Album clause in grey........		40p	£20.00
				B. 3rd Series, Album clause in red.........		40p	£20.00
				C. 2nd Edition, 101–150		40p	£20.00
83	A	C	50	*Borough Arms (151–200), 4th series........		40p	£20.00
315	A	C	24	*Britain's Part in the War (Sep. 1917)		80p	£20.00
127	A	C	50	British Birds (May 1917)		60p	£30.00
	A	C	1	*Calendar for 1911 (Dec. 1910)		—	£12.00
	A	C	1	*Calendar for 1912 (Dec. 1911)		—	£6.00
	B	U	25	Celebrated Pictures (Feb. 1916):			
				A. Deep brown back		£1.00	£25.00
				B. Yellow-brown back		90p	£22.50
	B	U	25	Celebrated Pictures, 2nd Series (Nov. 1916)..		£1.00	£25.00
116	A	C	50	Celebrated Ships (Sep. 1911)...............		80p	£40.00
253	A	C	50	The Coronation Series (May 1911)..........		60p	£30.00
7	A	C	50	Cricketers (May 1908):—			
				A. 1–25 "Wills'S" at top front		£3.20	£80.00
				B. 1–50 "Wills's" at top front............		£3.20	£160.00
	B	C	25	Dogs (May 1914)		90p	£22.50
	B	C	25	Dogs, 2nd Series (Jun. 1915)...............		90p	£22.50
	A	C	50	Famous Inventions (Nov. 1915).............		50p	£25.00
	A	C	50	First Aid:—			
				A. Without Album Clause (Apr. 1913)		32p	£16.00
				B. With Album Clause (Jan. 1915)		32p	£16.00
272	A	C	50	Fish & Bait (May 1910)....................	H.65	40p	£20.00
	A	U	66	*Football Series (1902)	H.81	£2.50	£165.00
51	A	C	50	Garden Life (Oct. 1914)	H.449	32p	£16.00
	A	C	50	Gems of Belgian Architecture (Feb. 1915) ...		40p	£20.00
50	A	C	50	Gems of French Architecture (1917):—			
				A. White card..........................		90p	£45.00
				B. Bleuté card.........................		£1.00	—
				C. Rough brown card		£1.00	—
16	A	C	50	Gems of Russian Architecture (Feb. 1916)...		45p	£22.50
168	A	C	50	Historic Events (Jan. 1912)	H.464	60p	£30.00
	A	C	50	*Locomotive Engines and Rolling Stock, with I.T.C. Clause		£3.60	£180.00
				For issue without I.T.C. Clause see Period A.			
211	A	C	50	Military Motors (Oct. 1916):—			
				A. Without "Passed by Censor"		80p	£40.00
				B. With "Passed by Censor"..............		80p	£40.00
22	A	C	50	Mining (Jun. 1916)........................	H.450	45p	£22.50
21	A	C	50	Musical Celebrities (Apr. 1911)		80p	£40.00
	A	C	50	Musical Celebrities—Second Series (Sep. 1916):—	H.465		
				Set of 50 with 8 substituted cards...........		£1.60	£80.00
				8 original cards (later substituted)..........		£120.00	—
42	A	C	50	Naval Dress & Badges (Jul. 1909)	H.172	£1.20	£60.00
49	A	C	50	Nelson Series (Jul. 1905)...................		£1.30	£65.00
	A	C	50	Old English Garden Flowers (Jun. 1910)		32p	£16.00
304	A	C	50	Old English Garden Flowers, 2nd Series (Jan. 1913)................................		32p	£16.00
	A	C	50	Overseas Dominions (Australia) (Apr. 1915).	H.451	35p	£17.50
	A	C	50	Overseas Dominions (Canada) (Jun. 1914) ..		35p	£17.50
	A	C	50	Physical Culture (Feb. 1914)...............		40p	£20.00
132	A	U	100	*Portraits of European Royalty (1908):—			
				1–50 (Sept. 1908)......................		60p	£30.00
				51–100 (Dec. 1908)....................		60p	£30.00
	B	U	25	Punch Cartoons (Mar. 1916):—			
				A. Toned card		£2.20	£55.00
				B. Glossy white card		£3.50	—
	B	U	25	Punch Cartoons—Second Series (May 1917)		£9.00	—
307	A	C	12	Recruiting Posters (Apr. 1915)..............	H.452	£3.00	£36.00
325	A	C	50	Roses (Apr. 1912)........................		32p	£16.00
152	A	C	50	Roses, 2nd Series (1914)...................		32p	£16.00
323	A	C	50	School Arms (Nov. 1906)...................		50p	£25.00
330	A	C	50	Signalling Series (May 1911)................	H.453	60p	£30.00
313	A	C	50	Time & Money in Different Countries (May 1906)................................	H.454	£1.00	£50.00
	A	BW	66	Transvaal Series, "Capstan" back (1902)	H.360	£2.50	£165.00
				For other "Transvaal Series" see A Period.			
279	A	C	25	The World's Dreadnoughts (Jul. 1910)		£1.00	£25.00

C. Post-1920 Issues

Home issues, i.e., series with I.T.C. Clause. For export issues, see RB21.

	A	C		Air Raid Precautions (Aug. 1938):—	Ha.544		
			50	A. Home issue—adhesive back...........		13p	£6.50
			40	B. Irish issue—non-adhesive back........		40p	£16.00
151	A	C	48	Animalloys (sectional) (June 1934) (see RB21/200/124)		13p	£6.00
	B	C	25	Animals and Their Furs (Dec. 1929)........		70p	£17.50
	B	C	25	Arms of the British Empire—"First Series" (Nov. 1931)............................		50p	£12.50
	B	C	25	Arms of the British Empire—"Second Series" (Apr. 1932)......................		50p	£12.50
	B	C	42	Arms of Oxford & Cambridge Colleges (Oct. 1922).................................		£1.00	£42.00
365	B	C	25	Arms of Public Schools—"1st Series" (Aug. 1933).................................		50p	£12.50

Illus. No.	Size	Print- ing	Number in set		Handbook ref.	Price per card	Complete set
	B	C	25	Arms of Public Schools—"2nd Series" (Mar. 1934)		50p	£12.50
	B	C	25	Arms of Universities (May 1923)		90p	£22.50
	A	C	50	Association Footballers "Frameline" back (Nov. 1935) (see W/134)		20p	£10.00
118	A	C	50	Association Footballers—"No frameline" back (Nov. 1939):—			
				A. Home issue—adhesive back		20p	£10.00
				B. Irish issue—non-adhesive back		35p	£17.50
	B	C	25	Auction Bridge (July 1926)		80p	£20.00
	B	C	25	Beautiful Homes (Nov. 1930)		90p	£22.50
102	A	C	50	British Butterflies (June 1927) (see W/156)		32p	£16.00
	B	C	25	British Castles (Nov. 1925)		90p	£22.50
	B	C	25	British School of Painting (June 1927)		70p	£17.50
	—	BW	48	British Sporting Personalities (66 × 52 mm.) (Mar. 1937)		16p	£8.00
137	B	C	40	Butterflies & Moths (Oct. 1938)		35p	£14.00
	B	C	25	Cathedrals (Feb. 1933)		£1.00	£25.00
	A	C	25	Cinema Stars—"First Series" (Jan. 1928)		50p	£12.50
36	A	C	25	Cinema Stars—"Second Series" (Mar. 1928)		34p	£8.50
312	A	U	50	Cinema Stars—"Third Series" (June 1931)		50p	£25.00
	A	C	50	Cricketers, 1928 (Jan. 1928)		45p	£22.50
138	A	C	50	Cricketers—"2nd Series" (May 1929)		45p	£22.50
	A	C	50	Dogs—Light backgrounds (Sep. 1937) (see W/187):—			
				A. Home issue—adhesive back		14p	£7.00
				B. Irish issue—non-adhesive back		35p	£17.50
	A	C		Do You Know (see RB21/200/188):—			
349			50	"A Series of 50" (Sep. 1922)		16p	£8.00
120			50	"2nd Series of 50" (May 1924)		16p	£8.00
			50	"3rd Series of 50" (Feb. 1926)		16p	£8.00
164			50	"4th Series of 50" (July 1933)		20p	£10.00
	A	C	50	Engineering Wonders (Sep. 1927) (see W/193)		20p	£10.00
145	A	C	50	English Period Costumes (Aug. 1929) (see W/195)		35p	£17.50
	B	C	25	English Period Costumes (Jan. 1927)		70p	£17.50
	B	C	40	Famous British Authors (Aug. 1937)		35p	£14.00
	B	C	30	Famous British Liners—"First Series" (June 1934)		£1.50	£45.00
363	B	C	30	Famous British Liners—"Second Series" (June 1935)		90p	£27.00
	B	C	25	Famous Golfers (June 1930)		£1.20	£30.00
	A	C		A Famous Picture ... (sectional) (see RB21/200/210 to 212):—			
			48	Series No. 1—"Between Two Fires" (Mar. 1930)		20p	£10.00
			48	Series No. 2—"The Boyhood of Raleigh" (Aug. 1930)		18p	£9.00
			48	Series No. 3—"Mother and Son" (Feb. 1931)		16p	£8.00
			48	"The Toast" (June 1931):—			
				A. Home issue—Series No. 4		16p	£8.00
				B. Irish issue—Series No. 1		£1.00	—
			48	"The Laughing Cavalier" (Oct. 1931):—			
				A. Home issue—Series No. 5:—			
				1. No stop after numeral		20p	£10.00
				2. Full stop after numeral		20p	£10.00
				B. Irish issue—Series No. 2		£1.00	—
			49	Series No. 6—"And When did you Last See Your Father?" (Feb. 1932)		50p	£25.00
	A	C	25	Flags of the Empire (Nov. 1926 and Mar. 1929) (see W/215)		34p	£8.50
238	A	C	25	Flags of the Empire—"2nd Series" (Apr. 1929) (see W/216)		34p	£8.50
	A	C	50	Flower Culture in Pots (Feb. 1925) (see W/217)		14p	£7.00
	B	C	30	Flowering Shrubs (Feb. 1935)		50p	£15.00
9	A	C	50	Flowering Trees & Shrubs (July 1924)		17p	£8.50
	A	C	50	Garden Flowers (Jan. 1933)		13p	£6.00
	A	C	50	Garden Flowers by Richard Sudell (Jan. 1939) (see W/222):—			
				A. Home issue—four brands quoted at base		13p	£3.50
				B. Irish issue—no brands at base		14p	£7.00
	B	C	40	Garden Flowers—New Varieties—"A Series ..." (Jan. 1938)		13p	£3.50
	B	C	40	Garden Flowers—New Varieties—"2nd Series ..." (June 1939)		13p	£3.50
	A	C	50	Garden Hints (Jan. 1938) (see W/226):—			
				A. Home issue—Albums "one penny each"		13p	£3.00
				B. Irish issue—Album offer without price		14p	£7.00
	A	C	50	Gardening Hints (Mar. 1923) (see W/227)		16p	£8.00
	B	C	25	Golfing (June 1924)		£1.20	£30.00
	B	C	25	Heraldic Signs & Their Origin (May 1925) (see W/230)		70p	£17.50
100	A2	P	54	Homeland Events (Feb. 1932)		13p	£6.50
	A	C	50	Household Hints (Jan. 1927) (see W/234)		14p	£7.00
104	A	C	50	Household Hints—"2nd Series" (July 1930)		18p	£9.00

Illus. No.	Size	Printing	Number in set		Handbook ref.	Price per card	Complete set
	A	C	50	Household Hints (Sep. 1936) (see W/236)			
				A. Home issue—Albums "one penny each"		13p	£3.50
				B. Irish issue—Album offer without price .		14p	£7.00
240	A	BW	50	Hurlers (July 1927).........................		36p	£18.00
	A	C	25	Irish Beauty Spots (July 1929)		£2.40	£60.00
	A	C	25	Irish Holiday Resorts (May 1930)...........		£2.40	£60.00
264	A	C	50	Irish Industries (Feb. 1937):—			
				A. Back "This surface is adhesive...".....		—	—
				B. Back "Ask your retailer..."		36p	£18.00
	A	U	25	Irish Rugby Internationals (June 1928)......		£2.60	£65.00
	A	C	50	Irish Sportsmen (Oct. 1935)................		80p	£40.00
352	B	C	40	The King's Art Treasures (June 1938)		20p	£8.00
	B	C	25	Lawn Tennis, 1931 (May 1931)		80p	£20.00
	A	C	50	Life in the Royal Navy (July 1939) (see W/253).......................................		13p	£4.50
	A	C	50	Life in the Tree Tops (Oct. 1925) (see W/254)		18p	£9.00
	A	C	50	Lucky Charms (Oct. 1923) (see W/256)......		16p	£8.00
	A	C	50	Merchant Ships of the World (Oct. 1924) (see RB21/200/257)................................		45p	£22.50
	K2	C	53	*Miniature Playing Cards (1932–34) (see W/260):—			
				A. Home issue, blue back—"narrow 52" (2 printings)................................		40p	£20.00
				B. Home issue, blue back—"wide 52" (4 printings)................................		40p	£20.00
				C. Home issue, pink back (3 printings)		50p	—
				D. Irish issue, blue back (7 printings)......		80p	—
	B	C	25	Modern Architecture (Aug. 1931)...........		70p	£17.50
	B	U	30	Modern British Sculpture (Sep. 1928)		60p	£18.00
	B	C	25	Old Furniture—"1st Series" (Oct. 1923).....		90p	£22.50
	B	C	25	Old Furniture—"2nd Series" (Feb. 1924)....		90p	£22.50
	B	C	40	Old Inns—"A Series of 40" (July 1936).....		90p	£36.00
46	B	C	40	Old Inns—"Second Series of 40" (Sep. 1939)		50p	£20.00
	B	C	25	Old London (July 1929)		90p	£22.50
	B	C	30	Old Pottery & Porcelain (Oct. 1934).........		50p	£15.00
350	B	C	25	Old Silver (Nov. 1924).....................		80p	£20.00
	B	C	25	Old Sundials (Mar. 1928)		80p	£20.00
	A	BW	50	Our King and Queen (Feb. 1937) (see W/286)		13p	£4.50
	B	C	25	Public Schools (Nov. 1927)		70p	£17.50
	B	C	40	Racehorses & Jockeys, 1938 (Feb. 1939).....		40p	£16.00
	A	C	50	Radio Celebrities—"A Series ..." (Aug. 1934):—			
				A. Home issue—back "This surface..."...		25p	£12.50
				B. Irish issue—back "Note. This surface ...".................................		60p	—
	A	C	50	Radio Celebrities—"Second Series ..." (July 1935):—			
				A. Home issue—back "This surface..."...		25p	£12.50
				B. Irish issue—back "Note. This surface ...".................................		60p	—
114	A	C	50	Railway Engines (Jan. 1924) (see RB21/200/303)................................		50p	£25.00
	A	C	50	Railway Engines (May 1936):—			
				A. Home issue—back "This surface..."...		35p	£17.50
				B. Irish issue—back "Note. This surface ...".................................		60p	£30.00
	A	C	50	Railway Equipment (Apr. 1939) (see W/305)		13p	£4.00
343	A	C	50	Railway Locomotives (Dec. 1930)..........		60p	£30.00
	A	C	50	The Reign of H.M. King George V (Apr. 1935)......................................		15p	£7.50
	B	C	25	Rigs of Ships (Feb. 1929)		80p	£20.00
123	A	C	50	Romance of the Heavens (Aug. 1928) (see W/313):—			
				A. Thin card		35p	£17.50
				B. Thick card		32p	£16.00
	A	C	50	Roses (May 1926) (see W/94)		20p	£10.00
	B	C	40	Roses (Jan. 1936)		40p	£16.00
	—	BW	48	Round Europe (66 × 52 mm.) (Jan. 1937)....		13p	£6.50
	A	C	50	Rugby Internationals (Nov. 1929)..........		25p	£12.50
	A	C	50	Safety First (Dec. 1934) (see W/321):—			
				A. Home issue—"This surface...".......		14p	£7.00
				B. Irish issue—"Note. This surface ..." ...		50p	—
	A	C	50	The Sea-Shore (May 1938) (see W/322):—			
				A. Home issue—special album offer.......		13p	£4.00
				B. Irish issue—general album offer........		20p	£10.00
	A	U	40	Shannon Electric Power Scheme (1931)......		£1.00	£40.00
	A	C	50	Ships' Badges (June 1925) (see W/328)		22p	£11.00
106	A	C	50	Speed (Mar. 1930)........................		60p	£30.00
	A	C	50	Speed (Oct. 1938) (see W/330):—			
				A. Home issue—four brands quoted at base		13p	£5.00
				B. Irish issue—no brands at base..........		22p	£11.00
	A	C	50	Strange Craft (Dec. 1931).................		20p	£10.00
	B	C	40	Trees (Feb. 1937).........................		45p	£18.00
	B	C	25	University Hoods & Gowns (May 1926).....		£1.20	£30.00
163	A	C	50	Wild Flowers (June 1923):—			
				A. With dots in side panels..............		13p	£6.50
				B. Without dots in side panels		13p	£6.50

Illus. No.	Size	Print- ing	Number in set		Handbook ref.	Price per card	Complete set
157	A	C	50	Wild Flowers—"Series of 50" (Feb. 1936) (see W/346):—			£4.00
				A. Home issue—back "This surface...".		13p	
				B. Irish issue—back "Note. This surface ..."		40p	—
	A	C	50	Wild Flowers—"2nd Series ..." (May 1937) (see W/347):—			
				A. Home issue—adhesive back..........		13p	£3.50
				B. Irish issue—non-adhesive back........		20p	£10.00
	A	C	50	Wonders of the Past (Sep. 1926) (see W/348).		32p	£16.00
	A	C	50	Wonders of the Sea (Nov. 1928) (see W/349).		26p	£13.00

D. Post-1940 Issues

—		C	36	World of Firearms (70 × 44 mm) (1982)......		08p	£2.50
—		C	36	World of Speed (70 × 44 mm.) (1981)........		08p	£2.00

E. Unissued Series

	A	P	50	Gems of Italian Architecture (photographic reproduction of original series prepared in 1917) (1960).............................		09p	£4.50
	A	C	50	Life in the Hedgerow........................		15p	£7.50
	A	C	50	Life of King Edward VIII		—	£400.00
	A	C	25	Pond and Aquarium 1st Series		16p	£4.00
	A	C	25	Pond and Aquarium 2nd Series		16p	£4.00
	B	C	40	Puppies...................................		—	—
	A	C	50	Waterloo		£40.00	

F. Miscellaneous

			6	Boer War Medallions (see W/18)............		—	—
		C	12	The British Empire (133 × 101 mm.).........		£3.50	£42.00
		C	12	Cities of Britain (133 × 101 mm.)...........		£3.50	—
		C	6	Flags of the Allies (shaped) (see W/67)		£6.50	—
		C	32	Happy Families (non-insert) (91 × 63 mm.) ..		£4.00	—
		C	12	Industries of Britain (133 × 101 mm.)........		£3.50	—
			1	Pinchbeck Medallion (see W/18A)...........		—	—
				Three Castles Sailing Ship Model advertisement cards:—			
	A	C	1	A. View from Stern:—			
				I. Three Castles Cigarettes............		—	£0.80
				II. In the eighteenth century		—	£0.80
	A	C	1	B. View from Bows:—			
				I. Three Castles Filter		—	£0.80
				II. Three Castles Filter magnum		—	£0.80
	A	BW	1	C. Sailing Ship Black Line Drawing.......		—	£0.80
	A	BW	1	D. Three Castles Shield Black Line Drawing...............................		—	£0.80

G. Reprint Series by "Nostalgia"

	A	C	50	Cricketers 1896 (1982).....................		—	£6.00
	A	C	50	Cricketers 1901 (1983).....................		—	£6.00

WILSON & CO., Ely

Pre-1919 Issue

	A	C	50	War Portraits.............................	H.86	£40.00	—

W. WILSON, Birmingham

Pre-1919 Issues

	D	C	30	*Army Pictures, Cartoons, etc................	H.12	—	—
	A	C	50	War Portraits.............................	H.86	—	—

A. & M. WIX, London and Johannesburg

Post-1920 Issues

—		—		Cinema Cavalcade (50 coloured, 200 black and white; sizes—70 small, 110 large, 70 extra-large):—			
			250	"A Series of 250 ..." ("Max Cigarettes")...		25p	—
215			250	"2nd Series of 250 ..." ("Max Cigarettes").		16p	£40.00
	A2	C	100	Film Favourites—"Series of 100 ..."........	Ha.581-1	—	—
	A2	C	100	Film Favourites—"2nd Series of 100 ..."....	Ha.581-2	80p	—
	A2	C	100	Film Favourites—"3rd Series of 100":—	Ha.581-3		
				A. White card......................		—	—
				B. Cream card		45p	£45.00
	J1	C	100	*Men of Destiny (folders) (P.O. Box 5764, Johannesburg)........................		£2.00	—
	—	C	250	Speed Through the Ages (171 small, 79 large):—	Ha.583		
				A. Back in English & Afrikaans...........		30p	£75.00
				B. Back in English		30p	£75.00
206	—	C	250	This Age of Power & Wonder (170 small, 80 large) ("Max Cigarettes")		22p	£55.00

J. WIX & SONS LTD., London

A. Post-1920 Issues

	C	C	50	Builders of the Empire—"Kensitas".........		13p	£6.00
	A2	C	50	Coronation (1937):—			
				A. J. Wix back:—			
				1. Linen finish.................		13p	£5.50
				2. Varnished		13p	£6.50
				B. "Kensitas" back		13p	£5.50

Illus. No.	Size	Printing	Number in set		Handbook ref.	Price per card	Complete set
		C		Henry:—	Ha.625		
				"A Series of . . ." (1935):—			
	B1		50	A. Large size............................		20p	£10.00
	—		25	B. Extra-large size......................		90p	£22.50
				"2nd Series . . ." (1935):—			
	B1		50	A. Large size............................		60p	£30.00
	—		25	B. Extra-large size......................		90p	£22.50
	B1		50	3rd Series (1936)		30p	£15.00
	B1		50	4th Series (1936)		14p	£7.00
	B1		50	5th Series (1936)		13p	£5.00
		U	25	Love Scenes from Famous Films—"First Series":—			
	C2			A. Small size............................		£1.20	£30.00
	B1			B. Large size............................		£1.40	£35.00
	—			C. Extra-large size (127 × 88 mm.).........		£1.80	—
		U	19	Love Scenes from Famous Films—"Second Series" (Nos. 5, 9, 13, 20, 23, 24, withdrawn):—			
	C2			A. Small size......................		£1.20	£23.00
	B1			B. Large size......................		£1.40	£27.00
	—			C. Extra-large size, (127 × 88mm.)		£1.80	—
	K2	C	53	*Miniature Playing Cards (anonymous):—	Ha.535–3A		
				A. Scroll design:—			
				1. Red back		13p	£5.00
				2. Blue back........................		25p	£12.50
				B. Ship design:—			
				1. Red border—Nelson's "Victory"....		25p	£12.50
				2. Black border—Drake's "Revenge"..		30p	£15.00
		U	25	Scenes from Famous Films—"Third Series":—			
	C2			A. Small size....................		£1.20	£30.00
	—			B. Extra-large size (127 × 88 mm.)........		£1.80	—

B. Silks

	—	C	48	British Empire Flags—"Kensitas" (78 × 54 mm.) (1933):—	Ha.496–4		
				A. Inscribed "Printed in U.S.A."..........		50p	£24.00
				B. Without the above		50p	£24.00
	—	C	60	Kensitas Flowers—"First Series", small (68 × 40 mm.) (1934):—	Ha.496–1		
				1. Back of folder plain		75p	£45.00
				2. Back of folder printed in green:—			
				(a) Centre oval, 19 mm. deep..........		75p	£45.00
				(b) Centre oval, 22 mm. deep..........		75p	£45.00
				(c) As (b), inscribed "Kensitas Flowers are washable . . ." below number....		75p	£45.00
	—	C	60	Kensitas Flowers—"First Series", medium (76 × 55 mm.) (1934):—	Ha.496–1		
				A. Back of folder plain		90p	£55.00
				B. Back of folder printed in green		90p	£55.00
	fl	C	30	Kensitas Flowers—"First Series" extra-large (138 × 96 mm.) (1934):—	Ha.496–1		
				A. Back of folder plain		£7.00	—
				B. Back of folder printed in green		£7.00	—
	—	C	40	Kensitas Flowers—"Second Series" (1935):—	Ha.496–2		
				A. Small size, 68 × 40 mm................		£1.50	£60.00
				B. Medium size, 76 × 55 mm.		£1.60	—
	—	C	60	National Flags—"Kensitas" (78 × 54 mm.) (1934)................................	Ha.496–3	50p	£30.00

C. Post-1940 Issues

				Ken-cards (102 × 118 mm):—			
			12	Series 1. Starters/Snacks (1969)		—	£4.00
			12	Series 2. Main Courses (1969)................		—	£4.00
			12	Series 3. Desserts (1969)		—	£4.00
			12	Series 4. Motoring (1969)....................		—	£4.00
			12	Series 5. Gardening (1969)...................		—	£4.00
			12	Series 6. Do It Yourself (1969)		—	£4.00
			12	Series 7. Home Hints (1969)		—	£4.00
			12	Series 8. Fishing (1969)		—	£4.00

D. Miscellaneous

	—	C	50	Bridge Hands (140 × 105 mm.)..............		£4.50	—
			42	Card Tricks by Jasper Maskelyne:—	Ha.535–3B		
				A. Size 70 × 34 mm.		£1.50	—
				B. Size 70 × 48 mm.		£1.50	—
		U		Jenkynisms:—			
				A. "The K4's" Series (75–78 × 65 mm.):			
			101	I. Known as 1st Series................		50p	—
			50	II. Known as 2nd Series..............		50p	—
			30	III. Known as 3rd Series		50p	—
			1	IV. Known as 4th Series		—	—
				B. The Red Bordered series (2 sizes for each series):			
			17	I. Series of Quotations		£1.50	—
			? 42	II. "Today's Jenkynisms"		£1.50	—

WOOD BROS., England

	—	BW	28	Dominoes (63 × 29 mm.)		—	—

T. WOOD, Cleckheaton

Illus. No.	Size	Print-ing	Number in set		Handbook ref.	Price per card	Complete set
Pre-1919 issue							
	D	C	30	*Army Pictures, Cartoons, etc.	H.12	—	—

JOHN J WOODS, London

Pre-1919 Issue							
	A	BW	? 8	*Views of London	H.395	£90.00	—

W. H. & J. WOODS LTD., Preston

A. Pre-1919 Issue							
	A	C	25	*Types of Volunteers and Yeomanry	H.455	£15.00	£375.00
B. Post-1920 Issues							
	A2	U	25	Aesop's Fables	Ha.518	60p	£15.00
	A2	P	50	Modern Motor Cars		£1.50	£75.00
	D	C	25	Romance of the Royal Mail		24p	£6.00

J. & E. WOOLFE

Pre-1919 Issue							
	A	U	? 40	*Beauties—"KEWA"	H.139	—	—

M. H. WOOLER, London

Pre-1919 Issue							
	A	—	? 1	Beauties "BOCCA"		—	—

T. E. YEOMANS & SONS LTD., Derby

Pre-1919 Issues							
	—	C	72	Beautiful Women (75 × 55 mm.)	Ha.284	—	—
	A	U	50	War Portraits		—	—

JOHN YOUNG & SONS LTD., Bolton

Pre-1919 Issues							
	A2	C	? 4	Naval Skits	H.457/Ha.457	£110.00	—
	A2	C	12	*Russo-Japanese Series	H.456	£40.00	—

ANONYMOUS SERIES

A. Pre-1919 Issues. With letterpress on back of card

	A2	C	20	Animal Series: See Hill			
				A. "The cigarettes with which..." back		—	—
				B. Space at back		—	—
	A	U	? 40	*Beauties—"KEWA," "England Expects ..." back	H.139	—	—
	D	BW	25	*Boxers, green back. See Cohen Weenen		—	—
	A1	C	? 3	*Celebrities—Coloured, 1902 Calendar back		—	—
	D	C	39	*Celebrities—"GAINSBOROUGH I", 1902 Calendar back, gilt border to front. See Cohen Weenen	H.90	—	—
	A2	C	20	*Interesting Buildings and Views, 1902 Calendar back	Ha.96	—	—
	D2	C	20	*Nations, 1902 Calendar back	Ha.97	—	—
	A	C	25	*Types of British Soldiers, "General Favourite Onyx" back	H.144	—	—
	D	C	25	V.C. Heroes (Nos. 51–75—See Cohen Weenen)		—	—
	A	C	41	V.C. Heroes—"Pure Virginia Cigarettes"—Dobson Molle & Co. Ltd.—Printers	H.427	—	—
	D	U	50	*War Series (Cohen Weenen—Nos. 1–50)	H.103	—	—
	A	C	41	V.C. Heroes—See Thomson & Porteous	H.427	—	—

B. Pre-1919 Issues. With plain back

	A	U	25	*Actors and Actresses—"FROGA C"	H.20/Ha.20	—	—
	D2	U	? 5	*Actresses—"Anglo"	Ha.185	—	—
		U		*Actresses—"ANGOOD":—	H.187/Ha.187		
			? 13	A. Brown tinted—			
				i. Thick board		—	—
				ii. Thin board		—	—
			? 1	B. Green tinted		—	—
			? 10	C. Black tinted		—	—
	A1	BW	20	*Actresses—"BLARM"	H.23	£6.00	—
	D	U	20	*Actresses—Chocolate tinted. See Hill	H.207	—	—
	A	C	? 19	*Actresses—"DAVAN":—	Ha.124		
				A. Portrait in red only		—	—
				B. Portrait in colour		—	—
	D	BW	12	*Actresses—"FRAN". See Drapkin	H.175	—	—
	A	U	26	*Actresses—"FROGA A"	H.20	—	—

Illus. No.	Size	Print- ing	Number in set		Handbook ref.	Price per card	Complete set
A1	BW	? 15		*Actresses—"HAGG B"..................	H.24/Ha.24	£10.00	—
A	BW	15		*Actresses—"RUTAN" See Rutter..........	H.381	—	—
—	C	50		*Actresses Oval Card (as Phillips)	Ha.324	—	—
A1	U			*Actresses and Beauties—Collotype (See Ogden)	H.306	—	—
C	C	20		*Animal Series. See Hill		—	—
—	C	? 12		*Arms of Cambridge Colleges (17 × 25 mm.). See Kuit	H.458	—	—
—	C	? 12		*Arms of Companies (30 × 33 mm.). See Kuit	H.459	—	—
A2	BW	? 13		*Battleships. See Hill	H.208/Ha.208	—	—
A	C	? 14		*Beauties—"BOCCA"	H.39/Ha.39	£10.00	—
A		50		*Beauties—"CHOAB":—	H.21		—
	U			A. Unicoloured......................		—	—
	C			B. Coloured........................		£7.00	—
A				*Beauties—"FECKSA":—	H.58/Ha.58		—
	U	50		A. Plum-coloured front		—	—
	C	? 6		B. Coloured front....................		£8.00	—
D2	U	? 18		*Beauties—"FENA"	H.148/Ha.148	—	—
A2	C	25		*Beauties—"GRACC"	H.59	£8.00	—
A	C	26		*Beauties—"HOL"	H.192	£10.00	—
A	U	? 41		*Beauties—"KEWA"	H.139/Ha.139	—	—
—	C	30		*Beauties—Oval card (36 × 60 mm.) (See Phillips)	H.244	—	—
A	U	? 17		*Beauties—Collotype.....................	Ha.278	—	—
D1	U			*Bewlay's War Series:—	Ha.477		—
		12		1. Front without captions		—	—
		? 1		2. Front with captions		—	—
A2	BW	20		*Boer War Cartoons........................	H.42	—	—
A	C	? 25		*Boer War and General Interest:—	H.13		—
				A. Plain cream back		—	—
				B. Brown Leaf Design back		—	—
				C. Green Leaf Design back		—	—
				D. Green Daisy Design back..............		—	—
A2	BW	? 16		*Boer War Celebrities—"CAG"..............	H.79/Ha.79	—	—
A		? 8		Boer War Celebrities "RUTTER":—	Ha.382		—
	BW			A. Front in Black & White		—	—
				B. Front in light orange & Brown		—	—
A1	BW	20		*Boer War Generals—"CLAM"	H.61	—	—
A2	BW	? 12		*Boer War Generals—"FLAC"	H.47	—	—
D	C	25		*Boxer Rebellion—Sketches (1904)...........	H.46	£6.00	—
A	C	54		*British Beauties (Phillips) (1–54).............	H.328	—	—
A	C	54		*British Beauties (Phillips) (55–108) Matt.....	H.328	—	—
A	C	12		British Queens	Ha.480	—	—
A	BW	16		*British Royal Family.......................	H.28	£8.00	—
A	C	45		*Celebrities—Coloured (Cohen Weenen)	H.89	—	—
D	C	39		*Celebrities—"GAINSBOROUGH I". See Cohen Weenen..........................	H.90	—	—
D	BW	?147		*Celebrities—"GAINSBOROUGH II". See Cohen Weenen	H.91	—	—
A1	P	36		*Celebrities of the Great War (1916). See Major Drapkin & Co....................		—	—
A	BW	? 10		Celebrities of the Great War	Ha.236	—	—
A	C			*Colonial Troops:—	H.40		—
		30		A. Cream card		—	—
		50		B. White card		—	—
A	BW	20		Cricketers Series	H.29	—	—
A	C	50		Dogs (as Taddy)........................	Ha.487	£6.00	—
A	C	25		*England's Military Heroes. See Player:—	H.352		—
				A. Wide card...........................		—	—
				B. Narrow card		—	—
A	C	25		*England's Naval Heroes. See Player:—			—
				A. Wide card...........................		—	—
				B. Narrow card	H.353	—	—
A	C	20		*The European War Series	H.129	£3.00	—
A	C			*Flags, Arms and Types of Nations:—	H.115		—
		24		A. Numbered..........................		£5.00	—
		? 1		B. Unnumbered		—	—
A	C			*Flags and Flags with Soldiers:—	H.41		—
		30		A. Flagstaff Draped		£4.00	—
		15		B. Flagstaff not Draped (Flags only)		£4.00	—
A1	C	30		*Flags of Nations. See Cope..................	H.114	—	—
A1	C	24		*Girls, Flags and Arms of Countries. See Rutter	H.383	—	—
A	C	40		*Home and Colonial Regiments:—	H.69		—
				20. Caption in blue		—	—
				20. Caption in brown		£7.00	—
A	C	52		*Japanese Series, P.C. Inset. See Muratti		—	—
A1	P	? 2		*King Edward and Queen Alexandra	H.460	£15.00	—
D	C	20		*National Flag Series. See Hill		—	—
D	C	20		*Nations, gilt border. See Cohen Weenen......	H.97	—	—
D	C	40		*Naval and Military Phrases:—	H.14		—
				A. Plain front (no border)		£5.00	—
				B. Front with gilt border		—	—
—	U	? 1		*Portraits .See Drapkin & Millhoff (48 × 36 mm.)	H.461	—	—
A	U	? 47		*Pretty Girl Series—"BAGG"................	H.45/Ha.45	—	—
A1	C	20		*Prince of Wales Series. See Hill	H.22	—	—
D	C	30		*Proverbs................................	H.15	—	—
A	BW	19		Russo-Japanese Series	Ha.184	—	—
A	C	20		Russo-Japanese War Series	H.100	—	—

Illus. No.	Size	Printing	Number in set		Handbook ref.	Price per card	Complete set
	A	C	10	Scenes from San Toy. See Richard Lloyd.....	H.462	—	—
	A	C	25	Sports & Pastimes Series No. 1	H.225	£4.00	—
	A	C	25	*Star Girls	H.30	—	—
	A1	BW	? 28	*Statuary (Hill A–D)	H.218	—	—
	A	C	25	*Types of British and Colonial Troops.........	H.76	—	—
	A2	C	25	*Types of British Soldiers	H.144	—	—
	—	U	? 21	Views and Yachts (narrow, abt. 63 × 30 mm.) .	Ha.262–2	—	—
	D	BW	12	*Views of the World. See Drapkin	H.176	—	—
	D	BW	8	*Warships. See Drapkin	H.463/Ha.463	—	—
	D			*War Series:—	Ha.103		
		U	? 1	A. Front in brown........................		—	—
		BW	? 2	B. Front in black and white...............		—	—

C. Post-1920 Issues. With letterpress on back

		C	25	Cinema Stars—see Teofani:—	Ha.530		
	C2			A. Small size			
	—			B. Extra-large size (109 × 67 mm.)........			
	A2	U	50	Cinema Stars—Set 7—see United Kingdom Tobacco Co......................	Ha.515–7		
	D2	C	25	Cinema Stars—Set 8—see Moustafa........	Ha.515–8		
	A2	C	50	Evolution of the British Navy—see Godfrey Phillips................................			
	A2	BW	40	Famous Film Stars, text in Arabic (two series)—see Hill......................			
	A2	C	50	Famous Footballers—see Godfrey Phillips....			
	A2	C	35	Famous Stars—see Reliance Tobacco Mfg. Co...................................	Ha.572		
	C2	C	20	Great Inventors—see Teofani................	H.213		
	D2	U	48	Modern Movie Stars and Cinema Celebrities—see Teofani	Ha.569		
	D2	C	25	Pictures of World Interest—see Moustafa....			
	C2	U	24	Well-Known Racehorses—see Teofani	Ha.609		

D. Post-1920 Issues. With Designs on Back

	A	BW	25	Careless Moments		18p	£4.50
	D2	U	28	*Dominoes ("W.T.C." monogram back)—see Walker's Tobacco Co.....................	Ha.535–2		
	—	C	53	*Miniature Playing Cards (68 × 42 mm.) (red back, black cat trade mark in centre)—see Carreras...........................	Ha.535–1		
	K2	C	53	*Miniature Playing Cards (blue scroll back)— · see Godfrey Phillips			
	K2	C	53	*Miniature Playing Cards—see J. Wix:— A. Scroll design:— 1. Red back .... 2. Blue back .... B. Ship design:— 1. Red border—Nelson's "Victory".... 2. Black border—Drake's "Revenge"..	Ha.535–3		
		C		*Playing Cards and Dominoes—see Carreras:—	Ha.535–1		
		C	52	A. Small size:— 1. Numbered .... 2. Unnumbered			
	—		26	B. Large size (77 × 69 mm.):— 1. Numbered .... 2. Unnumbered			

E. Post-1920 Issues. With Plain Back

	A2	P	36	Australia, Second Series		13p	£2.25
	A2	P	18	*Beauties—see Marcovitch...................	Ha.627		
	A1	P	60	*British Beauty Spots—see Coudens	Ha.553		
	B1	P	50	*British Castles, Nd. S.J.51–S.J.100—see Pattreiouex...........................	Ha.595–3		
	—	C	108	*British Naval Crests (74 × 52 mm.)...........	Ha.504–4	—	—
	D2	CP	50	*Camera Studies—see Moustafa			
	B1	P	50	*Cathedrals and Abbeys, Nd. S.J.1–S.J.50—see Pattreiouex	Ha.595–3		
	A	C	25	*Charming Portraits—see Continental Cigarette Factory	Ha.549		
	A2	U	30	*Cinema Stars—Set 3	Ha.515–3	—	—
	A2	U	30	*Cinema Stars—Set 6	Ha.515–6	30p	£9.00
	—	C	110	*Crests & Badges of the British Army (74 × 52 mm.):— (a) Numbered........................... (b) Unnumbered	Ha.502–2	—	—
	—	BW	12	*Film Actors and Actresses (56 × 31 mm.)—see Teofani................................	Ha.618		
	A	C	20	*Head Dresses of Various Nations—see Teofani................................	Ha.619–1		
	A	—	20	*Inventors and Their Inventions—see Hill	H.213		
	—	C	? 9	*Irish Views (68 × 67 mm.)—see Lambkin	Ha.585		
	—	BW	12	*London Views (57 × 31 mm.)—see Teofani ...	Ha.620		
	A	C	50	*Natives in Costume—see Teofani	Ha.619–2		
	—	P	30	*Photographs (Animal Studies) (64 × 41 mm.) .	Ha.541	£1.00	—
	—	C	? 48	*Regimental Colours II (76 × 70 mm.).........	Ha.502–7	—	—
	—	P	22	*Teofani Gems I—Series of 22 (53 × 35 mm.)—see Teofani	Ha.621–1		
	—	P	28	*Teofani Gems II—Series of 28 (53 × 35 mm.)—see Teofani	Ha.621—2		
	—	P	36	*Teofani Gems III—Series of 36 (53 × 35 mm.)—see Teofani	Ha.621–3		
	A	C	50	*World's Smokers—see Teofani..............	Ha.619–3		

F. Post-1920 Issues. ANONYMOUS SERIES—Silks and Other Novelty Issues
    For Anonymous Metal Plaques—see International Tobacco Co.
    For Anonymous Metal Charms—see Rothman's.
    For Anonymous Miniature Rugs—see Godfrey Phillips.
    For Anonymous Lace Motifs—see Carreras.
    For Anonymous Woven Silks—see Anstie and J. Wix.
    For Anonymous Printed Silks with Blue Borders—see Themans.
Anonymous ordinary printed British silks which are found unbacked are listed below, with cross-reference to issuing
firms. Entries marked † are only anonymous when the paper backings are missing, and in these cases the indication
applies only to the silks without backings.

Arms of Countries and Territories—see Phillips	Ha.504–12
Battleship Crests I—see Morris†	Ha.504–3
British Admirals—see Phillips	Ha.504–5
British Butterflies and Moths II—see Phillips	Ha.505–6
British Naval Crests II—see Phillips	Ha.504–4
Butterflies I—see Phillips	Ha.505–5
Butterflies and Moths III—see Lea†	Ha.505–7
Clan Tartans—see Phillips	Ha.505–15
Colonial Army Badges—see Phillips	Ha.502–3
County Cricket Badges—see Phillips	Ha.505–8
Crests & Badges of the British Army II—see Phillips and Singleton & Cole†	Ha.502–2
English Flowers—see Morris†	Ha.505–4
English & Foreign Birds I—see Morris†	Ha.505–1
Flags—Set 1—see Gallaher†	Ha.501–1
Flags—Set 2—see Muratti	Ha.501–2
Flags—Set 3—see Muratti†	Ha.501–3
Flags—Set 4—see Phillips	Ha.501–4
Flags—Set 5—see Phillips	Ha.501–5
Flags—Set 6—see Phillips	Ha.501–6
Flags—Set 7—see Phillips	Ha.501–7
Flags—Set 8—see Muratti†	Ha.501–8
Flags—Set 9—see Phillips	Ha.501–9
Flags—Set 10 (7th, 10th and 12th Series)—see Phillips	Ha.501–10
Flags—Set 11 (Fourth to Seventh Series)—see John Sinclair	Ha.501–11
Flags—Set 12 ("Let 'em all come" and Allies grouped Flags)—see Phillips	Ha.501–12
Flags—Set 13—see Phillips	Ha.501–13
Flags—Set 14 (House Flags)—see Phillips	Ha.501–14
Flags—Set 15 (Pilot and Signal Flags)—see Phillips	Ha.501–15
Football Colours—see Phillips	Ha.505–9
Great War Leaders I—see Muratti†	Ha.504–6
Great War Leaders II—see Phillips	Ha.504–7
Great War Leaders III and Warships—see Phillips	Ha.504–10
Great War Leaders IV and Celebrities—see Phillips	Ha.504–11
Irish Patriots—see Phillips	Ha.505–11
Naval Badges of Rank and Military Headdress—see Phillips	Ha.504–9
Old Masters—Set 2—see Phillips	Ha.503–2
Old Masters—Set 3A—see Phillips	Ha.503–3A
Old Masters—Set 3B—see Phillips	Ha.503–3B
Old Masters—Set 4—see Phillips	Ha.503–4
Old Masters—Set 5—see Phillips	Ha.503–5
Old Masters—Set 7—see Phillips	Ha.503–7
Old Pottery—see Lea†	Ha.505–14
Orders of Chivalry I—see Phillips	Ha.504–14
Orders of Chivalry II—see Murray†	Ha.504–15
Pottery Types—see Salmon & Gluckstein† (see RB21/311)	
Regimental Badges I—see Muratti† and John Sinclair†	Ha.502–1
Regimental Colours I—see Muratti†	Ha.502–6
Regimental Colours II—see Phillips and John Sinclair	Ha.502–7
Regimental Colours III—see Phillips	Ha.502–8
Regimental Colours IV—see Morris	Ha.502–9
Regimental Colours V—see Muratti†	Ha.502–10
Regimental Colours & Badges of the Indian Army—see Drapkin†	Ha.502–5
Regimental Crests and Badges III—see Lea†	Ha.502–4
Religious Pictures—see Phillips	Ha.505–10
Victoria Cross Heroes I—see Phillips	Ha.504–1
Victoria Cross Heroes II—see Phillips and Cohen Weenen†	Ha.504–2
War Pictures—see Phillips	Ha.504–8

SECTION II
FOREIGN CIGARETTE CARDS

INDEX OF BRANDS

One of the Finest—see Buchner
Our Little Beauties—see Allen & Ginter
Oxford Cigarettes—see American Tobacco Co.

Pan Handle—see American Tobacco Co.
Perfection Cigarettes—see American Tobacco Co.
Peter Pan Cigarettes—see Sniders & Abrahams
Picadilly Little Cigars—see American Tobacco Co.
Piedmont Cigarettes—see American Tobacco Co.
Pinhead Cigarettes—see British American Tobacco Co.
Pirate Cigarettes—see Wills
Polo Bear Cigarettes—see American Tobacco Co.
Puritan Little Cigars—see American Tobacco Co.
Purple Mountain Cigarettes—see Wills

Recruit Little Cigars—see American Tobacco Co.
Red Cross—see Lorillard or American Tobacco Co.
Richmond Gem Cigarettes—see Allen & Ginter
Richmond Straight Cut Cigarettes—see American Tobacco Co.
Royal Bengal Little Cigars—see American Tobacco Co.

St. Leger Little Cigars—see American Tobacco Co.
Scots Cigarettes—see African Tobacco Mfrs.
Scrap Iron Scrap—see American Tobacco Co.
Senator Cigarettes—see Scerri
Sensation Cut Plug—see Lorillard
Silko Cigarettes—see American Tobacco Co.

Sovereign Cigarettes—see American Tobacco Co.
Springbok Cigarettes—see United Tobacco Co.
Standard Cigarettes—see Carreras or Sniders & Abrahams
Sub Rosa Cigarros—see American Tobacco Co.
Sultan Cigarettes—see American Tobacco Co.
Sweet Caporal—see Kinney or American Tobacco Co. or ITC Canada
Sweet Lavender—see Kimball

Teal Cigarettes—see British American Tobacco Co.
Three Bells Cigarettes—see Bell
Tiger Cigarettes—see British American Tobacco Co.
Tokio Cigarettes—see American Tobacco Co.
Tolstoy Cigarettes—see American Tobacco Co.
Trumps Long Cut—see Moore & Calvi
Turf Cigarettes—see Carreras
Turkey Red Cigarettes—see American Tobacco Co.
Turkish Trophy Cigarettes—see American Tobacco Co.
Twelfth Night Cigarettes—see American Tobacco Co.

U.S. Marine—see American Tobacco Co.
Uzit Cigarettes—see American Tobacco Co.

Vanity Fair Cigarettes—see Kimball
Vice Regal Cigarettes—see Wills
Virginia Brights Cigarettes—see Allen & Ginter

Wings Cigarettes—see Brown & Williamson

AFRICAN CIGARETTE CO. LTD. Egypt _____

| | | 50 | Actresses ALWICS (1905–08) .... | £4.50 | — |
| | L | 25 | Auction Bridge (1925–30) .... | £3.50 | — |

AFRICAN TOBACCO MANUFACTURERS, South Africa _____

A. Card Issues

	L	18	All Blacks South African Tour (1928)......................	—	—
		60	Animals (1920–25):—		
			A. Cut Outs	£2.50	—
			B. Not Cut Out..................................	£2.00	—
		25	The Arcadia Fair (1924)................................	£5.00	—
	MP	48	British Aircraft (1932)	£2.00	—
		50	Chinese Transport (1930)	£2.75	—
	MP	48	Cinema Artistes (1930).................................	£1.20	—
		50	Cinema Stars "OMBI" Officers Mess Issue 1st Series (1921)...	90p	£45.00
		50	Cinema Stars "OMBI" Officers Mess Issue 2nd Series (1921)..	90p	£45.00
	M	50	Famous & Beautiful Women (1938).......................	£1.00	—
	L	50	Famous & Beautiful Women (1938).......................	90p	—
		33	Houses of Parliament (1920–25).........................	£5.00	—
		58	Miniatures (1925–30)	£4.50	—
	MP	48	National Costume (1930)	£1.25	—
	K	53	Playing Cards MP–SA Virginia Cigarettes (1930–35)	60p	—
	K	53	Playing Cards OK Cigarettes (1930–35)...................	60p	—
	K	53	Playing Cards Scots Cigarettes (1930–35).................	60p	—
	MP	48	Popular Dogs (1930)...................................	£1.50	—
	M	100	Postage Stamps Rarest Varieties (1929)	70p	£70.00
	M	80	Prominent NZ & Australian Rugby Players & Springbok 1937 Touring Team (1937).................................	70p	—
	L	80	Prominent NZ & Australian Rugby Players & Springbok 1937 Touring Team (1937).................................	60p	—
		25	The Racecourse (1924).................................	£4.50	—
	M	132	S. African Members of the Legislative Assembly (1921).......	—	—
	M	100	The World of Sport (1938)	65p	—
	L	100	The World of Sport (1938)	65p	—

B. Silk Issues

	M	30	Some Beautiful Roses (1920–25).........................	£6.00	—
	M	25	Types of British Birds (1920–25)........................	£6.00	—
	M	20	Types of British Butterflies (1920–25)....................	£6.00	—
	M	25	Types of Railway Engines (1920–25)......................	£12.00	—
	M	25	Types of Sea Shells (1920–25)..........................	£7.00	—

ALLEN & GINTER, U.S.A. _____

All series issued 1885–95

		?	Actors & Actresses (Sepia Photographic)...................	£1.20	—
		?	Actresses & Beauties (Coloured).........................	£4.00	—
		50	American Editors.....................................	£10.00	—
	L	50	American Editors.....................................	£15.00	—
		50	Arms of All Nations	£8.00	—
		50	Birds of America	£5.00	£250.00
	L	50	Birds of America	£12.00	—
		50	Birds of the Tropics..................................	£6.00	£300.00
	L	50	Birds of the Tropics..................................	£12.00	—
		50	Celebrated American Indian Chiefs.......................	£7.00	£350.00
		50	City Flags	£5.00	—
		50	Fans of the Period	£10.00	—
		50	Fish from American Waters.............................	£5.00	—
	L	50	Fish from American Waters.............................	£12.00	—
		50	Flags of All Nations (Series Title Curved).................	£5.00	£250.00
		48	Flags of All Nations (Series Title in Straight Line)...........	£5.00	£240.00
		50	Flags of All Nations 2nd Series.........................	£5.00	£250.00
		47	Flags of the States & Territories	£5.00	—
		50	Fruits...	£10.00	—
		50	Game Birds	£5.00	£250.00
	L	50	Game Birds	£12.00	—
		50	General Government & State Capitol Buildings	£6.00	—
		50	Great Generals	£15.00	—
		50	Natives in Costume...................................	£15.00	—
		50	Naval Flags	£6.00	£300.00
		50	Parasol Drill	£10.00	£500.00
		50	Pirates of the Spanish Main	£10.00	£500.00
311		50	Prize and Game Chickens	£5.00	£250.00
		50	Quadrupeds..	£6.00	—
	L	50	Quadrupeds..	£12.00	—
		50	Racing Colors of the World:—		
			a) Front with White Frame.........................	£7.00	—
			b) Front without White Frame	£9.00	—
		50	Song Birds of the World	£5.00	£250.00
	L	50	Song Birds of the World	£12.00	—
		50	Types of All Nations..................................	£10.00	—
		50	Wild Animals of the World.............................	£6.00	£300.00
		50	The Worlds Beauties 1st Series	£8.00	£400.00
		50	The Worlds Beauties 2nd Series	£8.00	—
		50	The World's Champions 1st Series.......................	£6.00	£300.00
		50	The World's Champions 2nd Series.......................	£7.00	—
	L	50	The World's Champions 2nd Series.......................	£12.00	—
		50	The Worlds Decorations	£6.00	£300.00

ALLEN & GINTER, U.S.A. *(continued)*

	Size	No. in set		Price per card	Complete set
	L	50	The Worlds Decorations	£12.00	—
		50	Worlds Dudes	£8.00	—
		50	The Worlds Racers	£9.00	—
		50	Worlds Smokers	£8.00	£400.00
		50	World's Sovereigns	£12.00	—

ALLEN TOBACCO CO., U.S.A. ─────────────────────

	L	?	Views and Art Studies (1910–15)	£2.25	—

THE AMERICAN CIGARETTE CO., LTD., China ───────────

		25	Beauties Group 1 (1885–95)	£13.00	—
		?15	Beauties Group 2 (1885–95)	£16.00	—
		50	Flowers (1885–95)	£8.00	—

THE AMERICAN TOBACCO COMPANY, U.S.A. ─────────────

Issues 1890–1900
A. Typeset Back in Black

		Number in set		Price per card	Complete set
		28	Beauties Domino Girls......................................	£10.00	—
		25	Beauties Group 1 RB18/4	£2.50	—
		?1	Beauties Group 2 RB18/20	—	—
		25	Beauties Group 3 RB18/25	£2.50	—
		27	Beauties Group 3 RB18/26	£3.00	£80.00
		25	Beauties Group 3 RB18/27	£3.00	—
		25	Beauties Group 3 RB18/29	£3.50	—
			Beauties Group 4 RB18/36:—		
		50	a) Coloured	£2.00	£100.00
		?50	b) Sepia	£15.00	—
		52	Beauties P.C. Inset...	£4.00	£200.00
		25	Beauties – Star Girls	£9.00	—
		25	Dancers..	£5.00	—
		50	Dancing Women	£8.00	—
		50	Fancy Bathers..	£8.00	—
		36	Japanese Girls..	—	—
		25	Military Uniforms RB18/101................................	£6.00	—
		25	Military Uniforms RB18/102................................	£6.00	—
		27	Military Uniforms RB18/103................................	£3.75	£100.00
		50	Musical Instruments..	£8.00	—
		50	National Flag & Arms	£4.50	—
		25	National Flag & Flowers – Girls –	£9.00	—
		50	Savage Chiefs & Rulers	£8.00	—

B. Net Design Back in Green

		25	Beauties – black background RB18/62........................	£5.00	—
		25	Beauties – Curtain Background RB18/65	£4.00	£100.00
		25	Beauties Flower Girls RB18/67	£4.50	—
		25	Beauties Group 1 RB18/1	£2.00	£50.00
		27	Beauties Group 1 RB18/2	£2.50	—
		25	Beauties Group 1 RB18/3	£2.00	—
		24	Beauties Group 1 RB18/4	£3.00	—
		25	Beauties Group 1 RB18/5	£2.50	—
		25	Beauties Group 1 RB18/6	£2.00	£50.00
		50	Beauties Group 1 RB18/10	£2.00	—
		25	Beauties Group 2 RB18/16	£2.50	—
		25	Beauties Group 2 RB18/17	£2.50	—
		?24	Beauties Group 2 RB18/18	£2.50	—
		25	Beauties Group 2 RB18/19	£2.50	—
		25	Beauties Group 2 RB18/20	£2.50	—
		25	Beauties Group 2 RB18/21	£4.00	—
		36	Beauties Group 2 RB18/22	£5.00	—
		25	Beauties Group 3 RB18/25	£2.50	—
		?10	Beauties Group 3 RB18/28	—	—
		25	Beauties Group 3 RB18/30	£3.00	—
		25	Beauties Group 3 RB18/31	£7.50	—
		25	Beauties Group 3 RB18/32	£3.50	—
		50	Beauties Marine & Universe Girls	£7.00	—
		25	Beauties Palette Girls	£6.00	—
		25	Beauties Star Girls..	£9.00	—
		25	Beauties – stippled background RB18/78.....................	£4.50	—
		20	Beauties – thick border RB18/79............................	—	—
		52	Beauties with Playing Card inset Set 1 RB18/85	£4.00	—
		52	Beauties with Playing Card inset Set 2 RB18/86	£4.00	£200.00
		25	Boer War Series II – Series A:—		
			a) numbered...	£2.20	£55.00
			b) unnumbered	£2.20	—
			c) unnumbered and untitled "series A"..................	£4.50	—
		22	Boer War Series II – Series B	£2.50	£55.00
		25	Chinese Girls...	£7.50	—
		25	Fish from American Waters.................................	£3.50	—
		25	International Code of Signals	£4.50	—
		27	Military Uniforms numbered................................	£3.50	—
		25	Military Uniforms unnumbered	£5.00	—
		50	National Flags & Arms	—	—
		25	Old & Ancient Ships 1st Series.............................	£2.00	£50.00
		25	Old & Ancient Ships 2nd Series.............................	£4.00	£100.00

Illus. No.	Size	Number in set		Price per card	Complete set
		25	Star Series – Beauties	£8.00	—

C. Net Design Back in Blue

			Actresses:—		
	P	?300	A. Large Letter Back............................	£2.00	—
	P	?300	B. Small Letter Back............................	£3.00	—
		25	Beauties Blue Frameline:—		
			A. Matt	—	—
			B. Varnished	—	—
		28	Beauties – Domino Girls	£11.00	—
		28	Beauties Group 1 Dull Backgrounds...............	£4.00	—
		23	Beauties Group 1 Vivid Coloured backgrounds Set 1	£4.00	—
		25	Beauties Group 1 Vivid Coloured backgrounds Set 2	£4.00	—
		25	Beauties:—		
			A. Front in black and white	—	—
			B. Front in mauve	£4.00	—
		24	Beauties – Orange framelines.....................	£15.00	—
			Beauties – Playing cards:—		
		52	A. Inscribed 52 subjects	£4.00	—
		53	B. Inscribed 53 subjects	£4.00	—
		32	Celebrities...................................	£3.00	—
		25	Comic Scenes.................................	£4.50	—
	P	?149	Views	£1.60	—

D. "Old Gold" Back

		25	Beauties Group 1 RB18/1	£2.00	—
		27	Beauties Group 1 RB18/2	£2.00	—
		25	Beauties Group 1 RB18/3	£2.00	—
		24	Beauties Group 1 RB18/4	£2.00	—
		25	Beauties Group 1 RB18/5	£2.00	—
		25	Beauties Group 1 RB18/6	£2.00	—
		?47	Beauties Group 2 RB18/16,17,18	£2.00	—
		25	Beauties Group 2 RB18/22	£2.00	—
		25	Beauties Group 3 RB18/25	£2.00	£50.00
		27	Beauties Group 3 RB18/26	£2.00	£55.00
		25	Beauties Group 3 RB18/27	£2.00	—
		25	Beauties Group 3 RB18/28	£2.00	—
		25	Beauties Group 3 RB18/30	£2.00	—
		25	Flowers Inset on Beauties	£4.00	£100.00
		25	International Code of Signals:—		
			A. With Series Title...........................	£3.60	£90.00
			B. Without Series Title........................	£3.60	£90.00

E. Labels Back

		35	Beauties Group 1 RB18/2–3.....................	£2.00	—
		25	Beauties Group 2 1st Set RB18/15	£2.00	—
		25	Beauties Group 2 2nd Set RB18/16	£2.00	—
			Beauties Group 3 RB18/25–26:—		
		27	A. Old Gold Label............................	£2.00	—
		26	B. Brands Label	£2.00	—

F. Other Backs with Name of Firm

	P	100	Actresses RB18/91............................	£2.00	—
		44	Australian Parliament	£3.40	£150.00
		25	Battle Scenes	£5.00	—
		1	Columbian & Other Postage Stamps.............	—	£8.00
		50	Congress of Beauty – Worlds Fair	£9.00	—
93		50	Fish from American Waters.....................	£4.00	—
		50	Flags of All Nations	—	—
		25	Flower Inset on Beauties	£4.00	£100.00
		25	International Code of Signals	£4.00	£100.00
		25	Songs A:—		
			A. Thicker board size 70 × 39 mm..............	£5.00	—
			B. Thinner board size 67 × 39 mm	£5.00	£125.00
		25	Songs B:—		
			A. Size 70 × 39 mm..........................	£4.00	£100.00
			B. Size 67 × 39 mm..........................	£5.00	—
		25	Songs C 1st Series............................	£3.00	£75.00
		25	Songs C 2nd Series...........................	£4.00	—
		25	Songs D.....................................	£3.60	£90.00
		27	Songs E	£5.00	—
		25	Songs F	£5.00	—
		25	Songs G.....................................	£4.00	£100.00
		25	Songs H.....................................	£7.00	—
		25	Songs I......................................	£8.00	—

Issues 1900–1940

	L	50	Actors	£1.00	—
		80	Actress Series................................	—	—
	L	50	Actresses	—	—
	L	80	Animals:—		
			A. Descriptive back	80p	—
			B. Non Descriptive back	80p	—
	L	25	Arctic Scenes	£1.00	—
	M	15	Art Gallery Pictures	—	—
	M	50	Art Reproductions............................	—	—
		21	Art Series	—	—
		18	Ask Dad	—	—
	L	50	Assorted Standard Bearers of Different Countries	—	—
		25	Auto-drivers	£3.50	—

Illus. No.	Size	Number in set		Price per card	Complete set
	M	50	Automobile Series	—	—
	L	50	Baseball Folder Series (T201).................	£4.00	—
	M	121	Baseball Series (T204).......................	—	—
		208	Baseball Series (T205).......................	£5.00	—
		522	Baseball Series (T206).......................	£5.00	—
		200	Baseball Series (T207).......................	£12.00	—
		565	Baseball Series (T210).......................	—	—
		75	Baseball Series (T211).......................	—	—
		426	Baseball Series (T212).......................	—	—
		180	Baseball Series (T213).......................	—	—
		90	Baseball Series (T214).......................	—	—
		100	Baseball Series (T215).......................	—	—
	L	76	Baseball Triple Folders (T202)	£18.00	—
			Bird Series:—		
		50	A. With White Borders..................	65p	—
		50	B. With Gold Borders...................	65p	—
		30	Bird Series with Fancy Gold Frame...........	80p	—
	M	360	Birthday Horoscopes	£1.00	—
	M	24	British Buildings "Tareyton" issue............	£1.00	—
	M	42	British Sovereigns "Tareyton" issue	£1.00	—
	M	50	Butterfly Series	—	—
	L	153	Champion Athlete & Prize Fighter Series (Size 73 × 64 mm)...	60p	—
	L	50	Champion Athlete & Prize Fighter Series (Size 83 × 63 mm)...	£1.25	—
	L	50	Champion Pugilists..........................	£2.50	—
	EL	100	Champion Women Swimmers..................	£3.00	—
	M	150	College series..............................	50p	—
	M	50	Costumes & Scenery for All Countries of the World	£1.40	—
	L	49	Cowboy Series..............................	£1.25	—
	M	38	Cross Stitch	—	—
	M	17	Embarrassing Moments or Emotional Moments	—	—
	M	50	Emblem Series..............................	£1.00	—
	L	100	Fable Series	75p	—
	LP	53	Famous Baseball Players, American Athletic Champions & Photoplay Stars	—	—
		50	Fish Series inscribed "1 to 50" — 1st 50 subjects...........	65p	—
		50	Fish Series inscribed "1 to 100" — 2nd 50 subjects.	65p	—
172		200	Flags of All Nations	60p	—
	M	100	Flags of All Nations	—	—
		50	Foreign Stamp Series	—	—
	L	505	Fortune Series..............................	75p	—
	M	79	Henry "Tareyton" issue......................	70p	—
	L	50	Heroes of History...........................	£1.00	—
	M	50	Historic Homes.............................	70p	—
	L	25	Historical Events Series	£1.25	—
	M	25	Hudson – Fulton Series	—	—
	L	50	Indian Life in the 60's	£1.25	—
	L	221	Jig Saw Puzzle Pictures......................	£2.00	—
	L	50	Light House Series..........................	£1.25	—
	L	50	Men of History.............................	£1.00	—
		100	Military Series White borders	£2.00	—
		50	Military Series Gilt borders	£3.00	—
		50	Military Series "Recruit" issue:—		
			A. Uncut Cards.......................	£2.00	—
			B. Die-Cut Cards.....................	£2.00	—
		50	Movie Stars	—	—
	L	100	Movie Stars	—	—
		15	Moving Picture Stars	—	—
	EL	50	Murad Post Card Series......................	—	—
		100	Mutt & Jeff Series (Black & White)	£1.75	—
		100	Mutt & Jeff Series (Coloured)	£2.25	—
	EL	16	National League & American League Teams..............	—	—
		50	Pugilistic Subjects	—	—
	EL	18	Puzzle Picture Cards	—	—
	M	200	Riddle Series	70p	—
	EL	60	Royal Bengal Souvenir Cards	—	—
	M	150	Seals of the United States & Coats of Arms	60p	—
	L	25	Series of Champions	—	—
	L	50	Sights & Scenes of the World	£1.00	—
	L	50	Silhouettes	—	—
	L	25	Song Bird Series	—	—
		38	Sports Champions...........................	—	—
		45	Stage Stars	—	—
		25	State Girl Series	—	—
	L	50	Theatres Old & New Series...................	£1.25	—
	M	50	Toast Series	—	—
	M	550	Toast Series	—	—
	L	25	Toasts	—	—
		50	Types of Nations:—		
			A. Without Series Title..................	£1.00	—
			B. With Series Title.....................	£1.00	—
			C. Anonymous Back.....................	£1.00	—
	L	25	Up to date baseball Comics	—	—
	L	25	Up to date Comics..........................	—	—
	P	340	World Scenes & Portraits	—	—
		250	World War I Scenes.........................	75p	—
	L	50	Worlds Champion Athletes	—	—
	L	25	The Worlds Greatest Explorers...............	£1.00	—

THE AMERICAN TOBACCO CO. OF NEW SOUTH WALES LTD., Australia

Illus. No.	Size	Number in set		Price per card	Complete set
		25	Beauties Group 1 RB18/8 (1895–1905).....................	£4.50	—
		25	Beauties Group 2 (1895–1905)............................	£4.50	—

THE AMERICAN TOBACCO CO. OF VICTORIA LTD., Australia

		?87	Beauties Group 2 (1895–1905)............................	£5.50	—

ATLAM CIGARETTE FACTORY, Malta

	M	65	Beauties Back in Blue (1920–30).........................	£1.00	—
		¡50	Beauties Back in Brown (1920–30)........................	—	—
	M	519	Celebrities (1920–30)...................................	60p	—
	L	50	Views of Malta (1920–30)...............................	—	—
	M	128	Views of the World	£1.50	—

BANNER TOBACCO CO., U.S.A.

	L	25	Girls (1885–95)..	£13.00	—

THOMAS BEAR & SONS LTD.

		50	Aeroplanes (1926)	£1.50	—
		50	Cinema Artistes Set 2 (1928–33).........................	—	—
		50	Cinema Artistes Set 4 (1928–33).........................	—	—
		50	Cinema Stars Coloured (1930)............................	90p	£45.00
		50	Do You Know (1923)....................................	70p	£35.00
239		270	Javanese Series 1 Blue Background (1925–40)...............	60p	—
		100	Javanese Series 4 Yellow Background (1925–40).............	—	—
		50	Stage & Film Stars (1926)	£1.20	—

AUG BECK & CO. U.S.A.

		29	Picture Cards (1885–95).................................	£13.00	—

J. & F. BELL LTD., Denmark

		60	Rigvaabner (1920–30)..................................	£12.00	—
		60	Women of Nations (1924)................................	£14.00	—

BENSON & HEDGES (CANADA) LTD.

		48	Ancient & Modern Fire Fighting Equipment (1947)	£1.20	£60.00

BRITISH AMERICAN TOBACCO CO. LTD.

A   With Makers Name Net Design in Green

		Number		Price	Complete
		25	Beauties Art Series RB18/61.............................	£6.50	—
		25	Beauties – Black Background RB18/62	£5.00	—
		25	Beauties – Blossom Girls RB18/63........................	£20.00	—
		25	Beauties – Flower Girls RB18/67	£4.50	—
		25	Beauties – Fruit Girls RB18/68	£6.00	—
		25	Beauties – Girls in Costumes RB18/69	£5.50	—
		20	Beauties Group 1 RB18/9	£3.50	—
		25	Beauties – Lantern Girls RB18/70	£4.00	£100.00
		50	Beauties – Marine & Universe Girls RB18/71	£5.00	—
		25	Beauties – Palette Girls RB18/74:—		
			A. Plain Border to Front	£5.00	—
			B. Red Border to Front	£8.00	—
		24	Beauties – Smoke Girls RB18/75	£10.00	—
		25	Beauties – Star Girls RB18/76	£8.00	—
		25	Beauties – Stippled Background RB18/78...................	£4.00	£100.00
		25	Beauties – Water Girls RB18/80	£5.00	£125.00
		50	Buildings RB18/131	£4.00	—
		25	Chinese Girls "A" RB18/111.............................	£4.00	—
		25	Chinese Girls "B" RB18/112:—		
			A. Background Plain...................................	£4.00	—
			B. Background with Chinese Letters.....................	£4.00	£100.00
		25	Chinese Girls "C" RB18/113	£4.00	£100.00
		25	Chinese Girls "D" RB18/114............................	£4.00	£100.00
		25	Chinese Girls "E" RB18/115	£4.00	—
		25	Chinese Girls "F" Set 1 RB18/116........................	£4.00	—
		25	Chinese Girls "F" Set 2 RB18/116:—		
			A. Yellow Border......................................	£4.00	—
			B. Gold Border..	—	—
		50	Chinese Girls "F" Set 3:—		
			A. Plain Background....................................	£4.00	£200.00
			B. Chinese Characters Background	£6.00	—
		40	Chinese Trades	£3.00	—

Illus. *No.*	*Size*	*Number* *in set*		*Price* *per card*	*Complete* *set*
B	*With Makers Name Net Design in Blue*				
		25	Beauties – Numbered	£11.00	—
		53	Beauties – Playing Cards	£4.00	—
C	*With Makers Name Other Backs*				
	MP	50	Beauties (1925)	70p	£35.00
	MP	40	Beauties (1926)	70p	—
	M	50	Birds, Beast & Fishes (1925)..........................	70p	£35.00
		50	Danish Athletes (1905)................................	—	—
		28	Dominoes (1905)	£2.50	—
		48	Fairy Tales (1926)	—	—
		48	A Famous Picture – The Toast (1925–36)	—	—
		25	New York Views (1905–10)	—	—
		53	Playing Cards (1905)..................................	£4.00	—
	M	50	Wild Animals (1930–35)	70p	—
D	*Series with Brand Names*				
Albert Cigarettes					
	M	50	Aeroplanes (Civil) (1935).............................	—	—
		50	Artistes De Cinema Nd 1–50 (1932).....................	£1.20	—
		50	Artistes De Cinema Nd 51–100 (1933)	£1.20	—
	M	75	Belles Vues De Belgique (1925–30).....................	£1.00	—
	M	50	Butterflies (Girls) (1926)	£3.00	—
	M	50	Cinema Stars (Brown Photogravure) (1927–29)	—	—
	M	100	Cinema Stars (Numbered, Coloured) (1927–29)..........	£1.20	—
	M	208	Cinema Stars (Unnumbered, Coloured) (1927–29)..........	£1.20	—
	M	100	Circus Scenes (1925–35)...............................	£1.50	—
	M	100	Famous Beauties (1916)................................	£2.00	—
	M	50	L'Afrique Equitoriale De L'est A L'ouest (1930–35)	£1.50	—
	M	100	La Faune Congolaise (1930–35)	£1.00	—
	M	50	Les Grandes Paquebots Du Monde (1924)	£3.50	—
	M	50	Merveilles Du Monde (1927)	£1.50	—
	M	50	Women of Nations (Flag Girls) (1922)	—	—
Atlas Cigarettes					
		50	Buildings (1907)	£4.00	—
		25	Chinese Beauties (1912)	£1.00	£25.00
		50	Chinese Trades Set IV (1908)	80p	—
		85	Chinese Trades Set VI (1912)	£1.00	—
Battle Ax Cigarettes					
	M	100	Famous Beauties (1916)................................	£1.50	—
	M	50	Women of Nations (Flag Girls) (1917)	£2.50	—
Copain Cigarettes					
		52	Birds of Brilliant Plumage (1927)	£3.00	—
Domino Cigarettes					
		25	Animaux et Reptiles (1961)............................	10p	£1.50
		25	Corsaires et Baucaniers (1961).........................	10p	75p
		25	Figures Histeriques 1st Series (1961)	10p	£1.50
		25	Figures Histeriques 2nd Series (1961)	24p	£6.00
		25	Fleurs de Culture (1961)	10p	75p
		25	Les Oiseaux et L'Art Japanais (1961)	32p	£8.00
		25	Les Produits Du Monde (1961)	10p	75p
		50	Voitures Antiques (1961)..............................	32p	£16.00
Eagle Bird Cigarettes					
		50	Animals and Birds (1909)	£1.00	—
		50	Aviation Series (1912).................................	£1.20	—
		25	Birds of the East (1912)	80p	£20.00
		25	Chinese Famous Warriors (1911).......................	£1.00	£25.00
		25	Chinese Beauties 1st Series (1908):—		
			A. Vertical Back	£1.60	£40.00
			B. Horizontal Back	£1.60	—
		25	Chinese Beauties 2nd Series (1909):—		
			A. Front Without Framelines	£1.20	—
			B. Front With Framelines.............................	£1.20	—
		50	Chinese Trades (1908)	80p	£40.00
		25	Cock Fighting (1911)	£1.60	£40.00
		60	Flags & Pennons (1926)................................	60p	£36.00
		50	Romance of the Heavens (1929)	—	—
		50	Siamese Alphabet (1922)...............................	60p	£30.00
		50	Siamese Dreams & Their Meanings (1923)	70p	£35.00
		50	Siamese Horoscopes (1915–18).........................	60p	£30.00
		50	Siamese Play-Inao (1915–18)...........................	60p	£30.00
		50	Siamese Play-Khun Chang Khun Phaen 1st Series (1915–18)..	60p	£30.00
		50	Siamese Play-Khun Chang Khun Phaen 2nd Series (1915–18).	60p	£30.00
		36	Siamese Play-Phra Aphaiu 1st Series (1915–18)............	60p	£22.00
		36	Siamese Play-Phra Aphaiu 2nd Series (1919)	60p	£22.00
		150	Siamese Play – Ramakien I (1912–14)...................	60p	£90.00
		50	Siamese Play – Ramakien II (1914)	60p	£30.00
		50	Siamese Uniforms (1915)...............................	£1.00	£50.00
		50	Views of Siam (1928).................................	60p	£30.00
		50	Views of Siam (Bangkok) (1928)........................	60p	£30.00
		30	War Weapons (1914–15)	£1.10	£33.00
Kong Beng Cigarettes					
		60	Animals (cut-outs) (1912)	£4.00	—
Mascot Cigarettes					
		100	Cinema Stars (Nd 201–300) (1931)......................	£2.50	—
	M	208	Cinema Stars Unnumbered (1924).......................	£1.50	—
Millbank Cigarettes					
		60	Animals (Cut-Outs):—		
			A. "1516" at base of back (1922)......................	90p	—

Illus. No.	Size	Number in set		Price per card	Complete set
			B. "3971" at base of back (1923).........................	60p	£36.00
Nassa Cigarettes					
	M	50	Birds, Beasts & Fishes (1924).............	£3.00	—
Pedro Cigarettes (see also Imperial Tobacco Co. of India)					
		50	Actors & Actresses (1905–08).........................	—	—
		37	Nautch Girls Red Border (1905–07)	£1.00	—
Pinhead Cigarettes					
		50	Chinese Modern Beauties (1912).........................	90p	—
		33	Chinese Heroes Set 1 (1912)..............	90p	—
		50	Chinese Heroes Set 2 (1913–14).............	90p	—
212		50	Chinese Trades Set III (1908).................	70p	£35.00
		50	Chinese Trades Set IV (1909).................	70p	£35.00
		50	Chinese Trades Set V (1910).................	70p	£35.00
		50	Types of the British Army (1909)	£2.00	—
Railway Cigarettes (see also Imperial Tobacco Co. of India)					
		37	Nautch Girls Series (1907–08)	£1.00	£37.00
Teal Cigarettes					
		50	Cinema Stars (1930):—		
			A. Back in Blue......................................	90p	—
			B. Back in Red Brown	—	—
		30	Fish Series (1916)......................................	90p	£27.00
		50	War Incidents (1916)................................	£1.20	£60.00
Tiger Cigarettes					
		52	Nautch Girl Series (1911):—		
			A. Without frameline to front	£1.75	—
			B. With frameline to front		
			i) with crossed cigarettes on back	£1.00	£52.00
			ii) without crossed cigarettes on back..................	£1.25	—

E. Printed on back No Makers Name or Brand
(See also Imperial Tobacco Co. of Canada Ltd and United Tobacco Companies (South) Ltd)

Illus. No.	Size	Number in set		Price per card	Complete set
			Actresses "ALWICS" (1905–08):—		
		175	A. Portrait in Black......................	£1.25	—
		50	B. Portrait in Red.......................................	£3.00	—
		50	Aeroplanes (1926)	90p	£45.00
		50	Aeroplanes of Today (1936)......................	32p	£16.00
		25	Angling (1930)	80p	£20.00
		50	Arms and Armour (1910)	£2.50	—
		25	Army Life	£3.50	—
		50	Art Photogravures (1913–14)..................	70p	—
		1	Australia Day (1915)......................	—	£6.00
		22	Automobielen (1920–30)...........................	£3.00	—
		75	Aviation (1910).............................	£1.75	—
		50	Aviation Series (1911):—		
			A. With Album Clause....................	—	—
			B. Without Album Clause.................	£1.20	—
			Beauties Set I (1925):—		
	P	50	A. Black & White.....................	60p	£30.00
	MP	50	B. Coloured...........................	70p	—
	P	50	Beauties 2nd Series (1925–26):—		
			A. Black & White.....................	32p	£16.00
			B. Coloured	£1.00	—
	P	50	Beauties 3rd Series (1926)	30p	£15.00
		50	Beauties Red Tinted (1905–08)	90p	—
			Beauties Tobacco Leaf Back (1905–10):—		
		52	A. With P.C. Inset	£1.20	£62.00
		50	B. Without P.C. Inset.....................	£3.00	£150.00
	P	50	Beauties of Great Britain (1930):—		
			A. Non Stereoscopic.....................	32p	£16.00
			B. Stereoscopic.....................	80p	—
	P	50	Beautiful England (1928).................	20p	£10.00
	MP	60	La Belgique Monumentale et Pittoresque (1925–30)	£1.75	—
		50	Best Dogs of their Breed (1916)...................	90p	£45.00
		50	Billiards (1929)	90p	—
326		50	Birds, Beasts & Fishes (1937).....................	20p	£10.00
	M	50	Birds, Beasts & Fishes (1929).....................	70p	£35.00
		24	Birds of England (1924).....................	£1.20	£30.00
		50	Boy Scouts (1930) – without album clause..................	90p	£45.00
		50	Britains Defenders (1914–15):—		
			A. Blue Grey fronts.....................	80p	—
			B. Mauve fronts.....................	70p	£35.00
		50	British Butterflies (1930)	35p	£17.50
		50	British Empire Series (1913).....................	£1.25	—
		25	British Trees and Their Uses (1930)......................	80p	£20.00
		50	British Warships & Admirals (1915)	£2.00	—
		50	Butterflies & Moths (1911):—		
			A. With album clause.....................	£2.00	—
			B. Without album clause.....................	90p.	—
		50	Butterflies (Girls) (1928)	£1.20	£60.00
	M	50	Butterflies (Girls) (1928)	£1.50	£75.00
	M	50	Celebrities of Film & Stage (1930):—		
			A. Title on back in box.....................	60p	£30.00
			B. Title on back not in box	60p	£30.00
	LP	48	Channel Islands Past & Present (1939):—		
			A. Without "3rd Series".....................	£1.00	—
			B. With "3rd Series".....................	13p	£5.00
282		40	Characters from the Works of Charles Dickens (1919):—		
			A. Complete Set	—	£25.00
			B. 38 Different (— Nos. 33, 39)	20p	£8.00
		50	Cinema Artistes Black & White Set 1 (1928–33) (Nd 1–50)	50p	£25.00

Illus. No.	Size	Number in set		Price per card	Complete set
		50	Cinema Artistes Black & White Set 4 (1928–33) (Nd 101–150).	50p	£25.00
			Cinema Artistes Brown Set 1 (1928–33):—		
		60	A. With "Metro Golden Mayer"	50p	£30.00
		50	B. Without "Metro Golden Mayer"	70p	—
		50	Cinema Artistes Brown Set 2 (1928–33):—		
			A. Oblong Panel at Top Back	50p	£25.00
			B. Oval Panel at Top Back	70p	£35.00
	L	48	Cinema Artistes Set 3 (1928–33)	80p	£40.00
		48	Cinema Celebrities (C) (1935)	30p	£15.00
	L	48	Cinema Celebrities (C) (1935)	36p	£18.00
	L	56	Cinema Celebrities (D) (1936–39)	£1.20	—
		50	Cinema Favourites (1929)	£1.70	£85.00
		50	Cinema Stars Set 2 (No. 1–50) (1928–33)	30p	£15.00
		50	Cinema Stars Set 3 (No. 51–100) (1928–33)	75p	—
		50	Cinema Stars Set 4 (No. 101–150) (1928–33)	50p	—
		100	Cinema Stars "BAMT" (Coloured) (1931)	£1.10	£110.00
	P	50	Cinema Stars Set 1 (1924–30)	50p	—
	P	50	Cinema Stars Set 2 (1924–30)	32p	£16.00
	P	50	Cinema Stars Set 3 (1924–30)	55p	—
	MP	52	Cinema Stars Set 4 (1924–30)	80p	£40.00
	MP	52	Cinema Stars Set 5 (1924–30)	80p	—
	MP	52	Cinema Stars Set 6 (1924–30)	£1.50	—
	LP	48	Cinema Stars Set 7 (1924–30)	—	—
	P	50	Cinema Stars Set 8 (1924–30) (Nd 1–50)	60p	£30.00
	P	50	Cinema Stars Set 9 (1924–30) (Nd 51–100)	80p	£40.00
	P	50	Cinema Stars Set 10 (1924–30) (Nd 101–150)	80p	£40.00
	P	50	Cinema Stars Set 11 (1924–30) (Nd 151–200)	60p	£30.00
		25	Derby Day Series (1914)	£3.50	—
		50	Do You Know? (1923)	25p	£12.50
		50	Do You Know? 2nd Series (1931)	25p	£12.50
		25	Dracone Posthistoric (1930–40)	£4.00	—
		25	Dutch Scenes (1928)	£1.60	£40.00
		50	Engineering Wonders (1930)	25p	£12.50
236		40	English Costumes of Ten Centuries (1919)	80p	£32.00
	P	25	English Cricketers (1926)	£1.00	£25.00
		26	Etchings (of Dogs) (1926)	30p	£8.00
	P	50	Famous Bridges (1935)	35p	£17.50
		50	Famous Footballers Set 1 (1923)	90p	—
		50	Famous Footballers Set 2 (1924)	90p	—
		50	Famous Footballers Set 3 (1925)	90p	—
		25	Famous Racehorses (1926)	90p	£22.50
		25	Famous Railway Trains (1929)	£1.20	£30.00
		50	Favourite Flowers (1920–25)	35p	£17.50
		50	Film & Stage Favourites (1925–30)	60p	£30.00
		75	Film Favourites (1928)	60p	£45.00
		50	Flags of the Empire (1928)	50p	£25.00
		50	Foreign Birds (1930)	25p	£12.50
		50	Game Birds & Wild Fowl (1929)	60p	£30.00
	LP	45	Grace & Beauty (Nos 1–45) (1938–39)	20p	£9.00
	LP	45	Grace & Beauty (Nos 46–90) (1938–39)	13p	£3.50
	LP	48	Guernsey, Alderney & Sark Past & Present 1st Series (1937)	13p	£6.00
	LP	48	Guernsey, Alderney & Sark Past & Present 2nd Series (1938)	13p	£5.00
	L	80	Guernsey Footballers Priaulx League (1938)	20p	£16.00
	P	52	Here There & Everywhere:—		
			A. Non Stereoscopic (1929)	25p	£13.00
			B. Stereoscopic (1930)	25p	£13.00
		25	Hints & Tips for Motorists (1929)	90p	£22.50
	P	50	Homeland Events (1928)	45p	£22.50
		50	Horses of Today (1906)	£3.00	—
		32	Houses of Parliament (Red Back) (1912)	80p	£25.00
		32	Houses of Parliament (Brown Backs with verse) (1912)	£6.00	—
		50	Indian Chiefs (1930)	£1.60	£80.00
		50	Indian Regiment Series (1912)	£4.50	—
85		50	International Airliners (1937)	30p	£15.00
		25	Java Scenes (1929)	—	—
	LP	48	Jersey Then and Now 1st Series (1935)	22p	£11.00
	LP	48	Jersey Then and Now 2nd Series (1937)	13p	£5.50
		50	Jiu Jitsu (1911)	£1.40	—
		50	Keep Fit (1939)	25p	£12.50
		50	Leaders of Men (1929)	£1.50	—
		50	Life in the Tree Tops (1931)	30p	£15.00
		50	Lighthouses (1926)	50p	£25.00
		40	London Ceremonials (1929)	75p	£30.00
	P	50	London Zoo (1927)	50p	£25.00
		50	Lucky Charms (1930)	£1.20	—
		25	Marvels of the Universe Series (1925–30)	£1.20	£30.00
		45	Melbourne Cup Winners (1906)	£2.00	—
		50	Merchant Ships of the World (1925)	£1.75	—
		25	Merchant Ships of the World (1925)	—	—
		25	Military Portraits (1917)	£1.25	—
		36	Modern Beauties 1st Series (1938)	14p	£5.00
		36	Modern Beauties 2nd Series (1939)	13p	£3.00
	MP	54	Modern Beauties 1st Series (1937)	13p	£5.00
	MP	54	Modern Beauties 2nd Series (1938)	13p	£6.50
	MP	36	Modern Beauties 3rd Series (1938)	13p	£4.00
	MP	36	Modern Beauties 4th Series (1939)	13p	£4.00
	ELP	36	Modern Beauties 1st Series (1936)	50p	£18.00

Illus. No.	Size	Number in set		Price per card	Complete set
	ELP	36	Modern Beauties 2nd Series (1936)	25p	£9.00
	ELP	36	Modern Beauties 3rd Series (1937)	15p	£5.50
	ELP	36	Modern Beauties 4th Series (1937)	15p	£5.50
	ELP	36	Modern Beauties 5th Series (1938)	15p	£5.50
	ELP	36	Modern Beauties 6th Series (1938)	13p	£4.00
	ELP	36	Modern Beauties 7th Series (1938)	15p	£5.50
	LP	36	Modern Beauties 8th Series (1939)	20p	£7.50
	LP	36	Modern Beauties 9th Series (1939)	15p	£5.50
	LP	36	Modern Beauties (1939)	15p	£5.50
		50	Modern Warfare (1936)	30p	£15.00
		25	Modes of Conveyance (1928)	80p	£20.00
		48	Motor Cars Green Back (1926)	£2.00	—
		36	Motor Cars Brown Back (1929)	£2.25	—
		50	Motorcycles (1927)	£1.50	—
	P	50	Native Life in Many Lands (1932)	35p	£17.50
	P	50	Natural & Man Made Wonders of the World (1937)	25p	£12.50
	P	50	Nature Studies (1928)	32p	£16.00
	P	48	Nature Studies Stereoscopic (1930)	32p	£16.00
		50	Naval Portraits (1917)	£1.25	—
		25	Notabilities (1917)	£1.25	£32.50
		25	Past & Present (1929)	70p	£17.50
	P	48	Pictures of the East (1930):—		
			A. "A Series of 48" 17 mm long	25p	£12.50
			B. "A Series of 48" 14 mm long	25p	£12.50
	M	48	Picturesque China (1920–30):—		
			A. With 'P' at left of base	60p	£30.00
			B. Without 'P' at left of base	50p	£25.00
	M	53	Playing Cards Ace of Hearts Back (1933–40)	20p	£10.00
	K	53	Playing Cards Designed Back (1933–35):—		
			A. Blue Back	60p	—
			B. Red Back	50p	—
		36	Popular Stage, Cinema & Society Celebrities (1925–30)	£1.80	£65.00
219		25	Prehistoric Animals (1931)	70p	£17.50
		50	Prominent Australian & English Cricketers (1911)	£10.00	—
		25	Puzzle Series (1916)	£2.40	£60.00
		50	Railway Working (1927)	90p	£45.00
		10	Recruiting Posters (1915)	£4.00	—
		33	Regimental Pets (1911)	£3.00	—
		50	Regimental Uniforms (1936)	70p	£35.00
		50	Romance of the Heavens (1929)	30p	£15.00
	P	50	Round the World in Pictures Stereoscopic (1931)	35p	£17.50
		50	Royal Mail (1912)	£2.50	—
	P	50	Royal Navy (1930)	—	—
		27	Rulers of the World (1911)	—	—
		40	Safety First (1931)	30p	£12.00
		25	Ships' Flags and Cap Badges 1st Series (1930)	70p	£17.50
		25	Ships' Flags and Cap Badges 2nd Series (1930)	70p	£17.50
	P	50	Ships and Shipping (1928)	35p	£17.50
		50	Signalling Series (1913)	£1.50	—
		100	Soldiers of the World (Tobacco Leaf Back) (1902–05)	£6.00	—
		50	Speed (1938)	40p	£20.00
		25	Sports & Games in Many Lands (1930)	70p	£17.50
		50	Stage & Film Stars (1926)	90p	—
	M	50	Stars of Filmland (1927)	—	—
		48	Transport Then & Now (1940)	13p	£5.50
		32	Transport of the World (1917)	—	—
		20	Types of North American Indians (1930–40)	£3.00	—
	P	50	Types of the World (1936)	35p	£17.50
	P	270	Views of the World Stereoscopic (1908)	£1.20	—
		25	Warriors of All Nations (Gold Panel) (1937)	70p	£17.50
		50	War Incidents (Brown Back) (1915)	70p	£35.00
247		50	War Incidents (Blue Back) (1916)	60p	£30.00
		50	Warships (1926)	£2.00	—
		25	Whaling (1930)	90p	£22.50
	P	50	Who's Who in Sport (1926)	60p	£30.00
		50	Wild Animals of the World (Tobacco Leaf Back) (1902–05)	£3.50	—
		25	Wireless (1923)	£1.20	—
		50	Wonders of the Past (1930)	50p	£25.00
		50	Wonders of the Sea (1929)	40p	£20.00
141		25	Wonders of the World (1925–30)	30p	£7.50
		40	World Famous Cinema Artistes (1933)	50p	£20.00
	M	40	World Famous Cinema Artistes (1933)	50p	£20.00
		50	World's Products	25p	£12.50
	P	50	The World of Sport (1927)	60p	£30.00
	P	50	Zoo (1935)	40p	£20.00
		50	Zoological Studies (1928):—		
			A. Brown Back	32p	£16.00
			B. Black Back	—	—

F. Plain Backs

Illus. No.	Size	Number in set		Price per card	Complete set
		50	Actors & Actresses "WALP" (1905–08):—		
			A. Portraits in Black & White, Glossy	90p	£45.00
			B. Portraits Flesh Tinted, Matt	90p	£45.00
		50	Actresses "ALWICS" (1905–08)	£1.75	—
		50	Actresses, Four Colours Surround (1903–08)	£1.00	£50.00
		30	Actresses Unicoloured (1908–13):—		
			A. Fronts in Purple Brown	50p	£15.00
			B. Fronts in Light Brown	50p	£15.00
		50	Animals & Birds (1912)	£1.00	£50.00

Illus. No.	Size	Number in set		Price per card	Complete set
		60	Animals – Cut Outs (1912)	80p	—
		50	Art Photogravures (1912)	£1.00	—
		50	Aviation Series (1911)	£1.70	—
		40	Beauties Brown Tinted (1913)	£1.00	—
		50	Beauties with Backgrounds (1911)	£1.40	—
		32	Beauties Picture Hats I with borders (1914)	80p	£26.00
		45	Beauties Picture Hats II without borders (1914)	80p	—
		30	Beauties & Children (1910–15)	£4.50	—
		30	Beauties "Celebrated Actresses" (1910–15)	£1.40	—
		52	Birds of Brilliant Plumage P.C. Inset (1914)	£1.40	—
		25	Bonzo Series (1923):—		
			A. With Series Title	£1.40	£35.00
			B. Without Series Title	£1.40	—
		30	Boy Scouts Signalling (1920–25):—		
			A. Captions in English	£1.50	£45.00
			B. Captions in Siamese	£1.50	£45.00
		50	British Man of War Series (1910)	£4.50	—
		50	Butterflies & Moths (1910)	80p	—
		50	Cinema Artistes (1928–33)	—	—
		50	Cinema Stars (1925–35) RB21/259:—		
			A. Front Matt	50p	£25.00
			B. Front Glossy	80p	—
		50	Cinema Stars (1925–35) RB21/260 (Nd. 1–50)	50p	—
		50	Cinema Stars (1925–35) RB21/260 (Nd. 51–100)	60p	—
		50	Cinema Stars (1925–35) RB21/260 (Nd. 101–150)	60p	—
		100	Cinema Stars (1925–35) RB21/260 (Nd. 201–300)	40p	£40.00
		50	Cinema Stars "FLAG" (1925–35)	60p	—
		27	Dancing Girls (1913)	£1.20	—
		32	Drum Horses (1910)	£2.50	—
		50	English Period Costumes	50p	£25.00
		50	Flag Girls of All Nations (1911)	£1.00	—
			Flags Pennons & Signals (1905–10):—		
		70	A. Numbered 1–70	50p	—
		70	B. Unnumbered	35p	—
		50	C. Numbered 71–120	40p	—
		45	D. Numbered 121–165	60p	—
		20	Flowers (1915)	60p	£12.00
		50	Girls of All Nations (1908)	£1.00	—
		30	Heroic Deeds (1913)	80p	£24.00
		25	Hindou Gods (1909)	£3.00	—
		32	Houses of Parliament (1914)	£2.50	—
		25	Indian Mogul Paintings (1909)	£4.00	—
		53	Jockeys & Owners Colours P.C. Inset	£1.20	—
		30	Merrie England Female Studies (1922)	£4.00	—
	K	36	Modern Beauties 1st Series (1938)	—	—
		36	Modern Beauties 2nd Series (1939)	—	—
	P	48	Movie Stars (1925–30)	55p	—
		50	Music Hall Celebrities (1911):—		
			A. Blue Border	£2.00	—
			B. Gilt Border	£1.50	—
			C. Red Border	£2.00	—
			D. Yellow Border	£3.50	—
	P	50	New Zealand, Early Scenes & Maori Life (1925–30)	—	—
		50	Poultry & Pidgeons (1925–30)	—	—
		25	Products of the World (1914)	70p	£17.50
		50	Royal Mail (1912)	—	—
		36	Ships & Their Pennants (1913)	90p	—
		75	Soldiers of the World (1900–05)	£3.00	—
		30	Sporting Girls (1913)	£1.20	—
		50	Sports of the World (1917):—		
			A. Brown Front	—	—
			B. Coloured Front	70p	—
	M	50	Stars of Filmland (1927)	—	—
303		32	Transport of the World (1917)	50p	£16.00
		50	Types of the British Army (1908):—		
			A. Numbered	£1.20	—
			B. Unnumbered	£1.20	—
	P	50	Types of the World (1936)	—	—
	P	50	Units of the British Army & RAF (1925–30)	—	—
	M	50	Women of Nations (Flag Girls) (1922)	£1.50	—

G. Paper Backed Silks issued 1910–1917

	Size	Number in set		Price per card	Complete set
	M	25	Arabic Proverbs	£7.00	
	M	50	Arms of the British Empire:—		
			A. Back in Blue	£1.30	—
			B. Back in Brown	£2.50	—
	M	50	Australian Wild Flowers	£1.30	—
	M	50	Best Dogs of their Breed	£1.50	—
		110	Crests & Badges of the British Army	£2.00	—
	M	108	Crests & Badges of the British Army	£1.30	—
	M	50	Crests & Colours of Australian Universities, Colleges & Schools	£1.20	—

BRITISH AMERICAN TOBACCO COMPANY (CHINA) LTD. ___

		32	Sectional Picture – "Beauties of Old China" (1934)	£3.00	—

BRITISH AMERICAN TOBACCO CO. LTD., Switzerland _____

Illus. No.	Size	Number in set		Price per card	Complete set

| | | 30 | Series Actrices (1921) .... | £4.00 | — |

BROWN & WILLIAMSON TOBACCO CORP., U.S.A. (WINGS CIGARETTES) _____

M	50	Modern American Airplanes (1930's):—			
			A. Inscribed "Series A"	90p	—
			B. Without "Series A"	80p	£40.00
M	50	Modern American Airplanes "Series B" (1930's)	80p	£40.00
M	50	Modern American Airplanes "Series C" (1930's)	80p	£40.00

D. BUCHNER & CO. U.S.A. _____

	48	Actors (1885–92)	£11.00	—
L	50	Actresses (1885–92)	£13.00	—
	144	Baseball Players (1885–92)	£30.00	—
L	28	Butterflies & Bugs (1885–92)	£25.00	—
L	52	Morning Glory Maidens (1885–92)	£25.00	—
L	23	Musical Instruments (1885–92)	£30.00	—
L	21	Yacht Club Colours (1885–92)	£30.00	—

BUCKTROUT & CO. LTD., Guernsey. Chanel Islands _____

M	416	Around the World (1926–27):—			
		A. Inscribed "Places of Interest" Nd. 1–104	25p	£26.00
		B. Inscribed "Around the World" Nd. 105–208	25p	£26.00
		C. Inscribed "Around the World" Nd. 209–312	25p	£26.00
		D. Inscribed "Around the World" Nd. 313–416	25p	£26.00
	24	Birds of England (1923)	£1.40	£35.00
	50	Cinema Stars 1st Series (1921)	60p	£30.00
	50	Cinema Stars 2nd Series (1922)	£1.00	£50.00
M	50	Football Teams (1924)	80p	£40.00
M	22	Football Teams of the Bailiwick (1924)	30p	£6.50
	123	Guernsey Footballers (1910–15)	£1.20	—
	20	Inventors Series (1924)	25p	£5.00
	25	Marvels of the Universe Series (1923)	£1.20	£30.00
M	53	Playing Cards (1928–29)	40p	£20.00
	25	Sports & Pastimes (1925)	£1.60	£40.00

CALCUTTA CIGARETTE CO. India _____

	25	Actresses "ALWICS" (1905–08):—			
		A. Fronts in Blue	£8.00	—
		B. Fronts in chocolate	£10.00	£250.00

A. G. CAMERON & SIZER, U.S.A. (including Cameron & Cameron) _____

	25	The New Discovery:—			
		A. Without Overprint	£13.00	—
		B. With Overprint	£13.00	—
	24	Occupations, For Women	£26.00	—
		Photographic Cards			
	?1	Actresses	£5.00	—
L	?2	Actresses	—	—
	343	Framed Paintings	£2.50	—

V. CAMILLERI, Malta _____

MP	104	Popes of Rome (1922):—			
		A. Nd. 1–52	60p	£30.00
		B. Nd. 53–104	60p	£30.00

CAMLER TOBACCO COY Malta _____

P	?239	Footballers (1920–30)	—	—
M	96	Maltese Families Coats of Arms:—			
		A. Thick Board (1920–30)	45p	—
		B. Thin Board (1958–59)	80p	—

CARRERAS LTD., Australia _____

	72	Film Star Series (1933)	80p	—
	72	Football Series (1933)	80p	—
	24	Personality Series (1933)	80p	—
	72	Personality Series Film Stars (1933)	80p	—
	72	Personality Series Footballers (1933)	80p	—

CHING & CO. Jersey, Channel Islands

Illus. No.	Size	Number in set		Price per card	Complete set
210	L	24	Around & About in Jersey, 1st Series (1964)	10p	£2.50
	L	24	Around & About in Jersey, 2nd Series (1964)	80p	—
		25	Do You Know (1962)	10p	75p
			Album	—	£1.00
		48	Flowers (1962)	60p	£30.00
	L	24	Jersey Past & Present 1st Series (1960)	10p	75p
	L	24	Jersey Past & Present 2nd Series (1962)	10p	£2.50
			Album for 1st & 2nd series Combined	—	£1.50
	L	24	Jersey Past & Present 3rd Series (1963)	10p	75p
			Album	—	£1.25
		25	Ships & Their Workings (1961)	10p	75p
		50	Veteran & Vintage Cars (1960)	13p	£6.50
			Album	—	£2.00

W. A. & A. C. CHURCHMAN, Channel Islands

(All cards without ITC clause)

	Size	Number in set		Price per card	Complete set
	M	48	Air Raid Precautions (1938)	—	£24.00
	M	48	Holidays in Britain (Sepia) (1937)	—	£24.00
	M	48	Holidays in Britain (Coloured) (1938)	—	£24.00
	M	48	Modern Wonders (1938):—		
			A. ITC Clause blocked out in Silver	—	—
			B. Reprinted without ITC Clause	—	—
	M	48	The Navy at Work (1937)	—	£24.00
	M	48	The RAF at Work (1939)	—	£24.00
	M	48	Wings Over the Empire (1939)	—	£24.00

THE CIGARETTE COMPANY, Jersey, Channel Islands

		Number in set		Price per card	Complete set
		72	Jersey Footballers (1908–14)	£2.20	—

C. COLOMBOS, Malta

	Size	Number in set		Price per card	Complete set
	MP	200	Actresses (Pre 1918)	—	—
	MP	44	Actresses (Pre 1918)	—	—
		50	Actresses Coloured (Pre 1918)	—	—
	MP	55	Celebrities (Pre 1918)	—	—
	P	136	Dante's Devine Comedy (Pre 1918)	—	—
			Famous Oil Paintings (Pre 1918):—		
	MP	72	1) Series A	55p	—
	MP	108	2) Series B	55p	—
	MP	240	3) Series C	55p	—
	MP	100	4) Series D	55p	—
	LP	91	5) Large size	£3.00	—
	MP	100	Life of Napoleon Bonaparte (Pre 1918)	80p	—
	MP	70	Life of Nelson (Pre 1918)	80p	—
	MP	70	Life of Wellington (Pre 1918)	80p	—
	MP	100	National Types and Costumes (Pre 1918)	90p	—
	MP	20	Opera Singers (Pre 1918)	—	—
		120	Paintings and Statues (Pre 1918)	35p	£42.00
	M	112	Royalty & Celebrities (Pre 1918)	£1.40	—

D. CONDACHI & SON, Malta

Illus. No.		Number in set		Price per card	Complete set
237		?5	Beauties (1900–1910)	£6.00	—

CONSOLIDATED CIGARETTE CO., U.S.A.

		Number in set		Price per card	Complete set
		25	Ladies of the White House:—		
			A. Size 73 × 43 mm White borders	£20.00	—
			B. Size 70 × 38 mm No borders	£15.00	—

COPE BROS. & CO., LTD.

A. Indian Issue

		Number in set		Price per card	Complete set
		30	Flags of Nations (1896–1905)	£11.00	—

B. Danish Issues

		Number in set		Price per card	Complete set
		50	Jordklodens Hunde (1905–13)	—	—
		30	Scandinavian Actors & Actresses (1905–13)	£11.00	—
		35	Speider Billeder I Hver Pakke (1905–13)	—	—
		25	Uniformer A F Fremragende Britiske Regimenter (1905–13)	£11.00	—
		25	Vilde Dyr Og Fugle (1905–13)	—	—

A. G. COUSIS & CO. Malta

	Size	Number in set		Price per card	Complete set
			Actors & Actresses (Pre 1918):—		
	P	100	A. Back with Framework	—	—
	KP	100	B. Back without Framework	—	—
	K	254	Actors & Actresses (1920–30)	30p	—
	KP	100	Actresses Series I (Pre 1918)	—	—

Illus. No.	Size	Number in set		Price per card	Complete set
	KP	80	Actresses Series II (Pre 1918)	—	—
	P	100	Actresses (Pre 1918):—		
			A. Series I.	50p	—
			B. Series II.	60p	—
			C. Series III	60p	—
			D. Series IV	50p	—
			E. Series V.	70p	—
			F. Series VI	70p	—
			G. Series VII	70p	—
			H. Series VIII	—	—
			I. Series IX	70p	—
			J. Series X.	70p	—
			K. Series XI	70p	—
			L. Series XII	70p	—
			M. Series XIII	70p	—
			N. Series XIV	50p	—
			O. Series XV	60p	—
			P. Series XVI	70p	—
			Q. Series XVII	60p	—
			R. Series XVIII	70p	—
			S. Series XIX:—	—	—
			Actresses (Pre 1918):—		
	KP	1895	A. Miniature Size 50 × 30 mm	30p	—
	P	1160	B. Small Size 58 × 39 mm.	35p	—
	MP	248	Actresses, Celebrities & Warships (Pre 1918)	—	—
			Actresses, Partners & National Costumes (Pre 1918):—		
	KP	200	A. Miniature size 50 × 30 mm.	75p	—
	P	100	B. Small Size 60 × 39 mm.	75p	—
	MP	50	Beauties, Couples & Children (Pre 1918):—		
			A. Back inscribed "Collection No. 1"	80p	—
			B. Back inscribed "Collection No. 2"	80p	—
			C. Back inscribed "Collection No. 3"	80p	—
	K	50	Beauties, Couples & Children (Red Back) (1920–30).........	80p	—
	P	402	Celebrities Numbered Matt (Pre 1918):—		
			A. Front inscribed "Cousis's Dubec Cigarettes" Nd. 1–300	30p	—
			B. Front inscribed "Cousis's Cigarettes" Nd. 301–402	—	—
	P	2161	Celebrities Unnumbered (Pre 1918):—		
			A. Miniature size 50 × 30 mm.	25p	—
			B. Small size 59 × 39 mm	25p	—
	MP	72	Grand Masters of the Order of Jerusalem (Pre 1918).........	—	—
	P	100	National Costumes (Pre 1918)	80p	—
	MP	?57	Paris Exhibition 1900 (Pre 1918)	—	—
	MP	102	Paris Series (Pre 1918).	—	—
			Popes of Rome (Pre 1918):—		
	MP	182	A. Back inscribed "A.G. Cousis' Dubec Cigarettes"	40p	—
	MP	81	B. Back inscribed "Cousis' Dubec Cigarettes".............	90p	—
	P	100	Statues & Monuments (Pre 1918):—		
			A. Numbered.	80p	—
			B. Unnumbered	80p	—
	KP	127	Views of Malta (Pre 1918)	50p	—
	P	115	Views of Malta Numbered (Pre 1918)	50p	—
	MP	127	Views of Malta Numbered (Pre 1918)	40p	—
	MP	?65	Views of Malta Unnumbered (Pre 1918)	50p	—
	P	555	Views of the World (Pre 1918):—		
			A. Small size 59 × 39 mm	35p	—
			B. Medium size 65 × 45 mm	60p	—
	P	99	Warships White border (Pre 1918)	£1.20	—
			Warships, Liners & Other Vessels (Pre 1918):—		
	MP	64	A. "Cousis' Dubec Cigarettes"	£1.30	—
	MP	22	B. "Cousis' Excelsior Cigarettes".............	£1.30	—
	MP	37	C. "Cousis' Superior Cigarettes"	£2.00	—
	MP	850	D. "Cousis' Cigarettes"..................	60p	—
	KP	850	E. "Cousis' Cigarettes"	40p	—

CROWN TOBACCO CO. India

		?15	National Types, Costumes & Flags (1895–1905)..............	£17.00	—

DIXSON, Australia

		50	Australian MP's and Celebrities (1900–1902).................	£5.00	—

DOMINION TOBACCO CO., Canada

		50	The Smokers of the World (1900–05)	£20.00	—

DOMINION TOBACCO CO. LTD., New Zealand

		50	Coaches & Coaching Days (1925–30)	80p	—
		50	People and Places Famous in New Zealand History (1925–30)	£1.20	—
		50	Products of the World (1925–30)	50p	£25.00
		50	U.S.S. Co.'s Steamers (1925–30)...........................	£1.20	—

DUDGEON & ARNELL, Australia

Illus. No.	Size	Number in set		Price per card	Complete set
	K	16	1934 Australian Test Team (1934)	£3.00	£50.00
	K	55	Famous Ships (1933).................................	£1.50	—

W. DUKE SONS & CO., U.S.A.

	Size	Number in set		Price per card	Complete set
	EL	?	Actors & Actresses (Photographic) RB23/-D76–81...........	£1.00	—
		50	Actors & Actresses Series No. 1............................	£5.00	—
		50	Actors & Actresses Series No. 2............................	£5.00	—
		25	Actresses RB18/27......................................	£6.00	—
	EL	?	Actresses, Celebrities & Children (Photographic).............	£1.00	—
	EL	25	Albums of American Stars	£15.00	—
	EL	25	Battle Scenes	£10.00	—
	EL	25	Breeds of Horses..	£12.00	—
	EL	25	Bridges...	£9.00	—
	EL	25	Comic Characters	£9.00	—
		50	Coins of All Nations	£7.00	—
	EL	25	Cowboy Scenes..	£13.00	—
	EL	50	Fairest Flowers in the World	£10.00	—
		50	Fancy Dress Ball Costumes	£5.00	£250.00
	EL	50	Fancy Dress Ball Costumes	£12.00	—
		50	Fishers and Fish	£6.00	£300.00
	EL	25	Flags & Costumes	£12.00	—
		50	Floral Beauties & Language of Flowers	£6.00	—
	EL	25	French Novelties	£10.00	—
	EL	25	Gems of Beauty	£10.00	—
		50	Great Americans	£7.00	—
		25	Gymnastic Exercises	£12.00	—
	EL	25	Habitations of Man......................................	£10.00	—
		50	Histories of Generals (Booklets)..........................	£11.00	—
		50	Histories of Poor Boys who have become rich & other famous people	£11.00	—
		50	Holidays	£6.00	£300.00
	EL	25	Illustrated Songs..	£10.00	—
	EL	25	Industries of the States	£15.00	—
		50	Jokes...	£8.00	—
	EL	25	Lighthouses (Die Cut)	£10.00	—
	EL	25	Miniature Novelties	£10.00	—
		50	Musical Instruments	£8.00	—
		36	Ocean & River Steamers	£8.00	—
	M	240	Photographs from Life RB23/76–84	£2.50	—
		53	Playing Cards	£6.00	—
		50	Popular Songs & Dancers	£8.00	—
		50	Postage Stamps...	£8.00	—
			Rulers Flags & Coats of Arms (1888):—		
	EL	50	A. Thick Card Type..................................	£8.00	—
	EL	50	B. Thin Folders	£6.00	—
		50	Scenes of Perilous Occupations...........................	£10.00	—
	EL	25	Sea Captains	£12.00	—
		50	Shadows	£6.00	£300.00
	EL	25	Snap Shots from Puck	£10.00	—
	EL	25	Stars of the Stage 1st Series:—		
			A. With Duke	£10.00	£250.00
			B. Inscribed "3rd Series"............................	£10.00	—
	EL	25	Stars of the Stage 2nd Series.............................	£12.00	—
	EL	25	Stars of the Stage 3rd Series	£10.00	£250.00
	EL	25	Stars of the Stage 4th Series (Die Cut)....................	£10.00	—
	EL	48	State Governors, Coats of Arms...........................	£10.00	—
	EL	48	State Governors, Coats of Arms (Folders)	£7.00	—
		50	The Terrors of America & Their Doings	£6.00	—
	EL	50	The Terrors of America & Their Doings	£12.00	—
		50	Tinted Photos:—		
			A. Standard size	£10.00	—
			B. Die Cut to Shape	£10.00	—
	EL	25	Types of Vessels (Die Cut)	£10.00	—
		50	Vehicles of the World	£10.00	£500.00
		50	Yacht Colours of the World...............................	£6.00	—

Photographic Cards

		340	Actors & Actresses "Cross-Cut Cigarettes" with number and caption in design Group 1	£1.00	—
		260	Actors & Actresses "Cross-Cut Cigarettes" in design, number and caption at base Group 2...............................	£1.00	—
		?	Actors & Actresses "Cross-Cut Cigarettes" and all wording at base Group 3..	£1.00	—
		148	Actors & Actresses "Dukes Cameo Cigarettes" in design, number and caption at base Group 4	£1.00	—
		?	Actors & Actresses "Dukes Cameo Cigarettes" number and caption at base Group 5...................................	£1.00	—
		?	Actors & Actresses "Dukes Cigarettes" in design, number and caption at base Group 6...................................	£1.00	—
		?	Actors & Actresses "Dukes Cigarettes" and all wording at base Group 7..	£1.00	—
		?	Actors, Actresses & Celebrities. Printed Back:—		
			1. Horizontal "Dukes Cameo Cigarettes" back	£1.00	—
			2. Vertical "Sales 1888" back	£1.00	—
			3. Horizontal "Dukes Cigarettes" back	£1.00	—

H. ELLIS & CO., U.S.A.

| Illus. No. | Size | Number in set | | Price per card | Complete set |

Illus. No.	Size	Number in set		Price per card	Complete set
		25	Breeds of Dogs	£13.00	—
		25	Costumes of Women	—	—
		25	Generals of the Late Civil War	—	—
		25	Photographic Cards – Actresses	—	—

G. W. GAIL & AX., U.S.A.

	EL	25	Battle Scenes	£13.00	—
	EL	25	Bicycle & Trick Riders	—	—
	EL	25	French Novelties	£15.00	—
	EL	25	Industries of States	£15.00	—
	EL	25	Lighthouses (Die Cut)	—	—
	EL	25	Novelties (Die Cut)	£20.00	—
	EL	?	Photographic Cards	£2.00	—
	EL	25	Stars of the Stage	£15.00	—

GENERAL CIGAR COMPANY, Montreal, Canada

	EL	36	Northern Birds (1968)	80p	—

GOODWIN & CO., U.S.A.

		15	Beauties "PAC"	—	—
		50	Champions	£11.00	—
		50	Dogs of the World	£6.00	—
		50	Flowers	£8.00	—
		50	Games & Sports Series	£11.00	—
		50	Holidays	—	—
		50	Occupations for Women	£32.00	—
			Photographic Cards		
		?	Actors & Actresses	£1.00	—
		?	Baseball Players	£25.00	—
		?	Celebrities & Prizefighters	£4.00	—
		50	Vehicles of the World	£14.00	—

GUERNSEY TOBACCO CO., Channel Islands

			A Famous Picture:—		
		49	A. And When Did You Last See Your Father? (1934)	60p	£30.00
		48	B. The Laughing Cavalier (1935)	60p	£30.00
		48	C. The Toast (1936)	60p	£30.00
	K	52	Miniature Playing Cards (1933–36)	60p	—

THOS. H. HALL, U.S.A.

		4	Actresses RB23/-H6-1	£50.00	—
		14	Actresses RB23/-H6-2	£11.00	—
		140	Actors & Actresses RB23/-H6-3	£11.00	—
		112	Actresses & Actors RB23/-H6-4	£11.00	—
		?	Actresses & Actors RB23/-H6-5	£11.00	—
		?	Actresses & Actors RB23/-H6-6	£11.00	—
		49	Actresses RB23/-H6-7	—	—
		11	Actresses RB23/-H6-8	—	—
		25	Actresses RB23/-H6-9	£13.00	—
		11	Actresses RB23/-H6-10	—	—
		12	Athletes RB23/H6-3	—	—
		4	Presidential Candidates RB23/H6-1	—	—
		22	Presidents of the United States RB23/H6-11	£16.00	—
		25	Theatrical Types RB23/H6-12	£18.00	—

HIGNETT BROS. & CO., New Zealand

	MP	50	Beauties Set 1 (1926):—		
			A. Back without Framelines no brand mentioned	£1.20	—
			B. Back with Framelines "Chess Cigarettes"	60p	£30.00
	MP	50	Beauties Set 2 (1927)	80p	£40.00

R. & J. HILL LTD.

		10	Chinese Series (1911–17)	£18.00	—

THE HILSON CO., U.S.A.

Illus. No.	Size	Number in set		Price per card	Complete set
	EL	25	National Types (1898–1901)	£8.00	—

IMPERIAL TOBACCO COMPANY OF CANADA LTD., Canada

A. With Firms Name

Illus. No.	Size	Number in set		Price per card	Complete set
		25	Beauties – Girls in Costume (1903–05)	£20.00	—
		24	Beauties – Smoke Girls (1903–05)	£20.00	—
	M	50	Birds, Beasts & Fishes (1923–24)	£1.00	£50.00
	L	100	Birds of Canada (1924)	£1.60	—
	L	100	Birds of Canada (Western Canada)	—	—
80		50	British Birds (1923)	50p	£25.00
		48	Canadian History Series (1926)	60p	—
		50	Children of All Nations (1924)	50p	£25.00
		23	Dogs Series (1924)	60p	£14.00
		50	Dogs 2nd Series (1925)	50p	—
		50	Famous English Actresses (1924)	70p	£35.00
		50	Film Favourites (1925–6): —		
			A. English Issue: —		
			i) Numbered	£2.00	—
			ii) Unnumbered	£2.50	—
			B. French Issue: —		
			i) Numbered	£5.00	—
			ii) Unnumbered	£5.00	—
		50	Fish & Bait (1924)	70p	£35.00
		50	Fishes of the World (1924)	80p	£40.00
		50	Flower Culture in Pots (1925)	50p	£25.00
		30	Game Bird Series (1925)	60p	£18.00
		50	Gardening Hints (1923)	40p	£20.00
	M	25	Heraldic Signs & Their Origins (1925)	70p	£17.50
		50	How to Play Golf (1925)	£2.40	—
		50	Infantry Training (1915): —		
			A. Glossy Card	£1.40	—
			B. Matt Card	£1.40	—
	L	48	Mail Carriers and Stamps (1903–5)	—	—
		50	Merchant Ships of the World (1924)	50p	£25.00
		25	Military Portraits (1914–15)	£1.40	—
		50	Modern War Weapons 'Sweet Caporal" issue (1914–15)	£2.50	—
		56	Motor Cars (1924)	£1.00	£56.00
		50	Naval Portraits (1914–15)	£1.40	—
		25	Notabilities (1914–15)	£1.40	—
		53	Poker Hands (1924)	70p	—
		53	Poker Hands New Series (1925)	70p	—
		25	Poultry Alphabet (1924)	80p	—
		50	Railway Engines (1924): —		
			A. With Wills Blanked Out	90p	—
			B. Without Wills	60p	£30.00
128		50	The Reason Why	70p	£35.00
		127	Smokers Golf Cards (1925–26)	£1.70	—

B. Without Firms Name

Illus. No.	Size	Number in set		Price per card	Complete set
		50	Arms of the British Empire (1911)	£1.40	—
		50	Around the World (1910–15)	£2.50	—
		100	Baseball Series (1912)	—	—
		30	Bird Series (1910–15)	£1.20	—
		50	Boy Scouts (1911) – with album clause	£2.20	—
		50	Canadian Historical Portraits (1913–15)	£5.00	—
		50	Canadian History Series (1914)	80p	—
		50	Fish Series (1910–15)	£1.20	—
		50	Fowls, Pigeons and Dogs (1911)	£1.40	—
		45	Hockey Players (1912)	£3.40	—
		36	Hockey Series Coloured (1911)	£6.00	—
		50	How to do it (1910–15)	£2.00	—
		100	Lacrosse Series Leading Players (1910–15)	£2.40	—
		100	Lacrosse Series Coloured (1910–15)	£2.40	—
		50	Lacrosse Series Black & White (1910–15)	£2.40	—
		50	L'Historie Du Canada (1926)	90p	—
		50	Movie Stars	70p	—
	L	50	Pictures of Canadian Life (1910–15): —		
			A. Brown Front	—	—
			B. Green Front	£5.00	—
		50	Prominent Men of Canada (1910–15)	£2.00	—
		50	Tricks & Puzzles (1910–15)	£6.50	—
		50	Types of Nations	—	—
		25	V.C. Heroes (Blue Back) (1915)	£1.40	£35.00
	L	45	Views of the World (1910–15)	—	—
		25	The Worlds Dreadnoughts (1910)	£1.40	—

C. Silks Issued 1910–25

Illus. No.	Size	Number in set		Price per card	Complete set
	M	55	Animals with Flags	£1.60	—
	EL	50	Canadian History Series	£6.00	—
	M	121	Canadian Miscellany	£2.60	—
	M	55	Garden Flowers of the World	£1.20	£65.00
	M	55	Orders & Military Medals	£1.60	—
	M	55	Regimental Uniforms of Canada	£1.60	—
	M	50	Yachts Pennants & Views	£1.60	—

THE IMPERIAL TOBACCO CO. OF INDIA LTD., India

Illus. No.	Size	Number in set		Price per card	Complete set
		25	Indian Historical Views (1915):—		
			A. Set 1 First Arrangement	£1.40	£35.00
			B. Set 2 Second Arrangement	£1.40	£35.00
		40.	Nautch Girl Series:—		
			A. "Pedro Cigarettes" (1905–09)	£1.40	—
			B. "Railway Cigarettes" (1907–08)	£1.40	—
		52	Nautch Girl Series, P.C. Inset:—		
			A. "Pedro Cigarettes" (1905–09)	£1.40	£75.00
			B. "Railway Cigarettes" (1907–08)	£1.40	—
	K	53	Playing Cards Red Back (1919–20)	50p	—
	K	52	Playing Cards Blue Back (1933)	—	—

THE JERSEY TOBACCO CO. LTD., Channel Islands

Illus. No.	Size	Number in set		Price per card	Complete set
	K	53	Miniature Playing Cards (1933)	50p	—

JUST SO, U.S.A.

Illus. No.	Size	Number in set		Price per card	Complete set
	EL	?	Actresses (1885–95)	£3.50	—

KENTUCKY TOBACCO PTY. LTD., South Africa

Illus. No.	Size	Number in set		Price per card	Complete set
	L	120	The March of Mankind (1940)	80p	—

WM. S. KIMBALL & CO., U.S.A.

Illus. No.	Size	Number in set		Price per card	Complete set
		?25	Actresses	—	—
		72	Ancient Coins	£15.00	—
		48	Arms of Dominions	£10.00	—
		50	Ballet Queens	£10.00	—
		52	Beauties with Playing Card Insets	£10.00	—
	EL	20	Beautiful Bathers	£15.00	—
		50	Butterflies	£10.00	—
		50	Champions of Games & Sports	£12.00	—
		50	Dancing Girls of the World	£8.00	—
		50	Dancing Women	£8.00	—
		50	Fancy Bathers	£8.00	—
		50	Goddesses of the Greeks & Romans	—	—
	EL	25	Household Pets	£15.00	—
		?	Photographic Actresses RB23/K26–15–2	£2.00	—
	EL	20	Pretty Athletes	£15.00	—
		50	Savage & Semi Barbarous Chiefs and Rulers	£10.00	—

KINNEY BROS., U.S.A.

Illus. No.	Size	Number in set		Price per card	Complete set
		25	Actresses Group 1 Set 1 RB18/1	£3.40	£85.00
		25	Actresses Group 1 Set 2 RB18/2	£6.50	—
		25	Actresses Group 1 Set 3 RB18/3	£10.00	—
		25	Actresses Group 1 Set 4	—	—
		25	Actresses Group 1 Set 5	—	—
		25	Actresses Group 2 RB18/15	£4.00	—
		25	Actresses Group 2 RB18/16:—		
			A. Subjects named	£3.50	—
			B. Subjects unnamed	£3.00	—
		25	Actresses Group 3 RB18/26	£3.00	—
		25	Actresses Group 3 RB18/29	£3.00	—
		50	Actresses Group 4 RB18/36	£3.00	—
		150	Actresses Group 4	£2.50	—
		25	Animals	£8.00	—
		10	Butterflies of the World Light background	£8.00	—
		50	Butterflies of the World Gold background	£6.00	—
		25	Famous Gems of the World	£7.00	£175.00
		52	Harlequin Cards 1st Series	£8.00	—
		53	Harlequin Cards 2nd Series	£8.00	—
	L	50	International Cards	£15.00	—
	K	24	Jocular Oculars	—	—
		25	Leaders:—		
			A. Standard size	£7.00	£175.00
			B. Narrow card – officially cut	£7.00	£175.00
		50	Magic Changing Cards	£10.00	—
		622	Military Series	£2.00	—
		50	National Dances:—		
			A. Front with white border	£7.00	£350.00
			B. Front without border	£9.00	—
		25	Naval Vessels of the World	£8.00	—
		25	Novelties Type 1 Thick Circular No border	£15.00	—
		50	Novelties Type 2 Thin Circular with border	£5.00	—
			Novelties Type 3 Die Cut		
		25	A. Inscribed "25 Styles"	£4.00	—
		50	B. Inscribed "50 Styles"	£4.00	—
		75	C. Inscribed "75 Styles"	£4.00	—
		50	Novelties Type 5 Standard Size Cases Die Cut	£6.00	—

Illus. No.	Size	Number in set		Price per card	Complete set
		?11	Novelties Type 6 Oval............................	£15.00	—
			Photographic Cards		
		?	A. Actors & Actresses Horizontal Back with Kinneys Name	75p	—
		?	B. Actors & Actresses Vertical Sweet Caporal Backs.......	50p	—
		45	C. Famous Ships	£5.00	—
			Racehorses:—		
		25	1. American Horses:—		
			A. Back with series title "Famous Running Horses"	£6.00	—
			B. Back "Return 25 of these small cards" 11 lines of text	£6.00	—
		25	2. English Horses "Return 25 of these cards" with 6 lines of text	£5.00	£125.00
		25	3. Great American Trotters.........................	£10.00	—
		50	Surf Beauties	£8.00	£400.00
		52	Transparent Playing Cards......................	£9.00	—
		25	Types of Nationalities (Folders)	£12.00	—

KRAMERS TOBACCO CO. (PTY.) LTD., South Africa

| | | 50 | Badges of South African Rugby Football Clubs (1933) .... | £2.00 | |

LAMBERT & BUTLER

		50	Actors & Actresses "WALPS" (1905)......................	£1.60	—
255		250	Actresses "ALWICS" (1905–6):—		
			A. Portraits in Black, Border in Red	£1.60	—
			B. Portraits and Border in Black......................	£3.00	—
		50	Beauties Red Tinted (1906–10)	£1.60	—
		83	Danske Byvaabner (1910–15)	£7.00	—
	M	26	Etchings of Dogs (1926)......................	—	—
		25	Flag Girls of All Nations (1908)	£5.00	—
	P	50	Homeland Events (1928)......................	90p	£45.00
	P	50	London Zoo (1927)........................	£1.00	—
		50	Merchant Ships of the World (1924)	£1.20	—
		30	Music Hall Celebrities (1916)..................	£1.60	—
	P	50	Popular Film Stars (1926):—		
			A. Series title in one line, no brand quoted................	70p	£35.00
			B. Series title in two lines inscribed "Varsity Cigarettes" ...	£1.20	—
			C. Series title in two lines no brand quoted	70p	£35.00
	P	50	The Royal Family at Home & Abroad (1927)	60p	£30.00
		100	Royalty, Notabilities and Events in Russia, China, Japan and South Africa (1900–02)	£6.00	—
		100	Russo Japanese Series (1905)......................	£2.50	—
	P	50	Types of Modern Beauty (1927)	60p	—
	P	50	Who's Who in Sport (1926)	60p	£30.00
	P	50	The World of Sport (1927)	60p	£30.00

LEWIS & ALLEN CO. U.S.A.

| | L | 250 | Views & Art Studies (1910–15) .... | £2.00 | — |

LONE JACK CIGARETTE CO., U.S.A.

| | | 50 | Language of Flowers (1885–92) .... | £16.00 | — |

P. LORILLARD CO., U.S.A.

Issues 1885–98

	M	25	Actresses RB23/L70–4–3........................	£12.00	—
	M	25	Actresses RB23/L70–5.........................	£12.00	—
	EL	25	Actresses RB23/L70–6:—		
			A. "Red Cross" Long Cut........................	£12.00	—
			B. "Sensation Cut Plug" Front & Back	£12.00	—
			C. "Sensation Cut Plug" Front Only...................	£12.00	—
	EL	25	Actresses RB23/L70–8.........................	£12.00	—
	EL	25	Actresses in Opera Roles RB23/L70–9	£15.00	—
	M	25	Ancient Mythology Burlesqued RB23/L70–10	£8.00	—
	M	50	Beautiful Women RB23/L70–11:—		
			A. "5c Ante" Front & Back	£8.00	—
			B. "Lorillard's Snuff" Front & Back...................	£8.00	—
			C. "Tiger" Front & Back.....................	£8.00	—
	EL	25	Circus Scenes........................	£25.00	—
	EL	50	Prizefighters........................	£25.00	—
	M	25	Types of the Stage	£9.00	—

W. C. MACDONALD INC., Canada

| | | ? | Aeroplane & Warships (1926–47)................... | 40p | — |
| | M | 53 | Playing Cards (Different Designs) (1926–47) .... | 25p | — |

B. & J. B. MACHADO, Jamaica

Illus. No.	Size	Number in set		Price per card	Complete set
		25	British Naval Series (1916)	£7.00	—
		50	The Great War – Victoria Cross Heroes (1916–17)	£7.00	—
	P	50	Popular Film Stars (1926)	—	—
	P	50	The Royal Family at Home & Abroad (1927)	—	—
	P	52	Stars of the Cinema (1926)	—	—
	P	50	The World of Sport (1928)	—	—

MACLIN – ZIMMER – MCGILL TOB. CO. U.S.A.

	EL	53	Playing Cards – Actresses (1885–95)	£10.00	—

H. MANDELBAUM U.S.A.

		20	Types of People (1888–92)	£25.00	—

MARBURG BROS., U.S.A.

		48	National Costume Cards (1885–91)	—	—

P. H. MAYO & BROTHER, U.S.A.

		25	Actresses RB23/M80–1	£8.00	—
	M	25	Actresses RB23/M80–3	£13.00	—
	L	12	Actresses RB23/M80–4	£30.00	—
		?39	Actresses RB23/M80–5	£15.00	—
		40	Baseball Players	£30.00	—
		20	Costumes & Flowers	£13.00	—
		25	Head Dresses of Various Nations	£20.00	—
	M	25	National Flowers (Girl & Scene)	£15.00	—
		20	Naval Uniforms	£15.00	—
		35	Prizefighters	£13.00	—
		20	Shakespeare Characters	£15.00	—

M. MELACHRINO & CO., Switzerland

		52	Peuples Exotiques (1920–30) 1st Series	40p	£20.00
		52	Peuples Exotiques (1920–30) 2nd Series	40p	£20.00
		52	Peuples Exotiques (1920–30) 3rd Series	40p	£20.00

MIFSUF & AZZOPARDI, Malta

	KP	59	First Maltese Parliament (1922)	£3.00	—

L. MILLER & SONS, U.S.A.

	M	25	Battleships (1895–1905)	£15.00	—
	M	25	Generals & Admirals (Spanish War) (1895–1905)	£13.00	—
	M	24	Presidents of U.S. (1895–1905)	£13.00	—
	L	50	Rulers of the World (1895–1905)	£13.00	—

CHAS. J. MITCHELL & CO., Canada

		26	Actresses, "FROGA A" (1900–05):—		
			A. Backs in Brown	£16.00	—
			B. Backs in Green	£16.00	—

MITSUI & CO., Japan

		?	Japanese Women (1905–10)	£1.70	—

MOORE & CALVI, U.S.A.

	EL	53	Playing Cards – Actresses (1885–95):—		
			A. "Trumps Long Cut" Back	£12.00	—
			B. "Hard-A-Port" with Makers Name	£10.00	—
			C. "Hard-A-Port" without Makers Name	£10.00	—

MURAI BROS. & CO., Japan

		150	Actresses "ALWICS" (Pre 1918)	£2.50	—
		100	Beauties "THIBS"	£6.00	—
		50	Beauties Group 1	£8.00	—
		54	Chinese Girls Set 3	£4.50	—
		25	Chinese Beauties 1st Series Peacock Issue	£1.40	£35.00
		25	Chinese Beauties 3rd Series Peacock Issue	£1.60	—
		50	Chinese Beauties back in Red	£4.00	—
		50	Chinese Childrens Games without Border Peacock Issue	£1.20	£60.00

MURAI BROS. & CO., Japan *(continued)*

Illus. No.	Size	Number in set		Price per card	Complete set
		20	Chinese Childrens Games with Border Peacock Issue.........	£1.50	—
		50	Chinese Pagodas Peacock Issue.............................	£1.30	—
		30	Chinese Series Peacock Issue	£1.30	£40.00
		40	Chinese Trades I Back in Black	£2.00	—
		50	Dancing Girls of the World	£13.00	—

NATIONAL CIGARETTE AND TOBACCO CO., U.S.A.

Issued 1888–1905

	EL	13	Art Miniatures	£17.50	—
	EL	?	Cabinet Pictures..	£17.50	—
		25	National Types...	£10.00	£250.00
		44	National Types...	£10.00	—

Photographic Cards

		?	Actresses:—		
			A. Plain Back..	£2.00	—
			B. Printed Back	£3.00	—

OGDENS LIMITED

		51	Actresses Black & White Polo Issue (1906–08)...............	£2.20	—
		30	Actresses Unicoloured Polo Issue (1908):—		
			A. Tin Foil at back white.................................	£1.20	£36.00
			B. Tin Foil at back shaded	£1.40	£42.00
		17	Animals Polo Issue (1916)................................	£7.00	—
		60	Animals–Cut Outs:—		
			A. Ruler Issue (1912).....................................	£1.60	—
			B. Tabs Issue (1913):—		
			i) with captions	£1.60	—
			ii) without captions...................................	£3.20	—
		50	Aviation Series Tabs Issue (1912):—		
			A. Ogdens at base..	£1.60	—
			B. Ogdens England at base...............................	£1.80	—
		?98	Beauties Green Net Design Back (1901).....................	£8.00	—
		45	Beauties Picture Hats Polo Issue (1911)	£3.20	—
		50	Best Dogs of their Breed Polo Issue (1916):—		
			A. Back in Red	£3.50	—
			B. Back in Blue..	£3.50	—
		52	Birds of Brilliant Plumage Ruler Issue (1914):—		
			A. Fronts with Framelines	£1.25	£65.00
			B. Fronts without Framelines	£1.25	—
		25	British Trees & Their Uses Guinea Gold Issue (1927)	£1.20	£30.00
		25	China's Famous Warriors Ruler Issue (1913)...............	£2.50	—
		25	Famous Railway Trains Guinea Gold issue (1928)...........	£1.40	£35.00
		20	Flower's Polo Issue (1915):—		
			A. Without Eastern Inscription...........................	£3.50	—
			B. With Eastern Inscription	£3.50	—
		25	Indian Women Polo Issue (1919):—		
			A. Framework in Apple Green	£2.80	£70.00
			B. Framework in Emerald Green..........................	£2.80	£70.00
	K	52	Miniature Playing Cards Polo Issue (1922).................	—	—
			Music Hall Celebrities (1911):—		
		30	A. Polo Issue	£2.20	—
		50	B. Tabs Issue...	£2.20	—
		50	Riders of the World Polo Issue (1911).....................	£1.60	£80.00
		50	Russo-Japanese Series (1905).............................	—	—
		36	Ships & Their Pennants Polo Issue (1911)	£3.00	—
		32	Transport of the World Polo Issue (1917)	£3.00	—

OLD FASHION, U.S.A.

	L	?	Photographic Cards	£4.00	—

PENINSULAR TOBACCO CO. LTD., India

		50	Animals & Birds (1910)	£1.30	—
		52	Birds of Brilliant Plumage (1916):—		
			A. Back with single large packings........................	—	—
			B. Back with two small packings..........................	—	—
		25	Birds of the East 1st series (1912)	£1.00	—
167		25	Birds of the East 2nd Series (1912).......................	£1.00	£25.00
		25	Chinese Famous Warriors:—		
			A. Back "Monchyr India"	£1.20	£30.00
			B. Back "India" only	£1.00	£25.00
		50	Chinese Heroes (1913)	£1.40	—
		50	Chinese Modern Beauties (1912)...........................	£3.50	—
		50	Chinese Trades (1908):—		
			A. Back with "Monchyr"	—	—
			B. Back without "Monchyr"	—	—
		30	Fish Series (1916)..	—	—
		25	Hindoo Gods (1909)......................................	£1.20	£30.00
		37	Nautch Girl Series (1910–12)..............................	£3.50	—
		25	Products of the World (1915)..............................	£1.00	£25.00

PLANTERS' STORES & AGENCY CO. LTD., India

Illus. No.	Size	Number in set		Price per card	Complete set
		52	Interesting Places of the World (1920–40)	30p	£15.00
	P	25	International Footballers (1920–40)	—	—
	M	401	Malta Views (1920–40).	25p	—
209	M	51	Members of Parliament – Malta (1920–40)	16p	£8.00
		146	Prominent People (1920–40).	55p	—
	MP	100	Scenes from Films (1920–40)	55p	—
	LP	100	Talkie Stars (1920–40)	90p	—
	M	100	Worlds Famous Buildings (1920–40).	32p	£32.00

J. J. SCHUH TOBACCO CO. PTY. LTD., Australia

Issues 1920–25

		Number		Price	
		60	Australian Footballers Series A (half-full length)	£3.00	—
		40	Australian Footballers Series B (Rays).	£3.00	—
		59	Australian Footballers Series C (Oval Frame)	£6.00	—
			Australian Jockeys:—		
		30	A. Numbered.	—	—
		30	B. Unnumbered	—	—
	P	72	Cinema Stars	£1.00	—
		60	Cinema Stars	—	—
	L	12	Maxims of Success.	—	—
	P	72	Official War Photographs	£2.00	—
	P	96	Portraits of Our Leading Footballers	£2.00	—

G. SCLIVAGNOTTI, Malta

		50	Actresses & Cinema Stars (1923–24)	70p	£35.00
	MP	71	Grand Masters of the Orders of Jerusalem (1897–99)	—	—
	P	102	Opera Singers (1897–99)	—	—
	M	102	Opera Singers (1897–99)	—	—

SIMONETS LTD., Jersey, Channel Islands

	MP	36	Beautiful Women (1920–30).	£2.00	—
	P	24	Cinema Scenes Series (1920–30)	£1.50	£36.00
	P	27	Famous Actors & Actresses (1920–30)	£1.30	£35.00
		50	Local Footballers (1913–14).	£2.00	—
		25	Picture Series (1920–30).	£2.00	—
	P	27	Sporting Celebrities (1920–30).	£2.00	£55.00

THE SINSOCK & CO., Korea

		20	Korean Girls (1900–05)	£8.00	—

SNIDERS & ABRAHAMS PTY. LTD., Australia

Issues 1904–1920

		30	Actresses Gold Background	£5.00	—
		20	Actresses White Borders	£5.00	—
		20	Admirals and Warships of USA	£5.00	—
		60	Animals.	£1.00	—
		60	Animals and Birds:—		
			A. "Advertisement Gifts" issue	£1.00	—
			B. "Peter Pan" issue	£1.10	£66.00
		15	Australian Cricket Team (1905)	—	—
		16	Australian Football Incidents in Play	£4.00	—
		24	Australian Footballers (Full Length) Series A1 with Blue Framelines.	£6.00	—
		50	Australian Footballers (Full Length) Series AII without Framelines.	£6.00	—
		76	Australian Footballers ($\frac{1}{2}$ length) Series B	£5.00	—
		76	Australian Footballers ($\frac{1}{2}$ length) Series C	£5.00	—
		140	Australian Footballers (Head & Shoulders) Series D.	£4.00	—
		60	Australian Footballers (Head in Oval) Series E.	£4.00	—
		60	Australian Footballers (Head in Rays) Series F.	£4.00	—
		60	Australian Footballers (with Pennant) Series G	£4.00	—
		60	Australian Footballers (Head in Star) Series H	£4.00	—
		60	Australian Footballers (Head in Shield) Series I	£4.00	—
		56	Australian Footballers ($\frac{1-3}{2-4}$ length) Series J.	—	—
		48	Australian Jockeys Back in Blue.	£2.00	—
		83	Australian Jockeys Back in Brown.	£2.50	—
		56	Australian Racehorses Horizontal Back	£2.00	—
		56	Australian Racehorses Vertical Back	£2.00	—
		40	Australian Racing Scenes	£2.00	—
		132	Australian VC's and Officers	£3.00	—
		12	Billiard Tricks	£5.00	—
		60	Butterflies & Moths Captions in small letters	£1.00	—
		60	Butterflies & Moths Captions in block letters.	£1.00	—
		60	Cartoons & Caricatures.	£4.00	—
		12	Coin Tricks	£4.00	—
		64	Crests of British Warships.	£2.50	—
		40	Cricketers in Action	£8.00	—

SNIDERS & ABRAHAMS PTY. LTD., Australia *(continued)*

Illus. No.	Size	Number in set		Price per card	Complete set
		12	Cricket Terms	£7.00	—
		32	Dickens Series	£2.50	—
		16	Dogs:—		
			A. "Standard" issue..	£3.00	—
			B. "Peter Pan" issue:—		
			1. White Panel	£3.50	—
			2. Gilt Panel	£3.00	—
			C. "Coronet" Issue	£3.00	—
		6	Flags (Shaped Metal)	£2.00	—
		6	Flags (Shaped Card)	£2.00	—
		60	Great War Leaders & Warships:—		
			A. Front in Green...	£2.00	—
			B. Front in Sepia Brown	£2.00	—
		30	How to Keep Fit...	£3.50	—
		60	Jokes:—		
			A. "Aristocratica" issue....................................	£3.00	—
			B. "Standard" issue...	£2.00	—
		12	Match Puzzles...	£4.00	—
		48	Medals & Decorations	£4.00	—
	M	48	Melbourne Buildings	£5.00	—
		25	Natives of the World...	£5.00	—
		12	Naval Terms	£4.00	—
		29	Oscar Asche, Lily Brayton & Lady Smokers....................	£4.00	—
		40	Shakespeare Characters	£3.00	—
		30	Signalling – Semaphore & Morse	—	—
		14	Statuary...	—	—
		60	Street Criers in London (1907)	—	—
		32	Views of Victoria in 1857....................................	—	—
	P	174	Views of the World	£1.50	—

STAR TOBACCO CO., India

		52	Beauties (P/C inset) (1895–1905).............................	£18.00	—
		52	Indian Native Types (P/C inset) (1895–1905)	£18.00	—

TEOFANI & CO. LTD.

	MP	50	Teofani's Icelandic Employees (1930)	£2.50	—

TOBACCO PRODUCTS CORPORATION U.S.A.

		220	Movie Stars (1915)...	£1.00	—

TOBACCO PRODUCTS CORPORATION OF CANADA LTD.

		?45	Canadian Sports Champions (1920's).........................	—	—
		60	Do You Know (1924)...	£3.00	—
		60	Hockey Players (1926)	£6.00	—
		120	Movie Stars (1920's)	£1.75	—
		?163	Movie Stars Set 4 (1920's)	£1.75	—

TUCKETT LIMITED, Canada

		25	Autograph Series (1910–15)	£13.00	—
		160	Beauties & Scenes (1910–15).................................	£7.00	—
		25	Boy Scout Series (1910–15)..................................	—	—
	P	100	British Views without Tucketts on front (1910–15)............	£1.00	—
	P	?218	British Views with Tucketts on front (1910–15)..............	£1.00	—
	P	80	British Warships (1910–15)..................................	£3.50	—
	P	50	Canadian Scenes (1910–15)..................................	£1.00	—
		53	Playing Card Premium Certificates (1923–31)	£3.00	—
		52	Tucketts Aeroplane Series (1930)	£2.50	—
		52	Tucketts Aviation Series (1929)..............................	£2.50	—
		52	Tucketts Auction Bridge Series (1923–31)	£2.50	—

UNITED TOBACCO COMPANIES (SOUTH) LTD., South Africa

A. With Firms Name

		50	Aeroplanes of Today (1936):—		
			A. "Box 78 Capetown"	60p	£30.00
			B. "Box 1006 Capetown"	60p	£30.00
		50	Animals & Birds Koodoo Issue (1920–25).....................	£2.00	—
	L	24	Arms & Crests of Universities & Schools of South Africa (1930)	50p	£12.00
90	L	52	Boy Scouts, Girl Guide & Voortrekker Badges (1932).........	60p	£30.00
	L	62	British Rugby Tour of South Africa (1938)...................	40p	£25.00
		50	Children of All Nations (1928)	70p	—
		50	Cinema Stars "Flag Cigarettes" (1924).......................	80p	£40.00
		60	Do You Know? (1929)..	40p	£24.00
		50	Do You Know 2nd Series (1930)..............................	40p	£20.00
		50	Do You Know 3rd Series (1931)..............................	40p	£20.00
	K	28	Dominoes "Ruger Cigarettes" (1934).........................	—	—
	L	50	Exercises for Men & Women (1932)...........................	32p	£16.00

Illus. No.	Size	Number in set		Price per card	Complete set
		48	Fairy Tales 1st Series Flag Issue (1928)	80p	—
		48	Fairy Tales 2nd Series Flag Issue (1928)	80p	—
		24	Fairy Tales (1926) (Booklets)	—	—
	L	120	Farmyards of South Africa (1934)	22p	£26.00
	M	50	Household Tips (1926)	—	—
		25	Interesting Experiments (1930)	60p	£15.00
88	L	100	Medals & Decorations of the British commonwealth of Nations (1941)	35p	—
		50	Merchant Ships of the World (1925)	60p	£30.00
		50	Motor Cars (1923)	£2.00	—
	L	100	Our Land (1938)	13p	£10.00
	L	200	Our South Africa Past & Present (1938)	13p	£16.00
	L	24	Pastel Plates (1938)	60p	£15.00
	L	88	Philosophical Sayings (1938)	60p	—
		25	Picturesque People of the Empire (1929)	70p	£17.50
	K	53	Playing Cards "Flag" Cigarettes	£1.50	—
	K	53	Playing Cards "Lifeboat" Cigarettes (1934)	£1.20	—
	M	53	Playing Cards "Lotus Cigarettes" (1934–35)	—	—
	L	53	Playing Cards "Loyalist Cigarettes" (1934–35)	—	—
	K	53	Playing Cards "MP Cigarettes" (1934–35)	—	—
	K	53	Playing Cards "Ruger Cigarettes" (1934–35)	—	—
	L	50	Racehorses South Africa Set 1 (1929)	60p	—
	L	52	Racehorses South Africa Set 2 (1930):—		
			A. Inscribed "a series of 50"	60p	—
			B. Inscribed "a series of 52"	60p	—
		50	Regimental Uniforms (1937)	70p	£35.00
		50	Riders of the World (1931)	70p	£35.00
		25	South African Birds 1st Series (1927)	£1.00	—
		25	South African Birds 2nd Series (1927)	£1.00	—
	L	52	South African Butterflies (1937)	32p	£16.00
	L	52	South African Coats of Arms (1931)	30p	£15.00
	L	52	South African Flora (1935):—		
			A. With "CT Ltd"	40p	—
			B. Without "CT Ltd"	22p	£11.00
	L	65	South African Rugby Football Clubs (1933)	40p	£26.00
	L	52	Sports & Pastimes of South Africa (1936)	50p	£26.00
	L	47	Springbok Rugby and Cricket Teams (1931)	70p	—
	L	28	1912–13 Sprinkboks (1913)	—	—
		25	Studdy Dogs (1925)	£2.20	—
	L	40	Views of South African Scenery 1st Series (1918):—		
			A. Text Back	£2.00	—
			B. Anonymous Plain Back	£2.25	—
	L	36	Views of South African Scenery 2nd Series (1920)	£2.00	—
	/	25	Wild Flowers of South Africa 1st Series (1925)	£1.00	—
		25	Wild Flowers of South Africa 2nd Series (1926)	£1.00	—
		50	The World of Tomorrow (1938)	40p	£20.00

B. Without Firms Name

Illus. No.	Size	Number in set		Price per card	Complete set
74		50	African Fish (1937)	60p	£30.00
		50	British Aeroplanes (1933)	£1.00	—
	EL	25	Champion Dogs (1934)	£1.00	—
		30	Do You Know (1933)	50p	£15.00
		50	Eminent Film Personalities (1930)	90p	—
189		50	English Period Costumes (1932)	40p	£20.00
		25	Famous Figures from South African History (1932)	£1.20	—
	L	100	Famous Works of Art (1939)	13p	£10.00
		25	Flowers of Africa (1932)	£1.00	—
	M	50	Humour in Sport (1929)	£1.00	—
	L	100	Our Land (1938)	20p	—
	M	150	Our South African Birds (1942)	13p	£18.00
	L	150	Our South African Birds (1942)	13p	£18.00
	M	100	Our South African Flora (1940)	13p	£10.00
89	L	100	Our South African Flora (1940)	13p	£10.00
	M	100	Our South African National Parks (1941)	13p	£10.00
	L	100	Our South African National Parks (1941)	13p	£10.00
	L	50	Pictures of South Africa War Effort (1942)	20p	£10.00
		50	Riders of the World (1931)	70p	£35.00
		50	Safety First (1936)	40p	£20.00
	M	40	Ships of All Times (1931)	80p	—
		25	South African Birds 2nd Series	£2.00	—
	L	17	South African Cricket Touring Team (1929):—		
			A. Fronts with Autographs	£6.00	—
			B. Fronts without Autographs	£6.00	—
	M	100	South African Defence (1939)	13p	£10.00
	L	50	South African Places of Interest (1934)	20p	£10.00
	P	50	Stereoscopic Photographs Assorted Subjects (1928)	80p	—
	P	50	Stereoscopic Photographs of South Africa (1929)	80p	—
		50	The Story of Sand (1934)	50p	£25.00
	M	50	Tavern of the Seas (1939)	20p	£10.00
		25	Warriors of All Nations (Crossed Swords at Base) (1937)	80p	£20.00
		25	What's This (1929)	£1.00	£25.00
		50	Wild Animals of the World (1932)	60p	£30.00
	M	40	Wonders of the World (1931)	60p	—
	M	100	World Famous Boxers (1930–35)	70p	—

C. Silks Issues 1910–17

Illus. No.	Size	Number in set		Price per card	Complete set
	M	20	British Butterflies	—	—
	M	30	British Roses	—	—
	M	65	Flags of All Nations	£1.75	—

UNITED TOBACCO COMPANIES (SOUTH) LTD., South Africa *(continued)*

Illus. No.	Size	Number in set		Price per card	Complete set
	M	25	Old Masters	£5.00	—
	M	50	Pottery Types (1918–43)	£4.00	—
	M	50	South African Flowers Nd 1–50	£2.00	—
	M	50	South African Flowers Nd 51–100	£2.00	—

UNIVERSAL TOBACCO CO. PTY. LTD, South Africa _____

		835	Flags of All Nations (1935)	50p	—

S. W. VENABLE TOBACCO CO., U.S.A. _____

	EL	?	Actresses	£15.00	—

WESTMINSTER TOBACCO CO. LTD. _____

A. Card Issues

	Size	Number		Price	Complete
	M	332	Adamsons Oplevelser (1930)	—	—
	M	50	Beauties (1924)	£1.30	—
	MP	100	Beautiful Women (1915)	80p	—
	M	50	Birds, Beasts & Fishes (1923)	£1.30	—
	M	102	British Beauties (coloured) (1915)	£1.30	—
	M	102	British Beauties (uncoloured) (1915)	—	—
	P	48	British Royal & Ancient Buildings (1925)	50p	£25.00
	M	50	Butterflies & Moths (1920)	£1.50	—
	P	36	Canada 1st Series (1926)	60p	£22.00
	P	36	Canada 2nd Series (1928)	60p	£22.00
		30	Celebrated Actresses (1921)	£3.00	—
		100	Cinema Artistes Green Back (1929–33)	—	—
		50	Cinema Artistes Grey Back (1929–33)	—	—
		48	Cinema Celebrities (1935)	—	—
	P	50	Cinema Stars (1926)	£1.50	—
	MP	50	Cinema Stars Black and White (1930)	£2.00	—
	MP	50	Cinema Stars (1930) Hand coloured	£1.20	—
	M	27	Dancing Girls (1917)	£2.20	—
		50	Do You Know (1922)	£1.00	—
		24	Fairy Tale (Booklets) (1926)	—	—
	M	100	Famous Beauties (1916):—		
			A. Captions in Brown	£1.10	—
			B. Captions in Blue	£1.10	—
	MP	52	Film Favourites (1927):—		
			A. Uncoloured	£1.00	—
			B. Coloured	£1.00	—
	M	50	Film Personalities (1931)	£1.20	—
	M	50	Garden Flowers of the World (1917)	£1.20	—
		40	The Great War Celebrities (1914)	£4.00	—
	P	48	Indian Empire 1st Series (1925)	60p	£30.00
	P	48	Indian Empire 2nd Series (1926)	60p	£30.00
	LP	50	Islenzkar Eimskipamyndir (1931)	£1.30	—
	LP	50	Islenzkar Landslagmyndir (1928)	£1.30	£65.00
	LP	50	Islenzkar Landslagmyndir 2nd Series (1929)	£1.30	—
		40	Merrie England Studies (1914)	£3.00	—
		36	Modern Beauties (1938)	£3.00	—
	MP	52	Movie Stars (1925)	£1.30	—
	P	36	New Zealand 1st Series (1928)	60p	£22.00
	P	36	New Zealand 2nd Series (1929)	60p	£22.00
	K	53	Playing Cards (1934)	80p	—
	M	55	Playing Cards (1934):—		
			A. Blue Back	80p	—
			B. Red Back	80p	—
	P	50	Popular Film Stars (1926)	£1.00	—
	P	36	South Africa 1st Series (1928)	60p	£22.00
	P	36	South Africa 2nd Series (1928)	60p	£22.00
	M	49	South African Succulents (1936)	13p	£5.00
	M	100	Stage & Cinema Stars Captions in Grey (1921)	80p	—
	M	100	Stage & Cinema Stars Captions in Black (1921)	70p	—
	M	50	Stars of Filmland (1927)	£1.00	—
		50	Steamships of the World (1920)	£3.50	—
	M	50	Uniforms of All Ages (1917)	£4.50	—
	P	50	Views of Malaya (1930)	£3.50	—
		25	Wireless (1923)	£1.60	—
	M	49	Women of All Nations (1922)	£2.00	—
		50	The World of Tomorrow (1938)	32p	£16.00

B. Silk Issues

	M	50	Garden Flowers of the World (1914–18)	£1.70	—
	M	?	Miniature Rugs	£8.00	—

W. D. & H. O. WILLS _____

A. Channel Island Issues (without I.T.C. Clause)

		50	Air Raid Precautions	30p	£15.00
		50	Association Footballers (1936)	40p	£20.00
		50	Dogs (1937)	30p	£15.00
		50	Garden Flowers by Richard Sudell (1939)	20p	£10.00
		50	Garden Hints (1938)	20p	£10.00
		50	Household Hints (1936)	20p	£10.00

Illus. No.	Size	Number in set		Price per card	Complete set
		50	Life in the Royal Navy (1939)	13p	£6.50
		50	Our King & Queen (1937)	20p	£10.00
		50	Railway Equipment (1939)	20p	£10.00
		50	The Sea Shore (1938)	20p	£10.00
		50	Speed (1938).	20p	£10.00
		50	Wild Flowers 1st Series (1936)	30p	£15.00
		50	Wild Flowers 2nd Series (1937)	20p	£10.00

B. General Overseas Issues

Illus. No.	Size	Number in set		Price per card	Complete set
		50	Actors & Actresses Scroll Backs in Green (1903–10) Ref. 32		
			A. Portraits in Black & White	—	—
			B. Portraits Flesh Tinted........................	£1.30	—
		30	Actresses – Brown & Green (1905–10) Ref. 116 Scissors Issue .	£3.00	£90.00
		50	Actresses – Four Colours Surround (1903–08) Ref. 117:—		
			A. Scissors Issue.....................................	£3.50	—
			B. Green Scroll Back Issue	£1.30	—
		30	Actresses – Orange/Mauve Surround (1910–15) Scissors Issue Ref. 118:—		
			A. Surround in Orange................................	£1.30	£40.00
			B. Surround in Mauve	£1.00	£30.00
		100	Actresses (1903–10) Ref. 34:—		
			A. Capstan Issue.....................................	£1.50	—
			B. Vice Regal Issue	£1.50	—
		250	Actresses (1903–10) Ref. 33:—		
			A. Front Portrait in Black..................	£1.00	—
			B. Front Portrait in Red	—	—
		25	Actresses – Tabs Type Numbered Ref. 16	£6.00	—
		50	Actresses – Tabs Type Unnumbered Ref. 119 Scissors Issue ...	£10.00	—
		30	Actresses Unicoloured 1 (1908–13) Ref. 120:—		
			A. Scissors Issue Back in Red........................	90p	£27.00
			B. Scissors Issue Back in Purple Brown	£1.30	£40.00
		30	Actresses – Unicoloured 11 (1908–13) Ref. 121 Scissors Issue .	90p	£27.00
		50	Aeroplanes (1925)	£1.00	—
333		60	Animals (Cut-Outs) (1910–15):—		
			A. Havelock Issue....................................	60p	£36.00
			B. Wills Specialities Issue	40p	£24.00
		50	Animals & Birds (1910):—		
			A. With Text, Without Title...........................	£1.50	—
			B. Without Text, With Title (1912)	£1.50	—
			C. Without Text or Title	£1.50	—
		50	Arms & Armour (1910):—		
			A. Capstan Issue.....................................	80p	—
			B. Havelock Issue	—	—
			C. Vice Regal Issue	80p	—
			D. United Service Issue	£1.30	£65.00
		50	Arms of the British Empire (1910):—		
			A. Backs in Black....................................	50p	£25.00
			B. Wills Specialities Issue	70p	—
			C. Havelock Issue	£6.00	—
		25	Army Life 1910 Scissors Issue	£1.20	£30.00
		50	Art Photogravures 1st Series (1913–14):—		
			A. Size 67 × 33 mm..................................	40p	—
			B. Size 67 × 44 mm..................................	40p	—
		50	Art Photogravures 2nd Series (1913–14)	40p	—
		42	Australian Club Cricketers (1905) Ref. 59A:—		
			A. Dark Blue Backs..................................	£8.00	—
			B. Green Backs......................................	£8.00	—
			C. Pale Blue Backs...................................	£9.00	—
		25	Australian and English Cricketers (1903) Ref. 59B............	£7.00	—
		25	Australian and English Cricketers (1909) Ref. 59C:—		
			A. Capstan Issue:—		
			i) Framework in Scarlet............................	£7.00	—
			ii) Framework in Blue	£7.00	—
			B. Vice Regal Issue:—		
			i) Framework in Scarlet............................	£7.00	—
			ii) Framework in Blue	£7.00	—
		60	Australian and South African Cricketers (1910–11) Ref. 59D:—		
			A. Capstan Issue:—		
			i) Framework in Scarlet............................	£7.00	—
			ii) Framework in Blue	£7.00	—
			B. Havelock Issue:—		
			i) Framework in Scarlet............................	—	—
			ii) Framework in Blue	—	—
			C. Vice Regal Issue:—		
			i) Framework in Scarlet............................	£7.00	—
			ii) Framework in Blue	£7.00	—
	M	100	Australian Scenic Series (1928)	50p	—
		50	Australian Wild Flowers (1913):—		
			A. Will's Specialities Issue Grey-Brown Back.............	40p	£20.00
			B. Will's Specialities Issue Green Back	—	—
			C. Havelock Issue	£3.00	—
			Aviation (1910):—		
		85	A. Black Backs "Series of 85":—		
			i) Capstan Issue	£1.00	—
			ii) Vice Regal issue	£1.00	—
		75	B. Black Backs "Series of 75":—		
			i) Capstan Issue...................................	80p	—
			ii) Havelock Issue..................................	£1.50	—

Illus. No.	Size	Number in set		Price per card	Complete set
			iii) Vice Regal issue...........................	80p	—
		75	C. Green Back "Series of 75":—		
			i) Capstan Issue......................	90p	—
			ii) Havelock Issue.......................	£3.00	—
			iii) Vice Regal issue.....................	90p	—
		50	Aviation Series (1910–11):—		
			A. W. D. & H. D. Wills Back	£1.10	—
			B. Anonymous Backs with Album Clause.................	£1.20	—
			C. Anonymous Backs without Album Clause	£1.30	—
		?95	Baseball Series (1912) Pirate issue	£16.00	—
296		40	Beauties – Brown Tinted (1910–15):—		
			A. Scissors Issue..........................	80p	£32.00
			B. Star Circle and Leaves issue	£1.50	—
		30	Beauties – "Celebrated Actresses" Ref. 140 Scissors Issue.....	£3.00	£90.00
		52	Beauties – Heads and Shoulders Set in Background Ref. 141:—		
			A. Scissors Issue:—		
			i) Background to Packets Plain	£2.50	—
			ii) Background to Packets Latticework Design	£1.50	£80.00
			B. Star Circle and Leaves Issue	£2.50	—
	P	25	Beauties 1st Series (1924–25) Ref. 142......................	£1.30	—
	P	50	Beauties 2nd Series (1924–25) Ref. 143	£1.30	—
		32	Beauties – Picture Hats (1910–15) Ref. 144:—		
			A. Scissors Issue	£1.70	£55.00
			B. Star Circle and Leaves Issue	£2.50	—
	MP	72	Beauties – Red Star and Circle Back (1910–15) Ref. 145.......	£5.00	—
		50	Beauties – Red Tinted (1905–10) Ref. 146	£1.00	£50.00
		30	Beauties and Children (1910–15) Ref. 147 Scissors Issue	£1.40	£42.00
	P	50	Beautiful New Zealand (1925–30)	20p	£10.00
		50	Best Dogs of Their Breed (1916):—		
			A. Havelock Issue	£3.00	—
			B. Will's Specialities Issue	£1.40	—
			C. Anonymous Back, Will's on Front....................	£4.00	—
		30	Birds and Animals (1911) Ruby Queen Issue	£1.30	—
		50	Birds, Beasts & Fishes (1925–30)	30p	£15.00
		100	Birds of Australasia (1912):—		
			A. Green Backs:—		
			i) Capstan Issue......................	40p	£40.00
			ii) Havelock Issue......................	90p	—
			iii) Vice Regal Issue......................	40p	£40.00
			B. Yellow Backs:—		
			i) Havelock Issue	90p	—
			ii) Will's Specialities Issue......................	50p	—
		52	Birds of Brilliant Plumage:—		
			A. Four Aces Issue (1924)	£1.50	£80.00
			B. Pirate Issue:—		
			i) With border on front (1914).........................	£2.00	—
			ii) Without border on front (1916).....................	£2.00	—
			C. Red Star, Circle and Leaves Issue	£2.50	—
		25	Birds of the East 1st Series Ruby Queen Issue	60p	£15.00
		25	Birds of the East 2nd Series Ruby Queen Issue	60p	£15.00
		36	Boxers (1911–12)		
			A. Scissors Issue	£3.40	£120.00
			B. Green Star and Circle Issue........................	£3.40	£120.00
			Britains Defenders (1915–16):—		
			A. Will's Specialities Issue:—		
		50	i) Inscribed "S Series of 50"	£1.00	£50.00
		8	ii) Without Inscription "A Series of 50"	£6.00	—
		50	B. Havelock Issue	£2.00	—
		50	C. Scissors Issue:—		
			i) Red Upright "Scissors" Packet	70p	£35.00
			ii) Green Upright "Scissors" Packet	80p	£40.00
			iii) Red Slanting "Scissors" Packet	70p	£35.00
		50	D. Green Star and Circle Issue......................	£1.20	—
		43	British Army Boxers (1913–14) Scissors Issue	£1.50	£65.00
178		50	British Army Uniforms (1905–10):—		
			A. Wild Woodbine Issue	£3.50	£175.00
			B. Flag Issue	£2.80	—
			C. Scissors Issue	£2.80	£140.00
		100	British Beauties (1910–18).........................	90p	—
		50	British Empire Series (1913):—		
			A. Capstan Issue.........................	60p	£30.00
			B. Havelock Issue	£1.00	—
			C. Vice Regal Issue	60p	£30.00
	P	48	British Royal and Ancient Buildings (1925–30)..............	22p	£11.00
		45	British Rugby Players (1930)	90p	—
		50	Chateaux (1925–30).........................	£2.00	—
		50	Children of All Nations (1925–30).........................	30p	£15.00
		100	China's Famous Warriors (1911) Pirate Issue Ref. 357 (1911):—		
			A. First 25 Subjects	70p	£17.50
			B. Second 25 Subjects.........................	70p	£17.50
			C. Third 25 Subjects	70p	£17.50
			D. Fourth 25 Subjects.........................	70p	£17.50
		28	Chinese Actors and Actresses (1907) Pirate Issue Ref. 361.....	£1.20	—
		25	Chinese Beauties 1st Series Pirate Issue Ref. 362 (1907):—		
			A. Vertical Back	80p	£20.00
			B. Horizontal Back	£1.00	£25.00
		25	Chinese Beauties 2nd Series Pirate Issue Ref. 363 (1909):—		

Illus. No.	Size	Number in set		Price per card	Complete set
			A. With Framelines on Front............................	80p	£20.00
			B. Without Framelines on Front	80p	£20.00
		30	Chinese Children's Games (1905–15) Ruby Queen Issue Ref. 364	£1.00	—
		50	Chinese Costumes Pirate Issue (1928) Ref. 365	£1.60	—
	EL	25	Chinese Pagodas (1905–10) Pirate Issue Ref. 366	—	—
		50	Chinese Proverbs Brown Ref. 367 (1928):—		
			A. Pirate Issue....................................	80p	—
			B. Ruby Queen Issue................................	£1.50	—
		50	Chinese Proverbs Coloured (1914–16) Pirate Issue Ref. 368:—		
			A. Back in Blue:—		
			i) Without Overprint...........................	80p	
			ii) With Overprint	90p	—
			B. Back in Olive Green.............................	£1.00	—
		40	Chinese Trades (1900–05) Autocar Issue	—	—
		50	Chinese Transport (1914) Ref. 370 Ruby Queen Issue.........	£1.20	—
		50	Cinema Stars Four Aces Issue (1922–30):—		
			A. Numbered....................................	80p	£40.00
			B. Unnumbered	80p	£40.00
		25	Cinema Stars (1922–30) Scissors Issue	80p	£20.00
		50	Coaches and Coaching Days (1925–30)	60p	£30.00
			Conundrums:—		
		25	A. With Album Clause.............................	£5.00	—
		25	B. Without Album Clause...........................	£5.00	—
		25	C. Without Album Clause Redrawn	£5.00	—
		50	D. Without Album Clause Inscribed "50 Different ..."	£5.00	—
	M	68	Crests & Colours of Australian Universities, Colleges & Schools (1922)	30p	£20.00
	P	63	Cricketers Ref. 59E...................................	£4.00	—
		25	Cricketer Series Ref. 59F.............................	£45.00	—
		50	Cricketer Series (1901–02) Ref. 59G	£45.00	—
	P	48	Cricket Season (1928–29)	£1.40	—
		27	Dancing Girls (1915) Scissors Issue:—		
			A. Inscribed "28 Subjects" (No. 3 not issued).............	£1.70	£45.00
			B. Inscribed "27 Subjects"	£1.70	£45.00
		25	Derby Day Series (1910–25):—		
			A. Scissors Issue:—		
			i) With Title.................................	£1.40	£35.00
			ii) Without Title.............................	£3.50	—
			B. Star & Circle Issue	£3.50	—
		50	Dogs – Scenic Backgrounds (1925–26)	18p	£9.00
	M	20	Dogs – Heads 1st Series (1927–28):—		
			A. Will's World Renown Cigarettes Issue:—		
			i) With Album Clause...........................	80p	—
			ii) Without Album Clause	80p	—
			B. Three Castles and Vice Regal Cigarettes Issue	80p	—
	M	20	Dogs-Heads 2nd Series (1927–28)	60p	—
251		32	Drum Horses (1905–10):—		
			A. Scissors Issue:—		
			i) Vertical Format, Open Scissors Packet..............	£4.00	—
			ii) Horizontal Format, Closed Scissors Packet	£3.50	£110.00
			B. United Service Issue............................	£3.50	—
			C. Green Star Circle & Leaves Issue	£3.50	—
	P	25	English Cricketers (1926)................................	£1.20	£30.00
	M	25	English Period Costumes (1928):—		
			A. White Card....................................	80p	—
			B. Cream Card	60p	£15.00
			Etchings (of Dogs):—		
		26	A. Small Size English Language Issues:—		
			i) With "Gold Flake Cigarettes"......................	£2.50	—
			ii) Without Gold Flake Cigarettes (1925)	32p	£8.00
		26	B. Small Size Dutch Language Issues:—		
			i) With Framelines to back	£3.50	—
			ii) Without Framelines to back.......................	£3.50	—
	M	26	C. Medium Size (1925).............................	50p	£13.00
		25	The Evolution of the British Navy (1910–15)	£1.20	£30.00
			Famous Film Stars (1934):—		
		100	A. Small Size	30p	—
	M	100	B. Medium Size:—		
			i) White Card...................................	40p	—
			ii) Cream Card	40p	—
	MP	100	Famous Film Stars (1925–30)	90p	—
		50	Famous Footballers (1914–15):—		
			A. Scissors Issue..................................	£1.50	£75.00
			B. Star & Circle Issue	£2.50	—
		50	Famous Inventions (Without I.T.C. Clause) (1927)..........	40p	£20.00
		75	Film Favourites Four Aces Issue (1925–30)	80p	£60.00
		50	Fish of Australasia (1912):—		
			A. Capstan Issue..................................	50p	£25.00
			B. Havelock Issue	£1.00	—
			C. Vice Regal Issue	50p	£25.00
			Flag Girls of All Nations:—		
		50	A. Capstan Issue..................................	£1.20	—
		50	B. Vice-Regal Issue	£1.20	—
		25	C. United Service Issue.............................	£1.40	£35.00
		25	D. Scissors Issue:—		
			i) Numbered..................................	£2.50	—
			ii) Unnumbered	£3.50	—

Illus. No.	Size	Number in set		Price per card	Complete set
		25	E. Green Star Circle & Leaves Issue	£1.20	£30.00
		8	Flags Shaped Metal (1915)	£6.00	—
336		126	Flags & Ensigns (1903–10)	60p	£75.00
		25	Flags of the Empire (No I.T.C. Clause)	£3.50	—
			Flowers Purple Mountain Issue:—		
		20	A. Numbered	£5.50	—
		100	B. Unnumbered	£6.50	—
		50	Football Club Colours Scissors/Special Army Quality Issue (1905–10)	£2.20	—
		28	Football Club Colours and Flags (1905–15):—		
			A. Capstan Issue	£2.00	£55.00
			B. Havelock Issue	£4.00	—
		200	Footballers (1933):—		
			A. Small Size	40p	—
			B. Medium Size	80p	—
		50	Girls of All Nations (1905–10):—		
			A. Capstan Issue	£1.10	—
			B. Vice Regal Issue	£1.10	—
			C. Green Star Circle and Leaves Issue	£1.50	—
		25	Governors – General of India Scissors Issue (1911)	£3.60	£90.00
	M	25	Heraldic Signs and Their Origins (1925)	60p	£15.00
		30	Heroic Deeds (1914) Scissors Issue	£1.40	£42.00
		50	Historic Events (1912):—		
			A. Will's Specialities Issue	60p	£30.00
			B. Havelock Issue	£1.80	—
	M	25	History of Naval Dress (1930)	—	—
	P	50	Homeland Events (1925–30)	20p	£10.00
		50	Horses of Today (1906):—		
			A. Capstan Issue	80p	—
			B. Havelock Issue	£2.00	—
			C. Vice Regal Issue	80p	—
		50	Household Hints (1927–30):—		
			A. With "Will's Cigarettes" at Top Back	40p	—
			B. Without Will's Cigarettes at Top Back	60p	—
340			Houses of Parliament (1905–10):—		
		33	A. Pirate Issue	70p	£24.00
		32	B. Star and Circle Issue	80p	£25.00
		50	Indian Regiments (1905–10):—		
			A. Scissors Issue	£3.50	—
			B. Star and Circle Issue	£4.00	—
		50	Interesting Buildings (1905)	£1.00	£50.00
		67	International Footballers Season 1909–1910:—		
			A. Scissors Issue (1910)	£3.20	—
			B. United Services Issue (1910)	£3.20	—
			C. Flag Issue (1911)	£3.20	—
		50	Jiu-Jitsu (1905–10):—		
			A. Scissors Issue	£3.00	—
			B. Flag Issue	£2.50	—
		53	Jockeys and Owners Colours with P.C. Inset Scissors Issue (1905–10)	£4.00	—
		50	Lighthouses (1925–30)	30p	£15.00
		45	Melbourne Cup Winners (1906)	£2.20	—
		50	Merchant Ships of the World (1925–30) (Without I.T.C. Clause)	35p	£17.50
		40	Merrie England Studies (Male) (1905–15)	£2.50	—
		24	Merveilles du Monde (1927)	£3.20	—
		25	Military Portraits (1917) Scissors Issue	£3.00	—
	M	25	Miniatures – Oval Medallions (1914)	£35.00	—
	K	52	Miniature Playing Cards Scissors Issue	£4.50	—
		50	Modern War Weapons (1916):—		
			A. Wills Specialities Issue	80p	—
			B. Havelock Issue	£2.00	—
		25	Modes of Conveyance (1925–30) Four Aces Issue	90p	£22.50
		48	Motor Cars (1924)	80p	£40.00
	P	50	Motor Cars (1928)	60p	£30.00
		50	Motor Cycles (1926)	90p	£45.00
	P	48	Movie Stars (1925–30)	£3.00	—
		50	Music Hall Celebrities (1906–11) Scissors Issue	£3.00	£150.00
		50	National Flags and Arms (1930–35)	80p	—
	M	25	The Nation's Shrines (1925–30)	60p	£15.00
	P	50	Nature Studies (1925–30)	80p	—
		50	New Zealand Birds (1925–30)	50p	£25.00
	P	50	New Zealand – Early Scenes & Maori Life (1925–30)	25p	£12.50
		50	New Zealand Footballers (1928)	30p	£15.00
337		50	New Zealand Race Horses (1928):—		
			A. Cream Card	40p	£20.00
			B. White Card	60p	—
		50	N.Z. Butterflies, Moths & Beetles (1925–30)	40p	£20.00
		25	Past and Present (1929)	60p	£15.00
		50	Past and Present Champions (1905–10):—		
			A. Capstan Cigarette Issue	£3.00	—
			B. Capstan Tobacco Issue	£5.00	—
		25	Picturesque People of the Empire (1925–30)	60p	£15.00
		25	Pirates and Highwaymen (1925–30)	60p	£15.00
		25	Police of the World (1905–10)	£4.00	£100.00
	M	70	Practical Wireless (1922–30)	90p	—
			Products of the World – Maps and Scenes (1905–10):—		
		50	A. Pirate Issue	80p	—
		25	B. Green Star Circle and Leaves Issue	£1.00	—

Illus. No.	Size	Number in set		Price per card	Complete set
		50	Products of the World – Scenes only (1929).....................	30p	£15.00
		50	Prominent Australian and English Cricketers (1907) Ref. 59H	£7.00	—
		23	Prominent Australian and English Cricketers (1907–08) Ref. 59I	£7.00	
		59	Prominent Australian and English Cricketers (1911) Ref. 59J:—		
			A. Capstan Issue:—		
			i) "A Series of 50"	£7.00	—
			ii) "A Series of .../A Series of 59"	£7.00	—
			B. Vice Regal Issue:—		
			i) "A Series of 50"	£7.00	—
			ii) "A Series of .../A Series of 59"	£7.00	—
			C. Havelock Issue	£15.00	—
		25	Puzzle Series (1910–15) Scissors/United Service Issue	£3.40	—
		50	Races of Mankind (1905–10)	£6.00	—
334		50	Railway Engines (1924)	50p	£25.00
		50	Railway Working (1925–30)...............................	90p	£45.00
		50	Regimental colours and Cap Badges (1910–15):—		
			A. Scissors Issue	80p	£40.00
			B. United Service Issue:—		
			i) Red Back...	70p	£35.00
			ii) Blue Back	60p	£30.00
		33	Regimental Pets (1905–10) Scissors Issue.....................	£3.50	—
339		50	Regimental Standards and Cap Badges (1930)..............	32p	£16.00
		50	Riders of the World:—		
			A. Capstan/Vice Regal/Pennant/Will's Specialities Issue (1913).....................................	90p	—
			B. Havelock Issue (1913)................................	£2.00	—
			C. Back in Red-Brown (1925–30)	50p	£25.00
		50	Romance of the Heavens (1928) (No I.T.C. Clause)..........	70p	
		25	Roses (1912):—		
			A. Purple Mountain Issues:—		
			i) With Will's Cigarettes on Front	£3.50	
			ii) Without Will's Cigarettes on Front	£3.00	
			B. Plain Backs with Will's Cigarettes on Front	—	—
	P	50	The Royal Family at Home and Abroad (1930–35)	60p	—
		50	Royal Mail (With Will's Cigarettes on Fronts):—		
			A. Capstan Issue.....................................	80p	£40.00
			B. Havelock Issue	£2.00	—
			C. Vice Regal Issue	80p	£40.00
			D. With Anonymous Backs	£3.00	—
			E. With Plain Back	£3.00	—
	P	50	The Royal Navy (1925–30)...............................	80p	£40.00
		100	Royalty, Notabilities and Events in Russia, China and South Africa (1900–02)	£1.00	—
		27	Rulers of the World (1911)................................	£4.00	—
			Russo-Japanese Series (1905–06):—		
		100	A. Fronts in Black	85p	£85.00
		50	B. Fronts in Red......................................	£4.00	—
		50	Safety First (1934–35)....................................	50p	£25.00
	LP	48	Scenes from the Empire (1930–35).........................	90p	£45.00
		30	Semaphore Signalling (1910–15)............................	£1.10	£33.00
	P	50	Ships and Shipping (1928)................................	22p	£11.00
		36	Ships and Their Pennants (1910–15)	£2.00	—
		50	Ships' Badges (1926)	60p	£33.00
		50	Signalling Series (1913):—		
			A. Capstan Issue......................................	50p	£25.00
			B. Havelock Issue	70p	—
			C. Vice Regal Issue	50p	£25.00
		40	Sketches in Black and White (1900–05)	£1.40	—
			Soldiers of the World:—		
		50	A. Numbered..	£3.50	—
		75	B. Unnumbered	£5.00	—
		99	South African Personalities (1900).........................	—	—
		30	Sporting Girls (1900–10) Scissors Issue	£3.00	—
	P	50	A Sporting Holiday in New Zealand (1925–30):—		
			A. Small Size	25p	£12.50
			B. Medium Size	40p	£20.00
		25	Sporting Terms (1905–10):—		
			A. Capstan Issue......................................	£3.50	—
			B. Vice Regal Issue	£3.50	—
		50	Sports of the World (1917)	£1.60	—
		50	Stage & Music Hall Celebrities (1900–05) (Portrait in Oval Frame):—		
			A. Capstan Issue......................................	£1.20	—
			B. Vice Regal Issue	£1.20	—
			C. Havelock Issue	£2.50	—
		50	Stage and Music Hall Celebrities (1900–05) (Portrait in Oblong Frame)	£1.40	£70.00
	P	52	Stars of the Cinema (1925–26):—		
			A. Text Back	£2.50	—
			B. Four Aces Issue....................................	£1.50	—
		50	Time & Money in Different Countries (1908):—		
			A. Capstan Issue......................................	60p	—
			B. Havelock Issue	£1.50	—
			C. Vice Regal Issue:—		
			i) With album Clause	60p	£30.00
			ii) Without album clause...........................	60p	£30.00

W. D. & H. O. WILLS (continued)

Illus. No.	Size	Number in set		Price per card	Complete set
		50	A Tour Round the World (1907)	£1.20	—
		50	Types of the British Army (1905–10):—		
			A. Capstan Issue..	£1.50	—
			B. Vice Regal Issue	£1.50	—
		50	Types of the Commonwealth Military Forces (1910–15):—		
			A. Capstan Issue..	£1.50	—
			B. Vice Regal Issue	£1.50	—
			C. Havelock Issue	£3.00	—
		25	United States Warships (1911):—		
			A. Capstan Issue..	£1.20	—
			B. Havelock Issue	£2.50	—
			C. Vice Regal Issue	£1.20	—
	P	50	Units of the British Army and RAF (1925–30).............	22p	£11.00
		50	U.S.S. Co's Steamers (1930).............................	£1.00	—
		50	V.C.'s (1925–30).......................................	70p	£35.00
		25	Victoria Cross Heroes:—		
			A. Havelock Issue	£2.40	£60.00
			B. Will's Specialities Issue............................	£1.20	£30.00
			C. Scissors Issue	£1.40	£35.00
		10	Victorian Football Association (1905–10):—		
			A. Capstan on Front.....................................	£3.00	—
			B. Havelock on Front....................................	—	—
		19	Victorian Football League (1905–10):—		
			A. Capstan on Front.....................................	£3.00	—
			B. Havelock on Front....................................	£4.00	—
		215	Views of the World (1905–10):—		
			A. Numbers 1–50 Plain Backs (Anonymous)	40p	—
			B. Numbers 51–215 Blue Back Capstan Issue	40p	—
			C. Numbers 51–215 Green Back Vice Regal Issue	40p	—
		25	Village Models Series (1925–30):—		
			A. Small Size	90p	£22.50
			B. Medium Size	£1.50	—
24		50	War Incidents 1st Series (1916):—		
			A. Will's Specialities Issue............................	80p	—
			B. Havelock Issue	£1.50	—
			C. Scissors Issue	90p	£45.00
		50	War Incidents 2nd Series (1917):—		
			A. Will's Specialities Issue............................	80p	£40.00
			B. Havelock Issue	£4.00	—
		50	War Pictures (1915):—		
			A. Will's Specialities Issue............................	60p	£30.00
			B. Havelock Issue	£1.20	—
		50	Warships (1925)	70p	£35.00
		30	What It Means (1910–17) Scissors Issue....................	70p	£21.00
			Wild Animals:—		
		50	A. Small Size titled "Wild Animals" Heads...............	22p	£11.00
	M	25	B. Medium Size titled "Wild Animals"...................	50p	£12.50
		50	Wild Animals of the World:—		
			A. Bristol & London Issue..............................	£4.00	—
			B. Celebrated Cigarettes Issue..........................	£1.40	£70.00
			C. Star, Circle & Leaves Issue	£3.00	—
		25	Wonders of the World (1925–30)	40p	£10.00
		25	The World's Dreadnoughts (1910):—		
			A. Capstan Issue.......................................	70p	—
			B. Vice Regal Issue	70p	—
			C. No I.T.C. Clauses...................................	70p	£17.50
		50	Zoo (1925–30):—		
			A. Scissors Issue without descriptive back	—	—
			B. Will's Issue with descriptive back	20p	£10.00
		50	Zoological Series (1922–30)	80p	—

C. Silk Issues 1911–17

Illus. No.	Size	Number in set		Price per card	Complete set
	M	50	Arms of the British Empire..............................	£1.30	—
	M	50	Australian Butterflies	£1.30	—
	M	50	Birds & Animals of Australia............................	£1.30	—
	M	50	Crests & Colours of Australian Universities, Colleges & Schools	£1.30	—
	EL	1	Flag	—	—
		28	Flags of 1914–18 Allies:—		
			A. Backs with letterpress in Capitals	£1.20	—
			B. Backs with letterpress in small lettering	£1.20	—
		38	Kings & Queens of England.............................	£2.20	—
	M	50	Popular Flowers:—		
			A. Backs Inscribed "Now being inserted in the large packets"	£2.20	—
			B. Backs Inscribed "Now being inserted in the 1/- packets"	£2.20	—
	M	67	War Medals..	£1.80	—

J. WIX & SONS LTD.

Illus. No.	Size	Number in set		Price per card	Complete set
	P	24	Royal Tour of New Zealand (1925–30).....................	£5.50	—

GEO. F. YOUNG & BRO., U.S.A.

Illus. No.	Size	Number in set		Price per card	Complete set
	L	?	Actresses (1885–95).....................................	£15.00	—

AUCTIONS AND FAIRS IN LONDON

We hold regular cigarette card auctions and fairs at
The Eccleston Hotel, Victoria, London S.W.1,
conveniently situated immediately behind Victoria Rail and Coach stations.
Free car-parking in nearby streets

1986 Auction and Fair Dates

Saturday 15th March
Saturday 26th April
Saturday 21st June

Saturday 9th August
Saturday 11th October
Saturday 6th December

Viewing from 10.00 a.m.   Auction begins 1.30 p.m.
Bids also accepted by post.

Auction catalogue price 50p
post free from the address below
(free to "Cigarette Card News" subscribers).

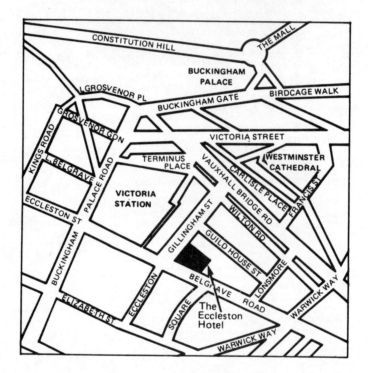

Also on display for sale throughout the day (except while the auction is in progress):
* Many hundreds of sets in mint condition from 75p
* Selection of rare sets in top condition
* Wide range of sets in fair to good condition at half price
* Thousands of pre-1918 odd cards and types individually priced
* The latest new issues and additions to stock
* Books, collectors aids and albums
* Specific requirements brought for viewing if requested in advance

Free admission.   Everybody welcome.

THE LONDON CIGARETTE CARD COMPANY LIMITED
SUTTON ROAD, SOMERTON, SOMERSET, ENGLAND. TA11 6QP

Telephone: 0458 73452